Marine Ecology

JOHN WILEY & SONS, INC.

New York · London · Sydney

Marine Ecology

HILARY B. MOORE

Professor of Marine Ecology
and Assistant Director Marine Laboratory
University of Miami

Research Associate
Woods Hole Oceanographic Institution

FIFTH PRINTING, NOVEMBER, 1966

Library of Congress Catalog Card Number: 58-10807

Printed in the United States of America

Preface

ECOLOGY IN RELATION TO OTHER SCIENCES

The science of ecology embraces all aspects of the interrelations of organisms and their environment, and since the organisms themselves are part of the environment, their own interrelations form part of the study. A field as broad as this of necessity makes contact with many other sciences. Within the limits of marine ecology as defined here, the ecologist is concerned with physical and chemical oceanography as well as with meteorology and marine geology in describing and explaining the physical and chemical aspects of the environment. He is concerned with physiology and animal behavior in understanding the reactions of the organisms to particular conditions. Taxonomy plays a vital role in defining the species, races, etc., with which he is dealing, and itself receives help from ecology in explaining problems of speciation and race formation. Biochemistry and biophysics similarly interlock with ecology, whereas mathematics, and particularly statistics, comprises a vital section of ecological studies. The list might obviously be extended further, but the point is already clear that this is no compact entity, self-sufficient, but rather a meeting place of many sciences.

Ecology in general has been surveyed in various texts, perhaps the most comprehensive of which, at least from the point of view of animals, is *Principles of Animal Ecology*, by Allee et al. (1949). Unfortunately, there is no such comprehensive treatment of the special field of marine ecology, which comprises, usually, only a minor portion of most general works. This minor role is understandable, since so many general principles of ecology can be best illustrated by land or fresh-water examples, and these two habitats are more accessible to the majority of students than is the ocean. There is, nevertheless, an extremely extensive literature pertaining to marine ecology, although widely scattered in different journals. In attempting to bring this together into a coherent book, there at once arises the problem of how much to include, and decisions are the more difficult with so many sciences contributing to the wide field of ecology.

It is intended that this book shall be of use to students of marine science. Already available to them are such texts as *The Oceans* by Sverdrup et al. (1946), Harvey's *Recent Advances in the Chemistry and Biology of Sea Water* (1945), and many others, and it seems unnecessary to duplicate what is well treated in them, simply for the sake of completeness in the present volume. It is sufficient to give references that will enable the student to locate such material when needed. It must be stressed, however, that ecology is concerned not merely with the environment as it affects the organism. Ecology must equally embrace the effects of the organism on the environment. A recently published treatise on marine palaeoecology* comes closest to covering the field, and includes both authoritative articles by a number of different authors and very valuable bibliographies.

SOURCE MATERIAL IN RELATED FIELDS

Throughout subsequent chapters, references will be found to source material from which the student may follow up lines of interest in greater detail than can be given here. Where possible, these have been chosen to include good bibliographies on the subject. Also, those written in English have been chosen wherever possible, and this certainly requires justification. A general text of this type should

* J. W. Hedgepeth, (Editor) (1957). Treatise on marine ecology and palaeoecology. Vol. I. *Geol. Soc. Am., Mem. No. 67*, 1-1296.

be as world-wide in application as possible. The research on which
it is based has been carried out in many countries and described in
various languages. It will, however, be read, in all probability, by
more English-speaking students than any others, and unfortunately
they are notoriously poor linguists. Additional reading, based on the
bibliography, will, then, undoubtedly meet the needs of the greatest
numbers if it is mainly in English, at least when an alternative exists.
This is a deliberate selection, and in no way reflects the value of the
work of other countries. It cannot be too strongly stressed, though,
that the student who reads only in his own language must realize the
wide field which he is missing thereby, and the unbalanced outlook
which he must inevitably have.

A work such as this is largely a compilation of the work of others,
and adequate acknowledgment should cover all those whose names
appear in the bibliography. Even this would be inadequate, since
so much selection has been necessary and so much important work
has had to be omitted. I am deeply indebted to Dr. J. A. Kitching
without whose collection of references and abstracts the work would
hardly have been possible. Dr. Gunner Thorson and Dr. D. P.
Wilson have read the manuscript and offered a wealth of suggestions.
Dr. W. R. Taylor not only helped with suggestions but also provided
the classification of the algae in the appendix. Among the many
others who have helped with suggestions and criticism, particular
mention should be made of Dr. G. L. Clarke, Dr. C. P. Idyll,
Mr. R. M. Ingle, Dr. B. H. Ketchum, Dr. A. C. Redfield, Dr. F. G. W.
Smith, and a succession of students at the Marine Laboratory of the
University of Miami. To all these, as well as to those authors and
publishers who have given permission for the reproduction of text
figures, I wish to express my great indebtedness.

HILARY B. MOORE

June 1958

Contents

1

Introduction

LITERATURE

In the opening section of Allee et al., *Principles of Animal Ecology* (1949), two chapters are devoted to the history of animal ecology. Although much of this material is non-marine, it also includes many marine works and covers the subject so fully that there seems little call to repeat it here. This work, incidentally, has 71 pages of bibliography which will prove invaluable to the student in search of further information on animal ecology. Gislén (1930) in his Epibioses of the Gullmer Fjord gives a very comprehensive bibliography of work on marine ecology up to that date, and Fischer-Piette (1940) has brought this further up to date for the intertidal region. Hesse's *Tiergeographie auf oekologischer grundlage* (1924), Hesse Allee, and Schmidt's *Ecological Animal Geography* (1951), and Ekman's *Zoogeography of the Sea* (1953) contain a wealth of additional material. A treatise on marine ecology and palaeoecology, to be published by the Geological Society of America, is now being prepared.

Flattely and Walton's *The Biology of the Sea Shore* (1922) is a work which, in its field, has not yet been superseded. In the field of marine biology, more recent works which will be invaluable to the student include Russell and Yonge's *The Seas* (1936) and Yonge's *The Sea Shore* (1949), Wilson's *Life of the Shore and Shallow Sea* (1951) and *They Live in the Sea* (1947), MacGinitie and MacGinitie's *Natural History of Marine Animals* (1949), and Buchsbaum's *Animals without Backbones* (1938). In all these, though, the more accessible shores have received the most attention, with progressively smaller space devoted to the less accessible ocean waters. For these the student must turn to sections of more general works such as Murray and Hjort's *The Depths of the Ocean* (1912) and Sverdrup et al. *The Oceans* (1946). For deeper water, two excellent books are Hardy's *The Open Ocean* (1956) and Marshall's *Aspects of Deep Sea Biology* (1954). Even with all these to draw on, we have no comprehensive work to turn to for the biological side of marine ecology, and the student will be forced to track down his facts laboriously through an extensive literature of more specialized and limited works.

Most books on marine biology are based mainly on the fauna and flora of a relatively small area. This can be very discouraging for the occupant of a region which shares few species in common with that of the book. It is true that a large proportion of the earlier work in this field has centered around the Naples laboratory and the various northern European laboratories, and later the laboratories on the northeast coast of the United States and on the California coast. More recently, though, much ecological work has been done in South America, South Africa, Japan, Australia, and elsewhere, and it seems proper to choose illustrations from as wide a field as possible, if a general point of view is to be obtained. This introduces the difficulty that most of the names of plants and animals referred to will be strange to all but the specialist. To meet this difficulty, a partial classification of the plant and animal kingdoms is given in an appendix; here all genera referred to in the text can be located.

Although some ecological research can make use of gross analyses of the total quantity of animal or plant material present in a region or being produced in it, still most of the work calls for a detailed knowledge of the species concerned. It is perhaps in this aspect, more than in any other, that ecology has lagged behind other sciences in mechanization. Modern oceanography has accelerated its routine by using such time-saving devices as the bathythermograph, the geomagnetic electrokinetograph, the echo sounder, and the salinity-temperature-depth recorder, to mention only a few. All have reduced enormously the time needed to make certain field observations and to interpret them in the desired form. Biochemistry, biophysics, and physiology have likewise accelerated many of their methods. Yet ecologists are still faced, in so many cases, with laborious sorting and identification of individual specimens. In the laboratory, they may be able to work with unispecific cultures and estimate their changing population density photometrically. In the field, such simplification is rarely possible.

The ecologist must, then, be able first to identify his material with certainty and then, having established the species with which he is concerned, to sort it with the least possible consumption of time. Where primary identification is concerned, he may usually submit material to specialists in that particular field, although these, even when available, usually have a heavy accumulation of similar material already awaiting their attention. Even with a named set of material available, the ecologist still requires good taxonomic training to be sure that his own later identifications are correct. To many non-taxonomists, the specialist often appears unjustifiably concerned with the erection of new subspecies and races. There is a purpose in this, however, which has very real significance to the ecologist. What today are considered as two subspecies may one day be more properly separated into distinct species. Ecologically, these may prove to be widely different. If this happens, earlier ecological work may prove valueless if it has not been made clear at the time with precisely what form the work was done. An example at the time of writing can be seen in the copepod *Calanus*. Prior to a few years ago, much classical work was done on *C. finmarchicus*. It now appears that this must be distinguished from *C. helgolandicus*, and it has not always been possible to refer back to preserved material to see which species was included in the earlier work (Russell, 1951).

To attempt to indicate available taxonomic literature is out of the question. For workers in the older marine laboratories there are usually available extensive fauna and flora lists such as the *Plymouth Marine Fauna* (Marine Biological Association, 1931), "A Biological Survey Of The Waters Of Woods Hole and Vicinity" (*Bull. U.S. Bur. Fisheries,* 1913), and "Manx Algae" (Knight and Parke, 1931). The bibliographies quoted in these usually afford an excellent starting point. For a few groups there are world-wide monographs (e.g. Mortensen's *A Monograph of the Echinoidea,* 1928–1950) or ones of wide application (e.g. the journal *Johnsonia* for east coast American molluscs), and the *Fiches d'Identification du Zooplankton* published by the International Council in Copenhagen. All too few groups have, however, been treated in this way, and for many parts of the oceans neither species lists nor comprehensive works exist. Descriptions of oceanic plankton and nekton, in particular, are largely confined to the various expedition reports concerned. Unfortunately, complete sets of these reports are not always readily accessible. The ecologist who must be able to recognize a wide array of species, particularly if he is to work in a region remote from a long-established marine laboratory, is faced with a difficult taxonomic problem. A long time delay may be involved before all his species have been identified, and early work may be invalidated by delay in distinguishing various species present. Nevertheless, the success with which the problems can be met may be seen in the teamwork of the members of the Great Barrier Reef expedition or of Stephenson and his co-workers in South Africa.

The embryology and life history of the organisms studied is a field in which even less information is available to the student. There are excellent textbooks of invertebrate embryology, such as *Textbook of Embryology* by MacBride (1914) and Dawydoff's *Traité d'embryologie comparée des invertébrés* (1928), and algal life histories are covered in such general texts as Smith's *Manual of Phycology* (1951) and Fritsch's *The Structure and Reproduction of the Algae* (1935, 1945). Nearly all the examples included, though, are selected types, usually from a limited region of the ocean. Even for such classical areas as Naples, Plymouth, or Woods Hole, the life history of only a small percentage of the local species is known. For most of the fauna and flora of the oceans, information on life histories is negligible. As with general marine biology, few comprehensive works exist. Probably for no other area is there a review as comprehensive as Thorson's "Reproduction and Larval Development of Danish Marine Bottom Invertebrates" (1946a). The latter work, incidentally, provides a valuable starting point in tracing further literature on particular forms, as well as containing a very extensive survey of the ecology of the larvae. A few comprehensive works on particular groups are available, such as Gurney's "Larvae of Decapod Crustacea" (1942) and Mortensen's "Contributions to the Study of the Development and Larval Forms of Echinoderms" (1931–1938), but these are the exception and the available literature is in general widely scattered. For most marine organisms, the life histories are still unknown.

There is no adequate textbook of physiology of marine invertebrates. Perhaps the most useful is *Comparative Animal Physiology* by Prosser et al. (1950), which has a particularly good bibliography. For the physiology and ecology of marine algae, there are sections in Smith's *Manual of Phycology* (1951) and Chapman's *An Introduction to the Study of Algae* (1941). With a few exceptions, marine organisms have been used by physiologists as convenient material for studying particular reactions rather than for the purpose of understanding the particular organism itself. This is of course true, though probably to a lesser extent, of other aspects of ecology. From the ecologist's point of view, though, it has had the unfortunate result of yielding an unbalanced picture. There is a tremendous wealth of knowledge concerning the physiology of the sea urchin egg, for example, but little is known about the adult sea urchin. Certain aspects of physiology have received more widespread treatment, of course. Examples may be found in Yonge's work on invertebrate digestion, that on respiratory pigments, done by various workers, etc. Again particular animals of economic importance, such as oysters, *C. finmarchicus,* etc., have been studied from many points of view. Once again, though, the ecologist is faced with the fact that if information is sought on the physiology of a particular species, the chances are very high that nothing is known about it.

The behavior of marine organisms has received some study, and the results are, on the whole, more immediately applicable ecologically than those of other fields so far discussed. The diurnal migration of zooplankton has yielded excellent material for the study of phototropic and geotropic reactions. The complex conditions in the intertidal zone have led to the examination of similar reactions in its inhabitants as well as of their reactions to desiccation, etc. Fish have been studied with regard to their schooling behavior, their ability to "learn," and their sensitivity to different stimuli. Although, again, no one book summarizes such information, reference may be made to Fraenkel and Gunn's *The Orientation of Animals* (1940), and "Physiological Mechanism in Animal Behaviour" (Society for Experimental Biology, 1950).

Turning from the organisms themselves, to the environment in which they live, we find a more encouraging series of texts available. Murray and Hjort's *The Depths of the Ocean* (1912) represents a landmark in the history of our knowledge of both the chemistry and physics of sea water. *The Oceans,* by Sverdrup et al. (1946) surveys the knowledge 60 years later. Three books by Harvey, *Biological Chemistry and Physics of Sea Water* (1928), *Recent Advances in the Chemistry and Biology of Sea Water* (1945), and *The Chemistry and Fertility of Sea Water* (1955) are also invaluable. Day (1951) gives an extensive discussion and bibliography of estuarine conditions. In most of these, oceanic waters tend to be more adequately covered than inshore ones, particularly those bathing the intertidal zone and those in estuaries. For these, reference must be made to individual papers. Tides, which comprise an important ecological factor near shore, are covered by Darwin (1898) and more recently by Russell and Mac-Millan (1952).

Meteorology impinges somewhat less on marine ecology, at least less directly. Sverdrup's *Oceanography for Meteorologists* (1943) contains some useful data not given in Sverdrup et al. (1946). On the whole, the ecologist most often finds his contact with meteorology limited to a study of weather records which are available in various government publications of different countries.

The influence of the organism on the environment has perhaps received more attention in geology than in any of the other sciences bordering on ecology, although it is true that, in a large proportion of cases, the organisms are most important geologically after they are dead. This is true of those sedimentary rocks formed largely from a rain of dead plankton, as well as for the oil content of some such deposits believed to have a similar origin. It is as true for rocks formed from ancient coral reefs, or dominated by fossil crinoids. On the other hand, much of both the cementation and the breakdown of intertidal and shallow water rocks may be due to the activities of living plants and animals, and both the consolidation of sediments into coarser fecal masses and their attrition may be due to passage through animal guts.

Such geological aspects of ecology are treated in many geological textbooks. The more limited subject of marine geology has been well surveyed in Kuenen's *Marine Geology* (1950), and Shepard's *Submarine Geology* (1948), and from them such special aspects as coral reef formation may be traced. Because of the economic importance of oil, the sediments in which it occurs have received very intensive study, as have the conditions under which such sediments accumulate. For an introduction to the field, Landes (1951) and Cloud (1952) may be mentioned of many others. Yet another aspect is found in paleoecology and in the attempt to deduce the nature of extinct environments from the known present-day requirements of the fauna and flora, or of their nearest living relations. Where recent species occur in the deposits, fairly valid conclusion about climate may be drawn, but when all the species have changed, such deductions must be made more cautiously; however, plants can hardly have grown, at any time, at a much greater depth than they do today, and the same is probably true of the reef corals, with their contained zooxanthellae. In this and similar ways, a comparatively accurate picture may be drawn of environmental conditions in previous eras. These are likely to be very greatly reinforced by the techniques now being developed, for the radioactive determination of both the age of fossils and the temperature at which some of their constituents must have been layed down (Urie, 1948; Urie et al., 1951).

This brief survey has been intended to point the way to additional sources of information for those who wish to explore particular fields in greater detail than is possible here. The bibliographies contained in the various works referred to should provide sufficient guides for these fields. Finally, the student is recommended to consult the ecology section, and particularly its oceanography subdivision, in *Biological Abstracts,* and the bibliography in *Journal du Conseil.* Further information may be found in the succeeding reference to ecological methods.

AUTECOLOGY AND SYNECOLOGY

During its evolution, ecology has tended to concentrate on two approaches to its problems. On the one hand there has been the study of the species as a unit, with an endeavor to arrive at as complete an understanding as possible of the internal and external relationships of one kind of animal or plant. This has come to be known as autecology. Rather sharply differentiated from this approach is synecology in which the unit studied is more complex. There we are concerned with communities, usually embracing many species of both animals and plants but characterized by the predominance of certain particular species. Unfortunately a rift has developed between the two schools of thought, and the protagonists of one sometimes fail to appreciate the true value of the other. It is manifest that either may be carried to extremes, and it is suggested that the proponents of both aut- and synecology should consider these as part of a three-way attack on the full understanding of ecology. The third facet is one that has so far been attempted only rarely but will certainly develop as our knowledge progresses: it might be termed integral ecology. The three parts form a circle, with synecology surveying the broad field, autecology differentiating this into its components, and integral ecology recombining these into the original whole.

Suppose we face the problem of understanding the interrelation of the animals and plants of a particular area. This may be the Dogger

Bank, with its economically important fishes, and the bottom-living and planktonic forms on which they prey. It may be an abyssal fauna, living too deep for living plants to exist; or it may be an intertidal rock pool, limited in size, but harboring its own peculiar forms of life and undergoing the rapid and drastic environmental changes characteristic of its location. In any of these, the first step is surely to define what life is present and what are the physical and chemical conditions under which it lives. From the biological aspect, the synecologists have devised descriptive terms covering various more or less homogeneous parts of the population. To these terms they have added estimation of the quantitative proportion of the major components, either numerically or by weight or volume. At the same time, environmental conditions are defined, and frequently a correlation becomes apparent between some of these and the dominance of particular species. The communities, or certain species in them, may be so sensitive to environmental conditions that they can be used as an index of those conditions—sometimes an easier or better index than can be obtained by a study of the conditions themselves. Furthermore, if the age of the older members of the community is known, we have evidence that environmental conditions did not vary beyond certain limits during that period. This fact could perhaps not be proved by direct methods. A classic example of such study of communities will be referred to later in describing some of Petersen's work in Danish waters. It is of interest to remember that this work was inspired by the need for an understanding of the biological productivity of these waters, particularly with reference to their fishing potential.

Now the environment in itself is sufficiently complex. In addition, no two species, or even two ages of the same species, react in quite the same way to the conditions they encounter. In unraveling the complicated network of interactions that exist in the community, it seems logical to examine it piecemeal. It may or may not be true that the whole, in such a case, is equal to the sum of the constituents. Perhaps they behave differently when isolated. Nevertheless, we cannot fail to benefit by their examination when isolated, and the possible errors which this method may introduce can be considered later.

It is this study of individual species that constitutes autecology. Study of the communities should have shown which are the most important species. These should now be examined separately. Unfortunately, there is a tendency to consider the communities in terms of their larger and more obvious members, omitting mention perhaps of much more significant but less apparent ones. An example of this may be seen in the concentration of the earlier phytoplankton studies on the diatoms and, to a lesser extent, on the armored dinoflagellates. Today, we are beginning to realize that the nannoplankton—forms so small that they pass freely through our finest nets—may constitute ten to a thousand times the bulk of the larger diatoms and armored dinoflagellates.

The study of individual species is a slow process. It has, rather naturally, centered mainly on commercially important species of fishes, molluscs, and crustaceans. Even these are not adequately known, and outside of them, there are probably not 50 species about which our knowledge is more than a very beginning. For of by far the greatest number of marine animals and plants no more is known than certain anatomical characteristics, a life cycle inferred from some related forms, and a rough idea of the type of habitat which seems to favor them. There are still whole groups, such as the nannoplankton and the marine fungi, whose very species are still almost unknown; the autecologist's task is then only in its infancy.

Among those species whose ecology is better known, it is still usually the more obvious characteristics that have been examined. The breeding cycle is probably known, as well as the growth rate. Seasonal and environmental variations in these will have been studied, and life span and the mortality rate determined. The feeding methods and food are probably known as well as the predators whose food the species provides. The relations of survival, growth, and behavior to a few environmental factors have probably been studied. The latter will include temperature and salinity—perhaps other factors such as oxygen and illumination. Something may be known of the organism's behavior and reaction to certain stimuli, and physiological studies probably include its respiration and food assimilation. Beyond these little will be known, and obviously far more needs to be done. Yet this list outlines our knowledge of only the few best-known forms. To those who have not worked in this field, it may be pointed out that even this much knowledge represents the combined efforts of many workers over a considerable time, all contributing their part to a study which is full of difficulties.

The first phase of an ecological survey is, then, the synecologist's survey of the whole situation. The second phase is the autecologist's study of the components into which the complex has been subdivided for ease of handling, and the third phase is the recombination of these components into a whole and the proof that this whole represents a reasonable approximation of the complex with which we started. When it is realized how few species have been adequately studied by the autecologist, it is not surprising that there has rarely been material available for an attempt at recombination. Properly speaking, it has not yet been accomplished. By making many simplifying assumptions, however, Riley has done this for the plankton community and has shown that the productivity of a water mass may be fairly closely predicted if the hydrographic conditions are known. Despite the necessary simplification of the problems, this is a big step forward and one that will, it is hoped, stimulate similar attempts in other fields. It is true that Riley's results have been seriously questioned (Nielsen, 1952; Riley, 1953); nevertheless they provide a valuable framework for future work. Furthermore, Riley's work has drawn attention to gaps in the work of the autecologists and provided a fresh stimulus toward filling them.

ECOLOGICAL METHODS

To survey ecological methods would be an impossible task, since so many sciences contribute to them. The most that can be done is to consider certain techniques of particularly widespread importance. Although some organisms can flourish under artificial conditions, when isolated from all other species, in nature they are always associated with many other forms. Always there is a greater or lesser extent of competition both within the species and between different species. The ecologist is concerned with defining and measuring the success of a species under particular conditions. The definition of such success is illusive, and Fischer-Piette (1948) has shown how the optimum external conditions for a species may differ according to the method used in estimating its "prosperity." In general, though, a workable index of the organism's well-being may usually be found in its growth rate, survival rate, and rate of reproduction. Population density is likely to be a less basic measure, though often an easier one, since it may be a resultant of all three.

The determination of growth rate must involve the estimation of size, and, although this may be simple in hard-bodied forms such as crustacea, or shelled gastropods, it is much more difficult in soft-bodied forms such as worms or algae. Even in forms such as molluscs, shell size does not necessarily reflect body size, since the latter may vary seasonally or from one locality to another. A linear measurement of a hard body is usually the easiest to make, but it is necessary to obtain an index whereby this may be converted to the equivalent tissue weight or volume, and a study has to be made of how this index varies in different circumstances. If shape does not vary with size, then body weight is proportional to the cube of the linear dimension, and the cube of the length is frequently a better description of size than is the length itself. Rigid bodies of irregular shape, in which growth is not uniform in different parts, are more difficult to measure. In the case of coral colonies, attempts have been made at measuring the area of the projected outline. In both these and algae, weight has been used, but since this involves weighing also the object to which they are attached, the accuracy of the weighing may be poor. Wieser (1951) gives a method utilizing the weight of the surface film of water as a means of estimating the surface area. Displacement methods have also been used with corals and algae, and in special cases, such as the long, strap-like fronds of *Laminaria,* the spacing of marks, incised on the plant, has yielded excellent growth data. In algae especially, a further problem arises in making allowance for loss by attrition or fragmentation.

For studies of growth of individuals, these may be relocated and recognized for repeated measurements if they are permanently attached forms. If not, it is necessary to attach numbered tags to them or paint numbers on some suitable surface. Tagging has been carried out most extensively and successfully with fish, and more rarely in other forms. Some account of the methods may be found in Rounsefell and Kask's "How to Mark Fish" (1943). For most invertebrates, no suitable tagging method has been evolved. In some molluscs, good results have been obtained by notching the edge of the shell and thereafter recording the growth beyond the scar left by the notch.

Various animals lay down some form of annual rings from which age and the size at successive year intervals can be determined. This method has been applied principally to the scales, otoliths, and bones of fishes, and to the shells of some lamellibranchs. Out of many papers on the subject, those of VanOosten (1929) and Lee (1920) may be suggested as a useful source of information. The method has also been used on the test plates of some echinoderms and could probably be applied in a few other forms also. Care is needed in applying the method, since some forms readily produce false rings, and proof must always be obtained that the rings are actually annual.

Population studies may provide a very valuable method of following growth. In a test panel or similar denuded surface, successive measurements of the few largest individuals give a measure of growth, although one that is liable to some error. If the breeding season or season of spat settlement is limited, then spat of a known age can be followed as a unit until the next spat group appears. Thereafter they may still be identified if an analysis of size distribution is made. When frequency is plotted against size in such data, two or more peaks may be obtained, each representing a separate year group or group of distinct age. With increasing size and decreasing annual linear increment, such peaks tend to overlap too much to be separable, although measurement of very large samples helps to extend the usefulness of this method. Occasionally an outstandingly successful year of spat settlement may so dominate the population that it is recognizable for many years thereafter. Finally, the growth of individuals may be studied in captivity, but then they are not living under natural conditions, and results so obtained can be applied to natural conditions only with reservations.

Studies of the rate of mortality at different ages have been made for surprisingly few marine forms. The greatest number of these are fishes of economic importance, and the reason for this lies not only in the economic value of the results but also in the availability of data on age in the fish scales. In most forms, the mortality rate is very much higher in the young stages than in the older ones. The mere fact that Danish bottom-living invertebrates which have planktonic larvae produce, on the average, about a million eggs per year each shows that larval mortality must be very high. There would not be space enough for any large proportion of these to settle on suitable territory, let alone grow up there. Those forms which protect their young in one way or another can afford to produce fewer eggs in proportion to the lower mortality rate in the young stages. A high mortality rate, as for intsance where predation is heavy, may well accompany conditions conducive to a high growth rate; in fact a high death rate may result in an increased growth rate by reducing the competition for the available food. Neither, by itself, can then be considered as an adequate index of well-being.

In a single-cell form, such as a diatom or protozoan, growth results in division, and reproduction and growth follow parallel paths. Even in higher and much larger forms, such as corals, growth may consist in repeated divisions of the individual. From the ecological point-of-view, the significance of both growth and reproduction lies largely in the increase in, or at least in the maintenance of, the territory occupied by the species. One vital significance in the production of eggs and larvae lies in the ability of the latter, very often to colonize regions beyond the reach of the parents. This is particularly advantageous when the parents are attached or are only feebly migratory. So effective is this mechanism that fringe populations of non-breeding individuals may exist as permanent and successful communities, yet rely entirely for their replenishment on larvae from other regions where conditions are more suitable for reproduction.

Reproductive rates vary enormously in different species and reflect the mortality rates to which the species is subject in its later stages. The production of numerous eggs is therefore no criterion of well-being, although, when this is combined with rapid maturation, it may result in great ability to take advantage rapidly of a favorable new environment. Within one species, though, the rate of egg production and the age at which this commences may be a valuable index of environmental conditions. Thus barnacles may become sexually mature at 1 to 3 years after settlement, or they may never mature, depending largely on tidal level and degree of exposure to wave action.

In some gastropods, and perhaps in other forms also, reproduction appears to be an alternative to growth, and the latter ceases permanently at sexual maturity. In many others, the energy drain involved in gonad maturation results in a marked decrease in growth rate. In the squid, *Loligo vulgaris,* growth ceases with egg production in the female but continues in the mature male (Tinbergen and Verwey, 1945), and in the shrimp, *Crangon vulgaris,* the female does not increase in weight at the molt which accompanies egg laying (Lloyd and Yonge, 1947). In some forms also, and notably in polychaetes, a species may be capable of several types of reproduction. Correlated with the resulting adaptability to a wide range of environmental conditions, there is usually a particularly wide geographic range in such species.

We have mentioned three aspects of success or well-being, and there are obviously many more. The zoogeographer may be concerned with the range of a species, considering only presence or absence. The ecologist also is concerned with those limiting conditions beyond which a species cannot survive. Within these limits, however, there are degrees of success of the species. Furthermore, a particular environmental factor does not usually have a fixed limiting value. The reaction of the species to each factor is conditioned by the suitability or otherwise of other factors. Thus a lowered salinity may well be tolerated at summer temperatures, whereas it could be lethal in winter.

In studying the effect of variation of one single factor, the ecologist is faced with the problem of the significance of his results when applied to natural conditions where many factors vary simultaneously. We come back, in fact, to the question raised earlier of to what extent the reactions of an organism to a complex environment can be expressed in terms of its reactions to a simple one. The corollary to this is the problem of whether a community is no more than the sum of its constituents. These seem to be particular aspects of the larger problem of whether all phenomena could be both explained and predicted if our knowledge were sufficient, or whether there are inherent unpredictables in the universe. In particular, there has long been debate about whether life is something over and above the phenomena of chemistry and physics. It would be profitless to argue this further here, and there seems little need for an attempt to answer the ecological aspects of the problem. Our immediate concern is with the reactions and interactions that we believe to be soluble.

The early marine biologists noted that, although some species were relatively constant in most of their characteristics, others were highly variable, with typical shape, color, and size for different localities. In many species these variations were attributed to environmental conditions with which they appeared to be correlated, and such causal relationships came to be widely accepted without ever having been proved. Sometimes later work has shown that the conclusions about cause and effect were false. Thus it was noted that limpets in wave-exposed locations tended to have flatter shells than those in sheltered areas, and it was explained that this was an adaptation fitting them better to withstand the shock of waves. Later investigations by Orton and others showed that the flatter shells were simply a reaction of the animal to being kept wet for a longer period, and that a tall shell could be induced to add flatter growth when kept permanently immersed in still water. Similarly, it was recorded that the color of the shell of the gastropod *Purpura* was dependent on the extent of wave action. Later work showed that it was dependent directly on the relative proportion of mussels to barnacles in its diet, and that the connection with wave action was the greater abundance of mussels in more wave-beaten places.

It is only rarely that a particular variation points to a single factor as being responsible, or as probably responsible. Gigantism in molluscs suggests the possibility of parasitic castration. An increased number of vertebrae in fishes is usually related to low temperatures during the young stages. More often only a guess can be made at the factor responsible, or there may be no indication at all of what it is. Or, again, more than one factor may, under different conditions, produce the same effect. Thus the rate of growth of diatoms may be controlled by the availability of nutrient salts, by illumination, and by temperature, any one of which may slow it down or accelerate it. When a given factor is suspected as the cause of a particular effect, it is frequently possible to test this hypothesis under experimental conditions, and this procedure has the added advantage of yielding a quantitative measure of the effect of the factor. Many organisms, though, do not live well or at all in captivity, or do not react normally when kept there. Under natural conditions, on the other hand, it is almost never possible to watch the effects of variation of a single factor while all other possible factors remain constant. Here statistical analysis of correlations is most useful, and Riley (1939) has discussed the applications of the method in marine ecology. In this method it is necessary to have, for a considerable series of localities or occasions, data on the several variations in the organism itself and of the status of each environmental factor which may be concerned. Correlation analyses then show the degree of connection between each. It must be emphasized that the correlation coefficients obtained indicate the degree of closeness with which changes in two observations parallel one another, but they do not show that there is any direct connection, or which one influences which. The method is very valuable, though, in pointing to the existence of a probable connection, and the solving of regression equations from the same data gives a numerical value to the amount of variation to be expected in one for a given change in the other. Furthermore, the calculation of partial correlation coefficients frequently helps in breaking down a complex of interrelations. Thus it may be found that, in a plankton population, both numbers of zooplankton and also numbers of phytoplankton are correlated with the amount of illumination. Partial correlations will show that the connection is strong between illumination and phytoplankton, and between phyto- and zooplankton, but weak or absent between illumination and zooplankton. This strongly suggests that the illumination affects the plants, and these in turn affect the animals.

It frequently happens that, under natural conditions, two possible factors vary together, and it is difficult to decide which of them is responsible for an observed effect. Such problems can sometimes be solved by finding exceptional circumstances in which the two factors vary abnormally in respect to one another. Thus, in certain French estuaries, it was shown that a number of intertidal species penetrated farther up the estuary in summer than in winter. Normally the summers there are periods of high salinity and high temperature, and low salinity and temperature are found in winter. Either salinity or temperature might have been limiting to the penetration of the species concerned. Observation of the estuary in seasons of unusually high and unusually low rainfall showed that it was the salinity which must be responsible. In the same way, in the example already referred to

of the interrelation of shell color in *Purpura* with either abundance
of mussels or wave action, a few exceptional localities were found
where mussels were abundant in shelter and where they were absent
at high wave exposure. In both of these places the color was found
to reflect the abundance of the mussels rather than the degree of
shelter.

In demonstrating such correlations, the significance of the results
is dependent on the amount of data available. Furthermore, for the
same degree of significance, the amount of data required increases
with increased numbers of variables present. The collection of sufficient data is likely to be the most serious difficulty in ecological problems of this type.

It must be clear from what has already been said that at the present
time the marine ecologist has touched little more than the fringe of
the problems that face him. Even when the wider field of land
ecology is included, it is remarkable how few general laws or principles have been enunciated as compared with other sciences. Properly controlled experiments, in which only one variable factor is permitted in the system at a time, must always be more difficult to achieve
with living material than in, say, chemistry or physics. Many of the
phenomena under consideration can hardly be reproduced in the laboratory, and so can never be controlled.

A survey of the present status of ecological knowledge cannot be
made to fit into a concise and orderly pattern and would, in fact, suffer
if so limited. There is too much interconnection of effects. In succeeding chapters, the various ecological factors are considered in turn,
and examples are given of the ways in which they have been found to
affect different organisms. After this an account is given of the more
important types of environment, together with an outline of the
variations and significance of the various factors in each. These
environments range from the comparatively stable and simple abyssal
regions to the highly complex intertidal zone. Finally, these same
environments are considered in terms of the organisms inhabiting them
with a discussion of the present status of knowledge of typical forms.

2

Physical Environmental Factors

TEMPERATURE

Probably no other environmental factor is as universally important as temperature. An increase in temperature accelerates chemical reactions: according to van't Hoff's law, a rise of 10°C. doubles the reaction rate, although this law is not universally applicable. However, many body processes are the resultant of at least two reactions, one building up and the other breaking down, the two combining to give a reaction curve rising to a peak with increasing temperature and then dropping again. This may be seen, for example, in various enzyme reactions. Any change in temperature is bound to affect the many chemical processes taking place simultaneously in plant or animal tissues, and so affect the organisms as a whole. In addition, many physical processes are dependent on temperature. For example, viscosity rises with decreased temperature. That of sea water is more than doubled with a drop from 30 to 0°C. The same range nearly doubles the solubility of oxygen in sea water.

Since the reaction of organisms to temperature is inevitably a highly complex process, it is to be expected that its details will be but rarely understood. There are very many cases in which a temperature dependence has been demonstrated, and a smaller number where the process principally involved is known, but very few where a particular chemical or physical process can be selected as accounting for all the observed facts. The ecological effects of temperature may conveniently be considered in this order.

The general relation of geographical distribution of both plants and animals to temperature has long been recognized and is the basis of

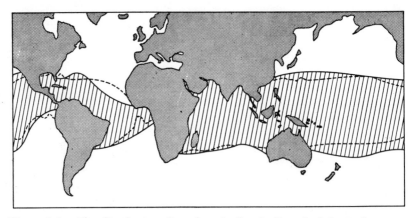

Figure 2–1. The distribution of coral reefs (hatched) and of the isotherm representing a minimum winter surface temperature of 70°F. (Modified from Hesse et al., 1937; Hutchins and Scharff, 1947.)

the classification of the world's fauna and flora in terms of certain temperature zones.   Perhaps the best-known case of close temperature control is that of the reef-building corals (Fig. 2–1). Coral reefs do not flourish where the minimum winter temperature is much below 21°C. The upper temperature limit may be much lower than this in other species, and an extreme case is the lamellibranch *Portlandia* (= *Yoldia*) *arctica* which is not found in water above 4°C. *Pecten groenlandicus,* in East Greenland, is never found above 0°C. (Jensen, 1942).   In contrast to such a form, the blue-green algae *Phormidium bijahense* and *Oscillaria filiformis* can live in fresh water up to 85.2°C., and some bacteria can live in a similar situation up to 88°C. (Copeland, 1936). Mayer (1914) has reviewed much of the earlier literature on the upper limiting temperatures of forms inhabiting warm waters; he brings out the important generalization that most of them

are living closer to their upper limiting temperature than to their lower
limit.

Climatic observations have established the upper and lower temperatures at the limits of a great many species of animals and plants.
It must not be supposed, though, that these represent lethal temperatures, since such mechanisms as feeding, reproduction, and general
activity are often modified at temperatures less extreme than those at
which immediate or rapid death occurs. For example, geographically,
there may be a non-breeding fringe within the absolute limits of distribution of a species. This fringe relies for its recruitment on a supply of migratory young or adults from an area where conditions are
suitable for breeding, and such a fringe cannot occur where there is no

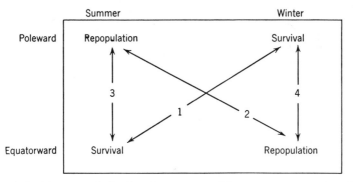

Figure 2–2. Diagram of the four basic types of limitation to extension of geographic range poleward and equatorward. The arrows indicate the ways in
which the pairs may combine. (After Hutchins, 1947.)

possibility of such migration. Hutchins (1947) has developed a
method for determining whether it is breeding or survival which constitutes a particular boundary for a species. For the poleward
boundary, the minimum winter temperature will determine the possibility of survival. On the other hand, it is the maximum summer
temperature that will determine the possibility of breeding. Equatorward the converse holds true, and it is the summer maximum which
determines the possibility of survival, whereas the winter minimum
determines the possibility of breeding. Since, then, both the poleward and the equatorward boundary may be set in two different ways,
there are, as indicated in Fig. 2–2, four possible types of distribution
limitation.

If the distribution of a species is wide enough, it is possible, by
inspection of isotherms, to determine the type to which it belongs.
For example, if the northern limit of the species is known for the east

coast of North America, the summer maximum and winter minimum temperatures may be determined for that spot. On the European coast, the localities where these same values occur will not coincide and will, in fact, be widely separated. If, then, the limit of European distribution of the species coincides with one or another of the localities, the nature of the limiting temperature control is indicated. The southern limits may be treated in the same way, and, where the distri-

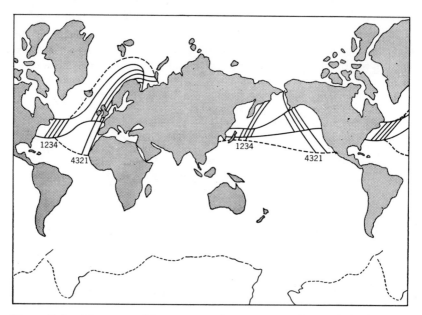

Figure 2–3. The geographic extent on the major coast lines, of the four zone types, numbered as in Fig. 2–2 based on water temperatures at Newfoundland and Cape Hatteras. In this case the four zones are coextensive on the American Atlantic coast but have different, distinctive patterns on the other coasts. (After Hutchins, 1947.)

bution extends into the Pacific, verification of both boundary conditions may be obtained from that ocean. Typical distributions of the four types of control are shown in Fig. 2–3, and Hutchins was able to show that such distribution patterns agreed well with the known distribution of several marine forms. The two mechanisms of survival and breeding are, undoubtedly, of major importance in determining distribution, but others are involved, and Hutchins' analysis would undoubtedly be an oversimplification for many species. In elaboration of this, Thorson (1946) points out that the process of spawning involves at least the two processes of maturation of the genital products and of release of these products, and that each has its critical temperature. There will also be critical temperatures involved after spawning, since, in general, early cleavage stages have a smaller temperature tolerance range than do the larvae, and these in turn than the adults.

The upper lethal temperature has been determined experimentally for a fairly wide range of forms (Broekhuysen, 1940; Gowanloch and Hayes, 1927; Henderson, 1929; Mayer, 1918; Newcombe et al., 1936; Shelford, 1916). Much of the earlier work on the subject has been summarized by Mayer (1914). Catastrophic mortality resulting from abnormally high temperature has been witnessed on various occasions under natural conditions, and there is no doubt that this may be a serious limiting factor in the distribution of many organisms. For instance, the death of numbers of the sea urchin *Diadema*, of *Octopus*, and of *Fissurella* and other gastropods, as well as of small fish was observed on the reef at Dry Tortugas on an occasion when water temperatures rose as high as 33–38°C. It has been suggested that the actual mechanism involved might be coagulation of certain proteins, or asphyxiation. The first of these seems unlikely, since death usually occurs at too low a temperature for coagulation to occur. It is unlikely, also, that the increase in temperature could lower the oxygen concentration of the water to a lethal value unless the body's oxygen requirements were simultaneously increased at the high temperature. It seems more likely that the failure of an enzyme system is involved, possibly one connected with respiration.

Less information is available on the effects of low temperatures and on lower lethal·limits, and much of it concerns unusually cold winters in which actual freezing took place. Usually there is a marked difference in the susceptibility of different species. Blegvad (1929) reports the effect of about two months freezing on the population of a sandy beach in Denmark. The polychaete *Scoloplos armiger* and the molluscs *Mytilus edulis, Scrobicularia plana*, and *Littorina littorea* suffered 100 per cent mortality, *Arenicola marina* 95 per cent, *Cardium edule* 80 per cent, *Nereis diversicolor* 70 per cent, and *Macoma baltica* 33 per cent. Caullery (1929) records a very cold spell which coincided with low spring tides in the Boulogne region in which all exposed *Laminaria flexicaulis* and *L. saccharina*, and some of the more delicate red algae, were killed, but there was no effect on *Fucus* spp. or *Chondrus crispus*. Orton and Lewis (1931) record that temperatures 2–6°C. below normal in the Blackwater estuary were associated with the death of all the *Murex* and many of the *Purpura* ($=$ *Thais*), whereas there was no mortality among the *Urosalpinx*. These three gastropods are all serious pests on the local oyster beds, and the selective mortality modified the carnivore-prey relationship on these beds for some time thereafter. In the same way, Delphy (1917) found that abnormally cold weather at Île Tatihou selectively killed a large part of the *Octopus* population and resulted in a subsequent marked increase in the population of the crabs and lobsters on which they normally preyed. Smidt (1944) reviews other records on the same subject.

Various mechanisms are postulated to account for these effects of cold. In the intertidal region, the presence of ice may cut off the oxygen supply from organisms living below it, even if these are not themselves within the frozen zone. Where actual freezing of the organism takes place, death may be caused by rupture of the cells by ice crystals, but it must be remembered that a considerable degree of supercooling is often possible before such crystals form. In this connection, Salt and Mail (1943) have found that certain insects may be supercooled to as low as −40 to −50°C. Recent work by Scholander et al. (1953) on the survival of fresh-water and land forms in the Arctic may apply also to marine forms. Freezing is normally preceded by considerable desiccation and may prove fatal if this does not occur. Ice formation is mainly in the intercellular spaces, and its extent is proportional to the lowering of the temperature, but some liquid remains within the cells and is unfrozen. This liquid is not supercooled. Along with freezing there is a great reduction in the rate of respiration, and this reduction also increases as the temperature is lowered. Blegvad (1929) states that, in the Arctic, various intertidal forms such as *L. littorea* tend to avoid freezing conditions in winter by moving down to below low watermark, and that there is a very high mortality among those individuals remaining in the intertidal zone.

There are, of course, other circumstances in which mortality is associated with the lowering of temperature, but at temperatures well above the freezing point. A well-known example of this is the catastrophic mortality which occurred in the tile fish, *Lopholatilus chamaelionticeps*, on the east coast of the United States. In 1882 this fish was almost completely wiped out, the sea surface for some 150 miles being reported covered with dead and dying fish, and the mortality was attributed to the intrusion of abnormally cold water into the area. There is another mechanism that may be operative under estuarine conditions. In general, lowered temperature tends to reduce the tolerance of estuarine species to low salinities (Broekema, 1941), and it may be that the mortality among oyster drills, recorded by Orton in the Blackwater estuary, was caused by inability to tolerate, at very low temperatures, a salinity well within their tolerance range at normal temperatures.

We have so far considered only general effects of temperature, with little reference to particular mechanisms and processes involved. We

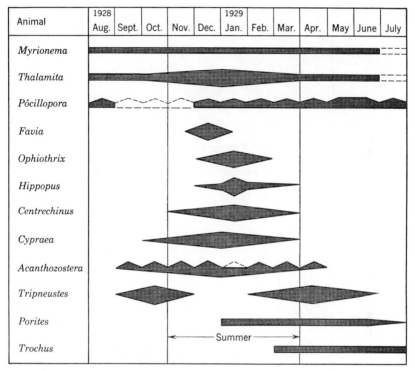

Animal	1928 Aug.	Sept.	Oct.	Nov.	Dec.	1929 Jan.	Feb.	Mar.	Apr.	May	June	July
Myrionema												
Thalamita												
Pócillopora												
Favia												
Ophiothrix												
Hippopus												
Centrechinus												
Cypraea												
Acanthozostera												
Tripneustes												
Porites												
Trochus												

Summer

Figure 2–4. Diagram of the probable spawning periods of forms studied at Low Isles, on the Great Barrier Reef. The broken lines show presumed conditions during periods for which no data are available. Periodicity is indicated by a series of peaks which have not, however, been adjusted to the correct phase of the moon. The widened center of the diamond indicates increased breeding activity in *Thalamita* and *Hippopus* but is conventional in the remainder. The abrupt beginning of breeding in *Porites* and *Trochus* is due to absence of information for the preceeding period. (After Stephenson, 1934.)

have treated, also, extremes of temperature rather than those that lie within the tolerance range of the species concerned. All shallower water marine forms undergo some, and usually considerable, seasonal variation in temperature. In addition, many of them also undergo diurnal variations in temperature. In different organisms, all types of seasonal breeding may occur. There are critical temperatures for both the maturation and the liberation of genital products. Some forms breed more or less uniformly throughout the year, others mainly in the summer or mainly in the winter; still others have two breeding periods, one in the spring and the other in the fall. Superimposed on this general pattern may be a lunar or other spawning rhythm. Examples of these various types, taken from the Australian Great Barrier Reef, are

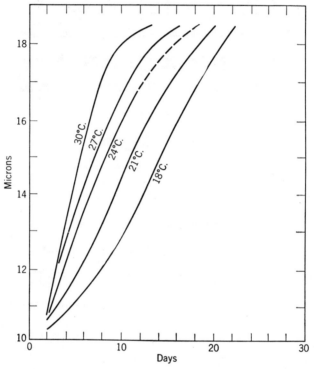

Figure 2–5. The relation of growth of the larvae of the lamellibranch *Venus mercenaria* to temperature. (After Loosanoff et al., 1951.)

shown in Fig. 2–4. Besides temperature, other factors such as illumination vary seasonally, so it is not always certain that temperature is the controlling factor. In many species, though, the relationship appears to be well established (Orton, 1920). Thus Thorson (1946), comparing the breeding periods of a number of species of Danish invertebrates, shows that there is tendency for earlier spawning among those inhabiting the shallower waters which warm up earlier in the year; the deeper waters are slower to warm up, and their inhabitants tend to spawn correspondingly later in the summer. From the extensive work on commercial species of oyster, it is clear that there is a

definite temperature at which spawning begins.   However, local physiological races have been developed in the oyster so that the spawning
temperature, although relatively constant at any one place, differs
markedly on different parts of the coast.   Thus Stauber (1950) states
that spawning of oysters begins at about the same time of year at
Delaware Bay, Bideford River, and Long Island Sound, but that the
corresponding temperatures are respectively 25, 20, and 16.4°C.

The temperature tolerance range of developing eggs and larvae
tends, as we have already stated, to increase as they grow older.
Within the range, growth rate is usually strongly accelerated at higher
temperature.   Figure 2–5 shows the effect of temperature on the development of the larvae of the clam *Venus mercenaria,* and Fig. 2–6

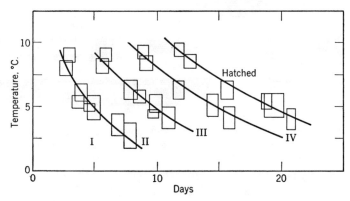

Figure 2–6. The relation of growth of haddock eggs at successive stages to
temperature.   (After Dannevig, 1895; in Walford, 1938.)

on the different stages of haddock eggs.   *Ostrea edulis* has a free-
swimming life of 1 week at 24–27°C., 13 days at 23–24°C., 17 days at
20°C., and at least 21 days at still lower temperatures (Thorson, 1946).
Such prolongation of free-swimming life at low temperatures may be
of considerable importance both in allowing a longer period for the
larvae to be distributed under the influence of currents, and in extending the period when they are open to predation.

Growth is in itself a complex process, but for simplicity it may be
considered as the manifestation of assimilated food not diverted to
such other purposes as respiration and muscular activity.   Where ova,
sperm, or spores are produced, these, as they mature, represent only
temporary growth which will ultimately be lost as far as the total organism is concerned.   The same is true of tissue lost in the molting of
crustacea, in the fragmentation of algae, etc.   In many organisms

growth continues throughout life. In some molluscs, such as *Purpura lapillus,* body growth occurs only during immaturity, being apparently completely diverted to gonad production at maturity (Moore, 1938).

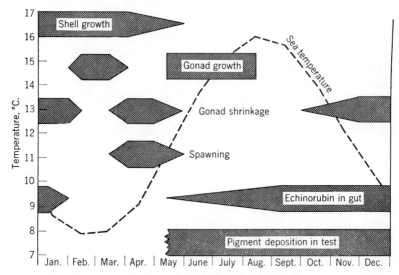

Figure 2–7. The seasonal cycles of shell and gonad growth, spawning, and pigment formation in the sea urchin, *Echinus esculentus.* (After Moore, 1937.)

In still others, periods of body growth alternate with periods of gonad growth, as in the sea urchin *Echinus esculentus* (Fig. 2–7). Under experimental conditions, a relation has been demonstrated between the

TABLE 2–1

Relation between Growth of *Ostrea virginica* and Temperature during the Period February 15–March 16, 1949

(Loosanoff and Nomejko, 1949)

Per Cent Increment, mm.	Temperature, °C.			
	10	15	20	25
Length	1.4	9.2	8.2	4.8
Width	1.4	10.8	10.3	4.4

growth rate of various animals and the temperature. In such animals as the oyster, Table 2–1, there is an optimum temperature, above or below which growth decreases.

The average or maximum size attained in a population does not of necessity reflect the growth rate. Large size may be evidence of long-continued growth rather than of rapid growth. There are many instances of a geographical variation in size in which temperature appears to be the controlling factor, however, we do not know whether the regions characterized by the larger sizes are areas of rapid growth or of long-continued slow growth. Although there is a rather general impression that larger forms tend to be found in cold waters, there are many exceptions (e.g. Odhner, 1915). For example, Wimpenny (1936) shows that the diatoms of warm waters tend, on the whole, to be larger than those of colder waters. His data are shown in Table 2–2.

TABLE 2–2

Distribution of Larger and Smaller Forms of Diatoms

(Wimpenny, 1936)

Genera Showing Species of Smallest Diameter in Cold Areas	Genera Showing Species of Smallest Diameter in Warm Areas	Genera Showing Species of Largest and Smallest Diameter in Cold Areas	Genera Showing Species of Largest Diameter in Cold Areas
Melosira	*Lauderia*	*Schröderella*	*Biddulphia*
Coscinodiscus	*Leptocylindrus*		*Thalassiothrix*
Chaetoceros	*Bacteriastrum*		
Rhizosolenia			
Thalassiosira			
Stephanopyxis			
Fragillaria			
Asterionella			
Achnanthes			
Navicula			
Nitzschia			
Actinoptychus			
Asteromphalus			

Among animals, the sea urchin *E. esculentus* (Moore, 1937) and the gastropod *Urosalpinx cinerea* (Fraser, 1931) both show a larger maximum size in warmer waters. It seems reasonable to suppose that for all organisms there is an optimum temperature for development of maximum size. For some this lies within the range of habitats suitable for survival of the species, and in such cases there will be a decrease in size in both warmer and colder waters. For others the optimum temperature may never be encountered under natural conditions; then there will be a decrease in size with increasing distance from the poles or tropics, as the case may be. In yet other species, some different factor becomes limiting before any appreciable change of temperature is possible. Thus a species adapted to abyssal life could not enter water much above 0°C., without at the same time being subjected to non-abyssal conditions. Among marine animals which exhibit an optimum temperature for developing maximum size there is *P. lapillus*, a temperate form, whose maximum size decreases slightly poleward and markedly toward the equator (Moore, 1936). In the same way, an optimum is found in the antarctic diatom *Rhizosolenia curvata*, as shown in Table 2–3.

TABLE 2–3

Average Diameters of *Rhizosolenia curvata* in Relation to Temperature

(Hart, 1937)

Temperature, °C.	Average Diameter, μ
0	57.2
0–1	58.1
1–2	58.5
2–3	61.5
3–4	63.3
4–5	68.8
5–6	64.4
6–7	64.7
7–8	60.4

Where growth is known to be dependent on temperature, the size attained in a given place may reflect the duration of suitable temperatures there. Thus Orton (1928) has shown that the growth of the oyster *Ostrea edulis* in the Fal and Blackwater estuaries occurs only between 10 and 11°C., during the rising spring temperatures, and between 16 and 14°C. in the fall. In Florida waters, Ingle (in litt.) has found that suitable growing temperatures for *O. virginica* persist throughout the year, and the resulting continuous growth produces, at the end of the year, a size of oyster that would take 2 or 3 years to grow further north. In the gastropod *U. cinerea*, Federighi (1931) found that spawning did not take place below 20°C. and that feeding stopped below 15°C., activity below 10°C. Presumably, then, prolonged subjection to temperature below 15°C. would result in cessation of growth. Stauber (1950) showed that different physiological races of this species occurred in Hampton Roads, Virginia, and in

Delaware Bay. The critical lower limiting temperatures are shown in
Table 2–4. Figure 2–8 shows the relation between the number of egg
masses deposited in the traps set to catch them and the temperature,

TABLE 2–4

**Minimum Temperatures for Certain Activities of *Urosalpinx cinerea* in
Two Physiological Races**

(Stauber, 1950)

Activity	Hampton Roads Race, °C.	Delaware Bay Race, °C.
Oviposition	20	15
Drilling of oysters	15	10
Movement	10	5

and how closely the critical temperature for the occurrence of such
masses agrees in 3 different years.

Large size may, as we have stated, reflect long-continued, rather
than rapid, growth. An example of this is seen in the chaetognath

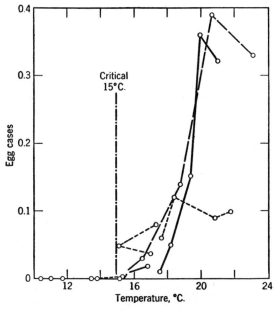

Figure 2–8. The relation of egg deposition to water temperature in the gastropod *Urosalpinx cinerea*. The deposition rate is shown as the number of egg
cases per trap per day. Solid line, 1936; broken line, 1937; dotted line, 1938.
(After Stauber, 1950.)

Sagitta elegans (Fig. 2–9; Russell, 1932a). In this species, the winter brood takes a great deal longer to reach sexual maturity than the summer brood does and, despite the poorer winter feeding conditions, reaches a much larger size.

Reduction of growth at low temperatures may result from a decrease in available food in winter, particularly where this is of planktonic origin. In some animals it may also be the result of reduced feeding activity, despite the fact that sufficient food is available. In the carnivorous *Urosalpinx* referred to earlier, predation ceases before

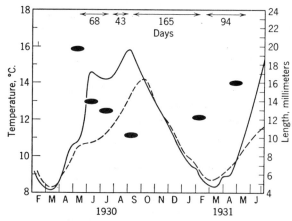

Figure 2–9. Spawning of the chaetognath *Sagitta elegans* in relation to water temperature at the surface (solid line) and at 25 meters (broken line). The black areas represent the spawning periods of the successive broods and the length of the adults comprising these broods; the arrows at the top indicate the duration of the spawning periods. (After Russell, 1932.)

a sufficiently low temperature has been encountered to stop all activity. In the barnacle *Balanus balanoides,* practically the only active movement of the animal is sweeping its cirri through the water to filter out food particles. Cole (1929) reports that the rate of beat of the cirri increases regularly from 2 to 21°C; below 2° and above 21° the beat is irregular, and above 27° it is completely stopped. An increased rate of cirral beat presumably results in the catching of more food, and the growth rate of barnacles is known to be closely dependent on the availability of food; so, other things being equal, a relation between temperature and growth may be looked for in the barnacle. Fuller (1937) gives figures (Table 2–5) for the rate of filtration of water by the copepod *Calanus finmarchicus,* as determined from the rate of removal of the diatom *Nitzschia closterium* from suspension.

In experiments with plaice, *Pleuronectes platessa,* Dawes (1931) determined the amount of food necessary to maintain the body at a constant weight without any growth. This quantity was less in the winter than in summer. When given as much food as they would take, plaice consumed much less in winter than in summer, and the resulting growth was comparably less also, but the efficiency of utilization of this food for growth was somewhat larger in winter than in summer. It is interesting to note that the amount of food required per unit body weight for maintenance decreased in the larger fish. In a range of fish in which the largest was about twice the length of the smallest, the maintenance ratio of the largest was only about half that of the smallest.

TABLE 2–5

Filtration Rae in Relation to Temperature in *Calanus finmarchicus*

(Fuller, 1937)

Temperature, °C.	Water Filtered per Copepod per Day, cc.
3	0.35
8	2.83
13	1.09

Although there is little information on the relation in marine organisms between length of life, growth rate, and temperature, certain generalizations that emerge from experimental work in other forms are probably applicable. To begin with, length of life tends to be inversely proportional to temperature (Allee et al., 1949). This is true only within certain temperature limits. It applies only within any one species and may well be untrue if applied as a generalization to all species. Furthermore, in some cases, it can be applied only to a particular race of a species, and it can be untrue when different physiological races, if these exist, are compared. Within these limitations, a temperature-time summation may be made when the temperature fluctuates during the development of an organism. Thus, a basic temperature may be chosen, usually the minimum temperature at which development will take place. If the deviations from this basic temperature during development are multiplied by their duration, the sum of these products tends to be constant for the attainment of any designated stage of development.

There are yet other complications that enter into the temperature-growth relationship. Thus, Parker (1930) has shown that exposure of grasshopper eggs to temperature below the minimum at which development occurs results in accelerated development when higher temperatures are resumed. Again, various workers have shown that the maximum growth rate attainable at any fixed temperature may be exceeded in a fluctuating temperature. Moore (1952) proposes that the diurnal migration of at least some planktonic species involves oscillation between two optimum temperatures, one at the day level and one at the night level, and that such an alternation of temperature is more favorable to them than any one fixed temperature. The possibility that fluctuating temperatures may be more favorable than fixed ones, and may even be essential for completion of the life cycle, may prove of widespread importance. It is rather widely held that the abyssal environment, for example, is ideal in its constant-temperature conditions, whereas this may actually call for unusual specialization. There is no doubt that different body processes, such as the action of the various enzyme systems, respiration, muscular and nerve activity, gonad maturation, etc., show different temperature optima. It seems not unreasonable that a fluctuating temperature, which allows all these processes to enjoy optimal conditions for a part of the time, is better for the success of the organism as a whole than a constant temperature which, although optimal for some processes, is very far from optimal for others.

In the relation of the growth of plants to temperature, the analysis of the mechanisms involved has been carried further than for animals. Barker (1935) showed that for diatoms there was an optimum temperature at which the maximum growth rate occurred. The value of this optimum temperature varied in different species. Below the optimum, there was an approximately linear relation between growth rate and temperature. The extent of this temperature effect is strongly dependent, however, on the illumination. In one series of experiments Baly (1935) found that, at full illumination, a rise in temperature from 5 to 30°C. was accompanied by a sixfold increase in photosynthetic rate. When the illumination was reduced to 25 per cent of the original value, the same temperature range produced only a 2.4-fold increase in photosynthetic rate, and at 5 per cent illumination the increase was only 1.3-fold. The situation is still further complicated by the modification of both these effects by the availability of nutrient salts. Figure 2–10 (Riley et al., 1949) shows how both growth and photosynthesis of phytoplankton react to varying temperature illumination and phosphate concentration. The increase in rates with increased temperature is greater at high illumination than at low. Also, at high temperature a deficiency of phosphate has a pronounced effect on the rates only at very low concentrations, whereas at lower temperatures this effect is felt over a wider range of concentrations.

The difficulty of solving a complex mechanism of this type is obvious when it is remembered that, under natural conditions, low tem-

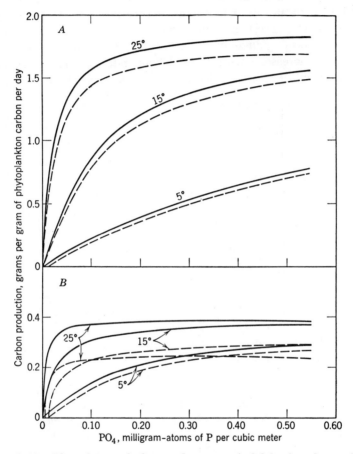

Figure 2–10. The relation of photosynthetic rate (solid line) and growth rate (broken line) to temperature, illumination, and phosphate concentration in phytoplankton. The upper figure (A) represents conditions at a radiation rate of 0.25 gm.-calories per square centimeter per minute, and the lower (B) those at a rate of 0.05 gm.-calories per square centimeter per minute. (After Riley et al., 1949.)

peratures are usually associated with low illumination, both in a bathymetric series and seasonally. Further, for animals the periods and depth of low temperatures and low illumination tend also to be associated with low food supply.

Another important aspect of temperature is its effect on respiration. Respiration is important, both as a basic mechanism for whose maintenance suitable external conditions must be available and also as a valuable index of growth and other activity. Figure 2–11 shows the respiratory rate of the mussel *M. edulis*, increasing with increased temperature up to an optimum and thereafter decreasing. In this case, the part of the curve below the optimum is almost a straight line, but in the copepod *C. finmarchicus* (Fig. 2–12), Q_{10}—the rate of increase per 10°C.—increases with increased temperature, whereas in another copepod, *Centropages*, Q_{10} decreases. Here, as in other phenomena,

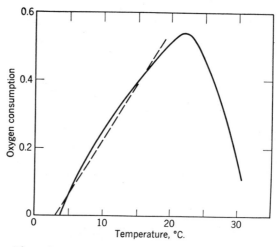

Figure 2–11. The relation of rate of respiration to temperature in the mussel *Mytilus edulis*. (After Bruce, 1926.)

the problem of physiological adaptation enters. In the case of *C. finmarchicus*, Marshall et al. (1935) found similar curves for summer and winter populations, with no indication of adaptation. On the other hand, Edwards and Irving (1943) found that the anomuran *Emerita talpoida*, although yielding a typical respiratory rate–temperature curve in short-period experiments, showed complete seasonal adaptation, so that the winter rate at 3°C. was the same as the summer rate at 15°C. In the same way Spärck (1936) records various lamellibranchs whose respiratory rates, at the average local temperature, were the same in Greenland and in the Mediterranean. Marked specific differences must therefore be expected, both in the nature of the respiration-temperature relationship, and in the degree of physiological adaptation involved. Zeuthen (1947) gives a comprehensive review of much work on the respiration of marine animals.

The effect of temperature changes on the respiration of plants varies widely in different forms. In many algae there is comparatively little change in rate within a rather wide temperature range, but a sharp increase above that range. In *Fucus serratus,* this increase begins at 30°C., in *Delesseria* at 25°C., and in *Plocamium* at 20°C. In *Enteromorpha,* on the other hand, there is a more or less uniform rise with increasing temperature (Ehrke, 1929, 1931). Since in some algae the rate of photosynthesis either rises less fast with increasing temperature than does the rate of respiration, or in some actually decreases, the balance between the two may vary with temperature. In the case of

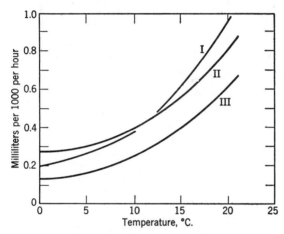

Figure 2–12. The relation of rate of respiration to temperature in males (I), females (II), and immatures (III) of the copepod *Calanus finmarchicus.* (After Marshall et al., 1935.)

Porphyra, for example, Montfort (1935) found that, as the temperature was raised from 5 to 21°C., the ratio of photosynthesis to respiration first rose and then fell. A critical depth in the sea is the "compensation point," where there is just sufficient illumination for photosynthesis to balance respiration.

Blinks (in G.M. Smith, 1951) quotes examples in which the compensation point at 10°C. is at 250–300-meter-candles illumination, whereas at 16°C. it is at 350–400 meter-candles. In such cases the compensation depth for the species would reflect not only the illumination but also the temperature in a particular locality.

An active avoidance of unfavorable temperature conditions is found in many animals. Among sessile forms and among plants this is, of course, not possible. When the young stages, either larvae or spores, are motile, some selection of a suitable adult habitat is possible. In some species a preferential settlement of young has been found to oc- cur in the neighborhood of already settled individuals of the species (Knight-Jones, 1951). Since lethal conditions of temperature and other factors cannot have occurred during the lifetime of the already settled specimens, this mechanism tends to concentrate larvae in places where unsuitable conditions are less likely to occur. We have already referred to the behavior of *L. littorea* in the Arctic. In winter it moves down from the intertidal zone to deeper and warmer condi- tions. Knight and Parke (1931) describe a change in level of various intertidal algae in which the upper limit of their distribution retreats down the shore during or after the period of maximum temperatures and insolation. It is probable that both these factors, and possibly others also, are involved, and the effective migration is, of course, due to selective mortality in the upper zones of the shore. Among inter- tidal organisms there is a general tendency for those that live at the highest levels, and so are exposed to the highest temperatures, to have the highest lethal temperatures. This will be seen in Table 2–6, in

TABLE 2–6

Relation of Lethal Temperature to Level of Occurrence on the Shore among South African Gastropods

(Broekhuysen, 1940)

Species in Order of Their Occurrence	Lowest Temperature at Which Death Occurred, °C.	Temperature at Which All Were Dead, °C.
Littorina knysnaensis	47.4	48.6
Oxystele variegata	41.5	42.1
Thais dubia	41.2	41.7
O. tigrina	38.9	40.5
Cominella cincta	38.9	c. 39.5
O. sinensis	38.0	39.6

which the various species are arranged in the order in which they oc- cur on the shore.

Broekhuysen (1940) shows a similar arrangement in a summary of the lethal temperatures for a range of intertidal forms from different parts of the world. Grouping these into sublittoral, lower intertidal, midtidal, and upper intertidal forms, he found the average lethal tem- peratures to be respectively 34.1, 39.5, 41.7, and 43.0°C. In his opin- ion, temperature was unlikely to be the operative limiting factor in the

South African forms, since there appeared to be an adequate factor of safety when lethal temperatures and observed maxima were compared.

Geotropism has been demonstrated in various active intertidal animals. Hayes (1927), working with the intertidal gastropod *L. littorea*, found no modification of the geotropism by temperature but did find that desiccation reduced the amount of negative geotropism. In zooplankton, only light and gravity can induce a directional response, but the reaction to either of these may be modified by other factors

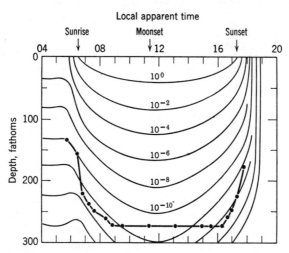

Figure 2–13. Diurnal changes in the level of the scattering layer in relation to temperature and illumination. The light lines show calculated levels of equal illumination (isolumes), spaced at intervals a hundredfold apart. The trace is interpreted as showing a layer descending under the control of illumination in the morning but ceasing to descend in the middle of the day when a critical low temperature is reached. Ascent begins in the afternoon as the illumination decreases again. (After Moore, 1949.)

such as temperature. Russell (1927) quotes an example in which increased temperature changes the animal from positively to negatively phototropic, whereas decreased temperature has the opposite effect. Figure 2–13 shows a record of the diurnal movement of the deep scattering layer, which is believed to consist of planktonic animals. During the period of morning descent, the organisms go deeper as the illumination increases, but apparently a low temperature barrier is encountered, and descent is arrested until a period in the afternoon when the animals follow the decreasing illumination toward the surface again.

In attempting to understand the ecological significance of temperature, the question arises, as with other factors, "What is the significant temperature with which we are concerned?" We have seen that maximum and minimum temperatures may be important limiting factors because of the lethal results if they are exceeded. On the other hand, we have seen that there may be other temperature ranges within this range which may limit particular processes such as activity, feeding, and breeding. Then, the period of exposure to a particular temperature may be important. In this connection, Doty and Archer (1950) exposed various species of intertidal algae to conditions of increased temperature and salinity of the order of those they might encounter during the period of exposure at low tide. For each species they determined the period of exposure to such conditions that was just sufficient to produce significant injury. When such a period was doubled or trebled, they found that death very often resulted. The maximum single period of exposure or immersion varies with level in the intertidal zone, and the way in which the results obtained by Doty and Archer bear on critical tidal levels will be discussed in a later section. The aspect of their experiments to be emphasized here is the need to concern ourselves not only with the lethal or damaging effects of particular temperatures but also with the duration of such temperatures.

There is another aspect of the effects of temperature which requires consideration here, although it applies equally to the effects of other environmental factors. The optimum, as well as the limiting, values for a factor vary according to how their effect is assessed. Thus, Fischer-Piette (1948) shows that the habitat in which the greatest population of the intertidal limpet, *Patella vulgata*, is found is not that in which they grow fastest, reach the greatest size, or mature earliest. Many organisms are less tolerant in their young stages than as adults of such adverse factors as insolation, and they change their habitat accordingly. For example, young *P. lapillus* move higher in the intertidal zone as they grow, and various intertidal algae require, at first, the protection of a cover of other algae but later grow to project beyond this cover. In such cases, optimal conditions, including those of temperature, vary with age. Although high temperatures result in rapid growth and early maturity, these are not of necessity more advantageous to the species than slower rates. Further, since the species is only one member of the community, the latter might find unfavorable a temperature which would be more advantageous to one of its constituents. It is clear, then, that the ecological effects of temperature are complex and that consideration must always be given, not only to the nature of the various processes involved but also to the type of temperature data needed.

SALINITY

Variations in the salinity of sea water may effect the organisms in the water through specific gravity control and variations in osmotic pressure. The specific gravity of most soft tissues is close to that of normal sea water. This is of importance to swimming forms, as well as to those that depend on the water to support most of their weight. Many bottom-living forms, both attached and motile, have very high specific gravities, for example, shelled gastropods and lamellibranchs, corals, and calcareous algae. At the other extreme, certain forms are modified for flotation at the surface and have gas bladders which counteract the excess weight of the tissues. Examples are found in the Sargasso weed, *Sargassum* spp., and the siphonophore *Physalia*. The closeness with which the specific gravities of many animals match that of the water in which they are found is shown in Table 2–7. The difference is, in most cases, considerably less than 10 per cent.

Gross and Raymont (1942) have measured the change in specific gravity with age in the planktonic copepod *C. finmarchicus*. The water in which they were living had a specific gravity of 1023.5 to 1025.0, and all stages except the fifth were denser than this, as shown in Table 2–8.

Salinity and specific gravity ranges are so small in the open ocean that it is doubtful whether they often limit the distribution of any particular organism. However, it appears possible that some deep-sea forms may be particularly sensitive to differences in specific gravity. Pickford (1949) suggested this to be true of the cephalopod *Vampyroteuthis infernalis*. When all known records are grouped together, as shown in Fig. 2–14, these are found to extend over quite a wide temperature and salinity range, but over a very narrow range of *in situ* density. Furthermore, it appears that the eggs sink to somewhat lower levels, with correlated higher density, than the adults.

In many teleost fishes there is a swim bladder, filled with gas, by means of which the specific gravity of the animal can be adjusted to that of the surrounding water. The mechanism has the disadvantage that any change in depth involves corresponding pressure changes, and the resulting variations in the size of the swim bladder will modify the specific gravity of the fish unless the gas content of the bladder is controllable. The mechanism involved will be discussed in greater detail when other effects of pressure are considered.

Since calcereous or siliceous skeletal material is considerably denser than water, its excess weight must be compensated for in armored

TABLE 2–7

Sinking Factors for Marine Animals

(Lowndes, 1942)

Species	Temperature, °C.	Sinking Factor*
CRUSTACEA		
BRANCHIOPODA		
Chirocephalus diaphanus	11.3	1011
Artemia salina	10.0	988
Daphnia pulex	7.0	1017
OSTRACODA		
Candona candida	7.6	1025
Herpetocypris reptans	8.8	1170
COPEPODA		
Calanus finmarchicus	15.4	1029
	15.4	1033
Anomalocera patersoni	16.2	1014
Diaptomus gracilis	8.0	1023
Tigriopus fulvus	15.6	1060
LEPTOSTRACA		
Nebalia bipes	7.4	1045
AMPHIPODA		
Gammarus pulex	20.0	1066
	20.0	1088
MYSIDACEA		
Hemimysis lamornae	6.4	1075
DECAPODA		
Leander serratus	15.2	1098.4
Palaemonetes varians	10.8	1071
Crangon vulgaris	17.2	1083
ANNELIDA		
POLYCHAETA		
Nereis diversicolor	7.4	1045
N. virens	9.6	1033
PISCES		
Conger vulgaris	10.0	1000
Gasterosteus aculeatus	10.0	1003
Crenilabrus melops	13.8	1004.5
Lepadogaster bimaculatus	15.0	1047
Pleuronectes platessa	6.8	1036.3
Cottus bubalis	6.4	1046
Scyllium canicula	17.2	1049

* Expressed as 1000 times the ratio of the specific gravity of the animal to that of the sea water in which it was living.

forms, if a specific gravity close to that of the surrounding water is to be maintained for the body as a whole. This is particularly important in weak-swimming or non-motile planktonic organisms, which often have droplets of light oil in their tissues; there is probably some mech-

TABLE 2–8

Specific Gravity of Stages of *Calanus finmarchicus*

(Gross and Raymont, 1942)

Stage	Specific Gravity
Eggs	1045 –1049
Newly hatched nauplii	1045 –1049
Stage V	1025.5–1026.5
Adult male	1043 –1045
Adult female	1043 –1047

anism for regulating the quantity of droplets as required. Gross and Zeuthen (1948) point out that different algae can accumulate, in their cell fluid, different specific ions, and that such an accumulation of light ions may help to balance the weight of the siliceous skeleton of plank-

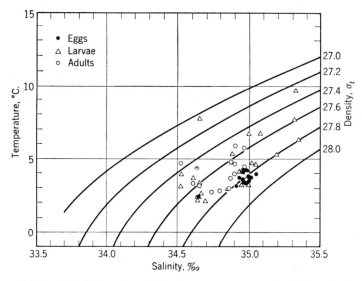

Figure 2–14. Distribution in relation to temperature and salinity, of the eggs, larvae, and adults of the cephalopod *Vampyroteuthis infernalis*. The records tend to lie along lines of equal density, with the eggs deepest and the adults shallowest. (After Pickford, 1949.)

tonic diatoms. They show that diatoms are normally in close equilibrium with the surrounding water, in which they can therefore float
suspended, but that spore formation involves contraction of the cell
contents, with the expression of liquid, and such spores are heavier
than the water and tend to sink. If sufficient vertical mixing takes
place in the water in which the diatoms live, it is not necessary for
them to be in equilibrium with the water, despite their inability to
swim. Those that sink may be carried down into water which will be
too deep for efficient photosynthesis, but there will always be some

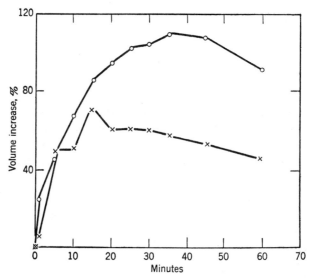

Figure 2–15. Rate of swelling of the flat worm *Gunda ulvae* in tap water deficient in calcium (upper curve) and in natural stream water containing calcium
(lower curve). (After Pantin, 1931; in Krogh, 1939.)

that are carried upward again by the mixing, and these can maintain
an adequate breeding stock in such rapidly reproducing forms.

The second important significance of salinity lies in resulting osmotic pressures. The salt content of the cells of marine organisms
tends, in general, to be close to that of average sea water, and if the
cells find themselves in water of other salinity, some osmoregulatory
mechanism is necessary to maintain this concentration. Krogh (1939)
states that in most estuarine animals, a first lowering of the salinity is
usually accompanied by a drop in the cell content salinity, and that
the osmoregulation does not come into play until a certain definite
drop in the external salinity has taken place. Methods of osmoregu-

lation include external protection from the surrounding water, protection at the cell membranes, and excretory mechanisms for getting rid of excess fresh water from the cells or bodies. Ability to withstand wide salinity fluctuations is found in widely separated groups from the protozoa to fishes.

For a given species, ability to withstand lowered salinity may be conditioned by other environmental factors. A good example of this is found in the platyhelminth *Gunda ulvae*, which occurs under stones in the intertidal zone, usually where there is a trickle of fresh water down the shore. In certain streams, *Gunda* is able to penetrate a considerable distance upstream in permanently fresh water, and this penetration has been shown to occur only where there is a concentration of at least 5 mg. of calcium per liter in the water. This calcium is essential for the process of osmoregulation, and in its absence the tissues imbibe water until they are killed, as shown in Fig. 2–15.

In various species it has been shown that the ability to tolerate low salinities is greater at higher temperatures. For example, Broekhuysen (1936) found that the lower limit for development of the eggs of the common shore crab, *carcinus maenas,* was about $20^0/_{00}$ at 16.3°C. but rose to $26^0/_{00}$ at 10°C. The result might be expected, since work must be done in the process of osmoregulation and higher temperature should favor the performance of this work. Figure 2–16 shows the increase in metabolic rate at low salinity in *C. maenas.* The optimum salinity also may decrease at higher temperatures, as in the shrimp *Crangon crangon* (Broekema, 1941).

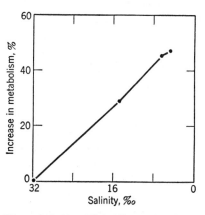

Figure. 2–16. The effect of salinity variation on the metabolic rate of the crab *Carcinus maenas.* (After Krogh, 1939.)

In some algae, such as *Enteromorpha, Fucus vesiculosus,* and *Porphyra,* respiratory rates are not affected by changes in salinity, where as in others, such as *F. serratus* and *Laminaria,* they rise as the salinity decreases (Hoffman, 1929). Photosynthesis also may be affected, and in *Fucus* and *Ulva* the rate has been found to be doubled when the salinity was decreased by about a third (Legendre, 1921).

In many estuaries, winter is the season of both lowest salinities and lowest temperatures. The two may work together to produce the observed result that many species penetrate farther into the estuary in summer than in winter. The ascidian *Polysyncraton lacazei,* in the estuary of La Rance, is a case in point (Fischer, 1928). It is not always clear whether such observed migrations are caused by temperature or salinity alone or by the combined effect of the two, but Fischer-Piette (1930, 1931), by comparing the distribution of various species during particularly dry and particularly wet winters, was able to show that, for many of them, salinity was the major limiting factor.

As is true of temperature, young organisms, in general, have smaller tolerance ranges for salinities than the adults. Fischer-Piette (1931) found that the eggs of the gastropod *P. lapillus* were killed at low salinities which were tolerated by the adults. Hayes (1929) gives the lower limit for development of the eggs of the gastropod *L. littorea* as $20^0/_{00}$ which is well above the limit for the adults. Broekhuysen (1936) found the same thing in the shore crab *C. maenas,* but with the unusual difference that the young were more tolerant of high salinities than the adults. There is less known about tolerance of high salinities, although these may be encountered both in inshore waters and where evaporation takes place in the intertidal zone. We have already referred to the work of Doty and Archer (1950) in which the salinity, as well as the temperature, was raised by an amount likely to be encountered during the period of exposure in the intertidal zone. When the minimum period of exposure to such salinity necessary to cause perceptible injury in various algae was determined, it was found that a doubling or trebling of the time of exposure was frequently fatal to them. Here again we see the importance not only of the magnitude of a harmful factor but also of the duration of exposure to it.

The sudden changes to be encountered in the intertidal zone are well described by H. D. Russell (1941) in an account of the habitat of the gastropod *Puperita pupa.* He says, "This species has been found inhabiting splash pools in Santo Domingo that were over 90°F. [32°C.] and exposed to the full brilliance of the tropical sun. A few minutes later a traveling cloud, or 'chawasco,' would pass. For perhaps twenty minutes the heavy rains deluged the coast. Then the weather would clear. . . . Not only the salinity, but also the temperature of the environment of *P. pupa* must, therefore, be radically changed in a short period of time. With a calm sea such as during the calms of August when there is little splash from the waves and the sun beats down on these pools, evaporating the water from them, the salt content must consequently rise considerably. . . ." Even in temperate climates such evaporation may be extreme, and Fraser (1936) states that the harpacticoid copepod, *Tigriopus fulvus,* occurs abundantly in pools on the English coast where salt crystals are actually being formed. However, when evaporation proceeds to the point at which the crystals dry out completely, the copepods die.

Algae growing in the intertidal zone can, in general, tolerate salinity changes proportionate to what they may encounter, and so to the level at which they are living. Most can tolerate for some hours, or even days, a range of 50 to 150 per cent sea water (about $12^\circ/_{00}$ to $47^\circ/_{00}$). Some, such as *Ulva, Enteromorpha,* and *Cladophora,* from high levels, can tolerate a range of 20 to 300 per cent for 24 hours. From about midtide level, *Polysiphonia, Rhodocorton, Membranoptera,* and *Ptilota* have a range of tolerance of only about 20 to 200 per cent sea water, and from still deeper levels, *Antithamnion, Trailiella, Brogniartella,* and *Plocamium* only from 40 to 150 per cent (Biebl, 1938).

Although some species are specifically adapted to living in estuarine conditions, others which can tolerate them show evidence of the unfavorableness of the habitat in the smaller size they attain there. Thus, Rawlinson (1934) describes a dwarf form of the anemone *Metridium dianthus* which is typical of the Mersey estuary, and Wright (1936) states that the gastropod *L. littorea* does not attain as great a size in permanently low salinity as it does in the sea. On the other hand, the barnacle *B. balanoides* benefits so greatly from the extra food in suspension in the estuarine water, and from the currents which bring this within its reach, that it grows faster and larger in some estuaries than it does in the sea (Moore 1936a). Continuous subjection to high salinities may also affect the size of an organism. Andrews (1940) describes certain ponds which have only periodic connection with the sea and in which evaporation raises the salinity markedly in the intervening periods. Populations of the gastropod *Neritina virginea* increased in numbers in the ponds during the periods of raised salinity, but the size of the individuals decreased.

In general, then, it seems probable that the range of salinity encountered in the open ocean will affect the osmoregulation of comparatively few forms. Accompanying changes in the specific gravity of the water may be important to some forms, although little is yet known about this. The wider range between such extremes as the Red Sea and polar areas may be more important. In inshore waters, and particularly in the intertidal zone and in estuaries, the range is sufficiently wide to have a very serious effect on osmoregulation. In such waters it may also affect flotation, through changes in specific gravity, but for many forms this will be relatively unimportant because of the much smaller depth of water involved.

PRESSURE

The actual compression undergone by either sea water or tissue even at abyssal depths is so small as to be negligible from the point of view of any distortion or similar change that occurs. Except where gases are concerned, the effects of pressure are not obvious. Unless held in rigid-walled containers, gases, and hence the vessels which contain them, suffer marked changes with pressure. Thus, the swim bladder of a fish which descends from the surface to a depth of about 10 meters will suffer an increase of 1 atmosphere in pressure and will decrease to half its original volume. With the correlated increase in pressure of about 15 pounds per square inch, the body of the fish can only partially resist this compression. In general, such compression is not met by strengthened container walls, although in the intertidal brown alga *Ascophyllum nodosum*, Damant (1937) has found that plants growing near low water, where they are subject to higher pressures, have thicker walled floats than those growing at higher levels on the shore.

If a fish, whose swim bladder volume is so adjusted that the fish as a whole has the same specific gravity as the surrounding water, changes level, the resulting change of volume in the bladder facilitates this movement. If the fish begins to move downward, the swim bladder is compressed and the specific gravity of the fish is thereby increased so that it continues to sink, even without muscular effort. Similarly, expansion of the bladder facilitates upward movement of the fish. Although this process may conceivably be of value, the fish will, when the vertical movement is arrested, no longer have the same specific gravity as the water and will have to expend muscular energy to maintain its depth, and further energy, if the movement is downward, to excrete additional gas into the bladder to bring the body back into equilibrium with the water. If the movement is upward, the balance may be regained, in those fishes whose swim bladders have an opening to the exterior, by venting some of the contents. For a fish moving downward, there would appear to be no particular barrier to the extent of the movement, provided the surrounding organs are not damaged by the compression of the swim bladder. The total volume of the bladder is only about 5 per cent of that of the fish, in marine forms (Jones, 1951), and no great muscular effort would seem to be called for to support this extra weight until buoyancy was regained by the secretion of more gas into the bladder. For the fish that can vent excess gas, there is no limit set by the bladder to upward movement, but for those that cannot, the limit is set at the point where the bladder ruptures as the gas in it expands. In a fresh-water perch, this occurred when the pressure was reduced about 60 per cent, so a fish can safely move upward from deep water to about half its previous depth. Beyond this point, the movement must be slow enough to allow resorption of the gas, and there is, at present, no information on how rapidly this can take place. In water less than about 10 meters deep, a reduction of pressure by a half would not, of course, occur even if the fish came directly to the surface. It is worth noting that, in abyssal depths, the gas in a swim bladder would be so highly compressed that it would be only a little lighter than water; so, to achieve the same buoyancy, a relatively much larger swim bladder would be called for, or else the heavy bony structure of the body would have to be correspondingly reduced.

Pressure also affects animals in various less direct or less obvious ways. Gases are much more soluble in water at high pressures, but since atmospheric gases are available for interchange with the water only at or near the surface, deep waters have little opportunity of obtaining the quantity of such gases that they are capable of dissolving, and so they do not differ very widely in content from surface waters. Carbon dioxide does, however, accumulate in them, and the higher concentration of this, combined with the high pressures, renders calcium carbonate more soluble in deep waters. Its secretion into shells and bones is correspondingly more difficult, and must, at least in part, account for the reduction in such structures in abyssal animals. The viscosity of sea water varies inappreciably within the pressure range found in the oceans, but that of protoplasm changes markedly, as has been shown by watching the behavior of *Amoeba* under pressure. Another effect, which is probably important, is that, according to Le Chatelier's theorem, colloid gels may be expected to take up more water under high pressures. A fuller account of pressure effects may be found in Johnson et al. (1954).

Most of the experiments on the effects of pressure on animals have been confined to particular tissues. Pease and Kitching (1939) showed that a sudden increase in pressure may temporarily increase the rate of beating of cilia, and a sudden decrease of pressure may temporarily reduce it, but in both cases there is a gradual resumption of the normal rate. Higher pressure increases both the action potential and rate of propagation in nerves and decreases their threshhold of stimulation. In a turtle heart, higher pressure increases the tension in isometric contraction. Increased pressure increases the isometric tension in a frog gastrocnemius muscle, at a temperature above

10–14°C., but decreases it below that temperature (Cattell, 1936). These statements apply only to moderate increases in pressure; the tissues of normally surface-living forms are killed by pressures approaching those found in abyssal water. It is generally assumed that the tissues of animals which inhabit such depths must be specially adapted for functioning at such high pressures, and that they are probably very different from those of shallower-living forms.

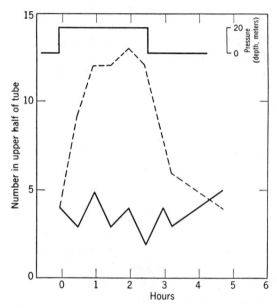

Figure 2–17. The effect of pressure on the vertical movements of crab megalopas. The top line shows the period during which hydrostatic pressure equivalent to a depth of 20 meters of water was applied. The broken line shows the distribution of the larvae in a vertical tube during this period, and the solid line shows the distribution of control animals to which no pressure was applied. (After Hardy and Bainbridge, 1951.)

It would seem that some basic chemical differences must exist between low- and high-pressure forms. However, there are many species of animals which show no apparent morphological change over a great range of depth. Thus, *Arca glacialis, Modiolaria discors, Natica groenlandica,* and *Ophiacantha bidentata* are found close to shore in East Greenland, but at depths of 2000 to 4000 meters farther south (Thorson, 1936). The holothurians *Elpidia* and *Myriotrocus* range from less than a hundred meters in the north to 6000 to 9000 meters in the tropics. On the other hand, Zobell and Oppenheimer

(1950) have demonstrated morphological differences in marine bacteria grown at different pressures. The problem of the effects of pressure on morphology and physiology has not yet been solved.

It would appear that physiological reactions of the type just described may be expected even within the pressure range encountered in the more extensive diurnal migrations of plankton and of certain pelagic fishes and cephalopods. Regnard (1885) applied pressures equivalent to 1000 meters of water to the crustaceans *Gammarus pulex, Daphnia* sp., etc., and recorded that, as the pressure increased, they first became more active and then died. Hardy and Bainbridge (1951) have demonstrated vertical migration of the megalopa stage of the larvae of two crabs, *Portunus* and *Carcinus,* in response to very much lower pressure changes. Figure 2–17 shows their upward movement in a vertical tube when a pressure equivalent to 20 meters of water was applied. A similar reaction was obtained with an increase of only 10 meters.

Reaction to even lower pressures than this is suggested in the case of the polychaete *Perinereis cultrifera.* This worm exhibits a lunar rhythm in its swarming, but the rhythm does not appear in a depth of less than 30 cm. of water (Herpin, 1928). It is suggested that the rhythm is maintained under the stimulus of varying water pressure.

ILLUMINATION

Light is of importance in marine ecology in connection with a wide range of phenomena including vision, photosynthesis, heating, and actinic damage. The eye is sensitive to a very wide range of illumination. Full moonlight, which appears relatively bright to the human eye, is about one half-millionth of the intensity of full sunlight. Waterman et al. (1939) have calculated that, at midday, there is sufficient light at a depth of about 600 fathoms in clear oceanic water to stimulate the eyes of certain crustacea. At this depth it is probable that only a few photons enter the eye per second, and although sufficient to induce a phototropic reaction, there might not be sufficient light to form a visual image. Beebe, working in the bathysphere, found that his ability to perceive non-illuminated objects was lost at depths far shallower than this. Although vision would appear to be highly advantageous, the deeper-water plankton affords many examples of eyed and eyeless forms living apparently equally successfully together. Many animals are nocturnal in their habits, apparently gaining advantages by their avoidance of various harmful effects of light. These include not only heating and actinic effects but also attack by predators. It has been suggested that the diurnal migration of zooplankton, which involves leaving the food-rich surface waters in the daytime, carries the advantage for the herbivores concerned with avoiding those predators which hunt by sight.

In considering the relation of illumination to photosynthesis, both the intensity and the wavelength of the light are important, and in comparing the amount of photosynthesis at different wavelengths, it is necessary to compare illuminations of equal energy, since the energy of light varies with the wavelength. Probably all plants show an optimum wavelength at which the most efficient photosynthesis occurs, but the value of this optimum varies in different forms, and between them they can utilize the entire visible spectrum. Klugh (1931) showed that the photosynthetic rate of the green alga *Enteromorpha linza* was very high in red light, much less so in blue, and very low in green. In the red alga *Porphyra umbilicalis* the rate was high in red light, but fairly high also in blue and green. In another red alga, *Delesseria sinuosa*, it was almost equally high in red and green light and slightly less in blue. Of these three species, *Enteromorpha* lives highest on the shore and *Porphyra* and *Delesseria* live lower and even down to some distance below low water. The trend toward greater utilization of the green and blue part of the spectrum by the deeper forms is correlated with the nature of the light available, the red being most rapidly removed during passage through intervening water. For the area where these experiments were carried out, the percentages of the red, green, and blue light reaching a depth of 5 meters were, respectively, 3.5, 16.0, and 7.0. Even within a species, there may be adaptation toward better utilization of the available light. In the species *Phormidium faveolarum*, Harder (1923) found that plants which had been grown in red light photosynthesized most rapidly in light of that color, and ones which had been grown in blue light showed an optimum in blue. Considering the range of pigments known to occur in different algae, it is not surprising that a wide range of adaptation to varying conditions can occur. These pigments include chlorophyll A and B, xanthophyll, carotin, fucoxanthin, phycoerythrin, and phycocyanin. The latter two have been shown to be fluorescent, and it has been suggested that both phycoerythrin and fucoxanthin may act as photosensitizers.

For most marine plants, full sunlight is too strong and may even be lethal. So far as photosynthesis is concerned, the optimum is much less than full sunlight. In *E. linza*, even though this is a form well adapted to intertidal life, increase in the illumination above 6 per cent sunlight does not result in increased photosynthesis (Fig. 2–18). For different species, the value of this optimum varies. Thus, Schreiber (1927) gives 1600 luxes as the optimum for the diatom

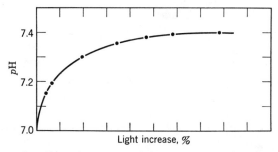

Figure 2–18. The effect of intensity of illumination on the photosynthetic rate (as indicated by pH change) in the green alga *Enteromorpha linza*. (After Klugh, 1931.)

Biddulphia mobiliensis and 3200 luxes for the green flagellate *Carteria* sp.

From the data shown in Table 2–9 (Gail, 1922), it will be seen that, in general, different species of algae are found at depths corresponding

TABLE 2–9

Relation between the Depth at Which Various Algae Were Collected and the Depth at Which They Receive Their Optimum Illumination

Species	Optimum Depth, meters	Habitat
Dasyopsis plumosa	15	—
Rhodymenia pertuosa	15	—
Halosaccion glandiforme	15	15–25 meters below low water
H. glandiforme	1	Low water
Agardhiella tenera	15	15–25 meters below low water
A. tenera	8	6–12 meters below low water
Prionitis Lyalli	1	Intertidal pool
Fucus evanescens	1	Intertidal pool
Costaria costata	8	Below low water
Laminaria sp.	8	Below low water
Desmarestia ligulata	15	Deeper water

to those at which their optimum illumination occurs, and that within the vertical range of a particular species those plants from the highest levels have a higher optimum illumination than those from the deeper levels.

Harder (1923) confirmed the ability of algae to adapt themselves, at least to some extent, to the illumination of their surroundings. He found that specimens which had been reared at a low illumination had a lower optimum than those reared at high illumination.

Since both the infrared and the red end of the spectrum are so rapidly absorbed by water, the heating effect of illumination need be considered only in the intertidal zone which is exposed directly to insolation. An exception must be made for intertidal pools and for very shallow bodies of water, in which the inhabitants may suffer from elevation of the temperature by insolation. In deeper water, mixing prevents this effect from being appreciable. Gardiner (1903) recorded a temperature of 56°C. in intertidal pools containing living coral at Minikoi, and Orr and Moorhouse measured a temperature of 44.8°C. inside rock oysters on exposed sand rock on the Great Barrier Reef. In such circumstances, the actual lethal temperature must have been closely approached. More frequently it is hard to tell whether the danger lies directly in elevation of the temperature or in the resulting increase in desiccation. The latent heat of evaporation involved in desiccation must play some part in cooling the organisms concerned, though possibly not an important one. Such evaporation also involves concentration of the salts in the tissues with resulting possibility of damage from hypertonicity. Both retardation of evaporation and some degree of protection from heating are obtained, among intertidal forms, by such mechanisms as thick protecting shells or a covering of mucus, as will be discussed in a later section.

Light is essential for photosynthesis but may also be beneficial in other ways to plant and animal tissues. It may and frequently does have a serious harmful effect also, and this harmful effect is mainly concentrated in the violet and ultraviolet part of the spectrum. Among the possible photochemical reactions involved in this effect is the rapid breakdown of certain vitamins in the presence of light. Ultraviolet radiation is too rapidly absorbed by water to be of much significance below the intertidal zone, but sufficient damaging radiation can penetrate to a considerable depth to limit most plankton to well below the surface in the daytime. Only a few specially adapted forms normally inhabit the extreme upper levels. Diatoms react to excessive illumination by systrophe, or a clumping together of the chromatophores. In *Coscinodiscus excentricus,* this occurs at 9.6 g.-calories per square centimeter per hour, which is equivalent to about a tenth of the surface illumination with overhead sunlight. This species would therefore be limited to below a depth of about 15 meters in clear oceanic water and one of fewer meters in more turbid water.

Many zooplankton animals have an optimum illumination which is far less than this, although it is not usually known whether higher illuminations would be lethal. Motile animals may avoid the excessive illumination by a diurnal migration, as in the case of zooplankton, or by hiding during the day in crannies or other shelter, as do many intertidal forms. Non-motile forms, such as corals, frequently expand their tentacles only at night, thus avoiding some of the harmful effects of insolation.

Specific differences in sensitivity to actinic rays may benefit less sensitive forms. For example, some flagellates can tolerate insolation which is fatal to the bacteria which might otherwise replace them in a culture, and sun-tolerant intertidal forms may benefit from the exclusion from the region of less tolerant competitors. There is, however, in white light a more direct beneficial action which appears to be widespread among both plants and animals. This lies in the accelerated recovery from tissue damage by ultraviolet radiation which takes place in the presence of white light. Whitaker (1942) found that, when the eggs of the brown alga *F. furcatus* were subjected to ultraviolet radiation, the normal rhizoid development was inhibited for some time. In one experiment, the time required for 50 per cent rhizoid development in such eggs was 50 hours when they were kept in the dark, but only 30 hours when they were kept in white light. Kelner (1949) and Novick and Szilard (1949) found that the effect of ultraviolet irradiation on the bacterium *Escherichia coli*, was partially neutralized by subsequent treatment with white light, the effect resembling that when a smaller dosage of ultraviolet was given. Neutralization was never complete, however. Similarly, among animals, the delay in normal cleavage induced in the eggs of the sea urchin *Strongylocentrotus purpuratus* by ultraviolet irradiation can be reduced by subsequent exposure to white light.

Among both plants and animals, many general correlations with light are known without the details of the mechanism involved being fully understood. Various intertidal animals are nocturnal in their habits. For example, the isopod *Ligia oceanica* emerges from the shelter of crevices only at night and may even remain in hiding in bright moonlight (Nicholls, 1931). The mussel *M. edulis* closes temporarily in response to any sudden change in illumination but at low temperatures opens only in the dark (Dodgson, 1928). Possibly as a result of the latter response its growth rate has been found to be nearly twice as great in the dark as in sunlight (Coulthard, 1929). *Chiton tuberculatus*, as already mentioned, lives only in shady habitats and is negatively phototropic when young. When older, it is positively phototropic and lives in full sunlight (Crozier and Arey, 1919). Among zooplankton, the young stages of many forms live at a different level from the adults, under conditions of corresponding differences in illumination. However, in some species it is the adults which live deeper and in others the young. Among algae, colonization of a denuded rock surface by *F. vesiculosus* takes place sooner on a northerly facing surface than on one facing west, and is less dense on an insolated rock than on a shaded one (Hatton, 1932). As an example of varying need for adequate illumination, adult plants of *F. evanescens* can survive at a level of illumination which is too low for younger plants. The vertical zonation of this species is also modified by the illumination, the lower limit being raised and the upper limit lowered in a habitat with a northern aspect (Gail, 1918). Additional examples of the relation of specific behavior and light will be found in later sections.

WAVES

Ecologically, waves are most important in the intertidal zone. In somewhat deeper water, their influence is felt to a reduced extent all the way to the bottom; and in oceanic waters, they influence aeration and light penetration at the surface and mixing to a moderate depth. Unfortunately, wave action is difficult to define or measure as an ecological factor. In deep water, the height and period of a wave are a function of the velocity of the wind producing it, of the duration of the wind, and of the fetch, or distance over which the wind is operative.

The wave so produced becomes longer and lower as it travels away from the area where it was born, but on entering shallow water its shape becomes modified and its height increases until it finally breaks. Caldwell (1949) gives, as an example, waves produced by a wind with a velocity of 48 km. per hour, acting for 24 hours over a fetch of 300 nautical miles. Waves would leave this storm area with a height of about 5 meters, a length of about 60 meters, and a period of 7.5 seconds. If these waves traveled over 2000 miles of open water, they would decay to a height of less than a meter and a length of about 400 meters. Change in form of the waves begins to appear when the depth of water is about half a wavelength, which would be about 200 meters in this example. At a depth of 3 meters, these waves would have grown to a height of nearly two meters and would break. They would also, as they entered shallow water, have swung round to bring their faces more or less parallel to the coast line.

In deep water, the extent of movement of the water particles is a function of the wavelength and decreases downward at such a rate as to be reduced to half its surface value at a depth of one-ninth the wavelength. Sufficient water movement to stir light sediments probably occurs on occasions at the bottom as far out as the edge of the continental shelf. Wave erosion of the bottom is recorded by Johnson (1919) at a depth of 40 meters in the English Channel, 50 meters in the Mediterranean, and 200 meters in the open ocean. Off the Chesil Bank, in the English Channel, shingle was shifted at a depth of 17 meters; and in the more exposed waters off Lands End, there is a record of stones weighing a pound being washed into lobster pots at a depth of 55 meters.

The maximum height which a simple wave is ever likely to attain is in the neighborhood of 17 meters, but this may be exceeded where two waves meet. Cornish (1934) records observed heights of 21 and 22 meters, and Patton and Marmer (1932) record 40 meters for a breaking wave. When an unbroken oscillatory wave hits a vertical face, it exerts only its hydrostatic pressure on that face (Johnson, 1919). However, in shallow water it becomes transformed into a wave of translation, and then its whole energy may be transformed into forward thrust, with resulting pressures up to nearly six times those of a corresponding oscillatory wave. Much of this energy may be dissipated if the bottom shallows gradually and the conversion into a wave of translation occurs far offshore, but where the bottom rises sharply most of this energy may reach land. Such a wave, 3 meters high and 30 meters long, can exert a pressure of about 8200 kg. per square meter on a vertical face which it strikes, and a wave 13 meters high and 150 meters long can exert 30,900 kg. per square meter. An actual record of a pressure of 29,700 kg. per square meter was made in Scotland (Johnson, 1919).

Such pressures are capable of moving very heavy objects and doing corresponding damage on and near the shore. Johnson (1919) gives the following observations. A stone weighing 76,200 kg., and situated 6 meters above sea level, was moved 22 meters across rough rocks. A block weighing 20,300 kg. was lifted 3.7 meters vertically and deposited on top of a pier above high watermark. Stones weighing 61 kg. have been thrown to a height of 30 meters, and windows have been broken by stones thrown by wave action to a height of 90 meters above sea level. The water itself, in falling back, may exert great pressures, and in one case broke strong timber, 30 by 30 cm. in section and 3 meters long, supported at the two ends.

It will be realized from such figures that an intertidal organism may have to endure relatively enormous destructive forces. The water itself can tear loose anything that is not adequately attached, and even a small pebble carried by the water may concentrate very heavy pressure in a small area. The banks of seaweed thrown ashore after a storm, often still attached to large stones which they have carried with them, bear witness to the former, and the crushed barnacles and limpets seen on rock surfaces after bad weather give evidence of the significance of the latter. In this connection, it is of interest to note the strength of some of the larger algae. Delf (1932) gives the following breaking stresses, in kilograms per square centimeter: *F. vesiculosus*, 45.5; *F. serratus*, 40.8; *Ascophyllum nodosum*, 37.6; *L. digitata*, 41.9. However, the holdfasts frequently become detached from the substratum at a tension less than that required to break the stipes. Even sand carried by the waves exercises a powerful abrasive action, and boulders bedded in sand are usually polished free from encrusting forms for some distance above the sand surface. In some such instances, the effect may be due rather to shifting level of the sand, which at its highest point may have smothered the organisms, leaving the rock clear as it receded again. The stones on a shore subject to wave action also suffer abrasion by grinding against one another, with little chance for survival of any forms growing on them, and a stony beach of this type is about the most barren type of shore that can be found. Some idea of the extent of the abrasion may be gained from the statement of Johnson (1919) that, on the wave-exposed beach at Cape Ann, Massachusetts, angular granite rocks become fairly well rounded within a year, and the amount of wear on pebbles amounts to several inches per year. The fauna and flora of the upper side of a rock differ greatly from those of the underside, with algae, barnacles, limpets, etc., dominating the upper side, and sponges, ascidians, etc., the underside. The overturning of such a rock, even without any abrasive action, has serious consequences, since a large proportion of the existing forms are killed, and it may take a year or more for full recolonization to take place. This too is reflected in the different inhabitants of sheltered and exposed rocky shores.

We have seen that high temperatures and desiccation are important limiting factors contributing to the vertical zonation of intertidal animals and plants. Wave action keeps the intertidal zone wet to a higher level than it would be in shelter, and the vertical distribution of the various species is correspondingly modified. In the brown alga

Pelvetia canaliculata and the lichen *Lichina pygmaea* both lower and upper limits move up the shore, with increasing wave exposure, but there is no marked widening of their zone (Figs. 2–19, 2–20). In the gastropod *L. neritoides* (Fig. 2–21) the upper limit moves up, and the lower limit down, as wave exposure increases, and there is a marked

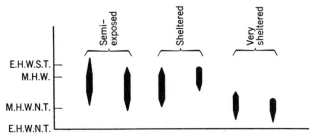

Figure 2–19. The relation of vertical distribution of the brown alga *Pelvetia canaliculata* to wave exposure. Tide levels are indicated by combinations of the letters: E. = equinoctial, M. = mean, H.W. = high water, L.W. = low water, N. = neap tides, S. = spring tides, M.T.L. = midtide level. The localities are classified as very exposed, exposed, semi-exposed, sheltered, and very sheltered. (After Evans, 1947.)

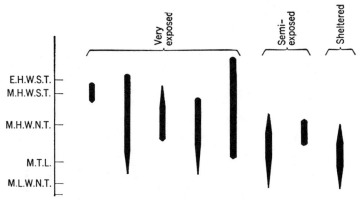

Figure 2–20. The relation of vertical distribution of the lichen *Lichina pygmaea* to wave exposure. Symbols as in Fig. 2–19. (After Evans, 1947.)

widening of the zone. In another brown alga, *F. serratus*, which extends in all places to low water, the upper limit moves upward as wave exposure increases (Fig. 2–22).

At present, the ecologist lacks any simple measure of wave action with which to compare conditions in different habitats. Moore (1935) has made use of the percentage of the year's winds blowing into the angular aperture of a locality, this aperture being estimated from the angle of open sea visible from the locality past land half a mile or less away. This method gives a useful crude figure for neighboring localities, but a better measure is needed for more widely separated places. It takes into account the prevalance of winds from certain quarters, but not the fact that they vary in strength; it makes no allowance for

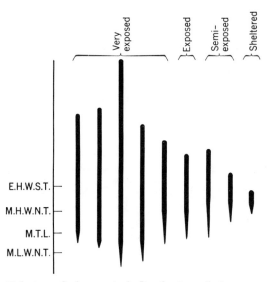

Figure 2–21. Relation of the vertical distribution of the gastropod *Littorina neritoides* to wave exposure. Symbols as in Fig. 2–19. (After Evans, 1947.)

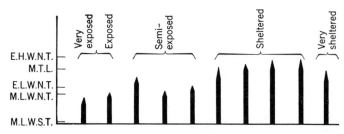

Figure 2–22. The relation of vertical distribution of the brown alga *Fucus serratus* to wave exposure. Symbols as in Fig. 2–19. (After Evans, 1947.)

modification of the waves by varying depth and nature of the offshore bottom, nor does it take into account fetch to more distant land. In intertidal zonation, a biological estimate may sometimes be made of the extent of the splash zone. On the coast of the British Isles, the barnacle *B. balanoides* has a rather sharp upper limit at high water of mean neap tides, and the amount by which it exceeds this in a given locality is closely correlated with wave action and may be used as a measure of the splash zone (Fig. 2–23).

Wave exposure in the intertidal and sublittoral zone may prove limiting to many forms which are damaged or covered up by movements of the substratum. A wave-beaten sandy beach is generally more barren than a sheltered one, for very few animals can tolerate the constant shifting of the sand. The barrenness of an exposed pebble beach has already been mentioned. On rocks, many forms may be excluded because of direct damage by wave action. This is undoubtedly true for many of the more delicate algae. The same is probably true of the

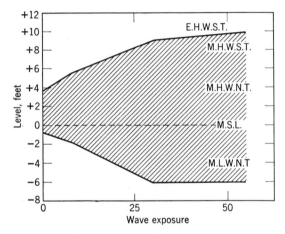

Figure 2–23. Relation of the vertical distribution of the barnacle *Balanus balanoides* to wave exposure (0 = complete shelter). (After Moore, 1935.)

hydroids recorded by Ricketts and Calvin (1948) as growing in both sheltered and wave-exposed habitats, but not producing any medusae in the latter. Among reef-building corals, many of the more delicately branching forms are restricted to sheltered locations, although there are exceptions to this, and in some there is a tendency for the wave-exposed colonies of a species to be less diffuse and delicate than those grown in shelter. Wave action may also dislodge forms such as *P. lapillus* from the rocks, and although this does not harm them, and many are able to regain their position in calmer weather, the final result is that they become scarcer in such areas. Forms such as *P. lapillus* may also be driven to shelter in crannies during stormy weather, and this limits their feeding, since they normally prey on the barnacles and mussels growing on open rock surfaces. Such curtailment of feeding time may be a serious limiting factor. It has been found, for example, that oysters growing in polluted estuarine waters may keep their shells closed during the part of the tidal cycle when the pollutants are most concentrated and thus avoid damage from them. As a result, though, they are able to open and feed for only a limited period, and this is believed, in some cases, to be the reason for observed poor condition of the oysters.

Wave action may, on the other hand, be beneficial or even essential to some species. In Bermuda, many of the corals and gorgonids and the sea urchin *Eucidaris tribuloides* are found only where there is at least moderate wave action. That it is actual water movement which

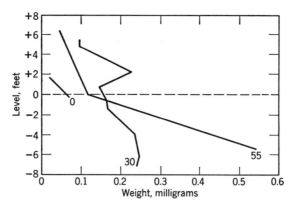

Figure 2–24. Relation of growth to tidal level and wave exposure in the barnacle *Balanus balanoides*. Growth is indicated by the tissue weight of first-year individuals (0 = complete shelter, 55 = high wave exposure.) (After Moore, 1935.)

is needed, and not proximity to oceanic type water, is shown by some of the gorgonids which can penetrate farther inshore in Bermuda where the wave action is replaced by strong currents. Similarly, wave action which frequently wets the upper zones of the shore with spray may be beneficial to certain species. A case in point is the lichen *L. pygmaea* which is absent from sheltered locations, where it is replaced by the related *L. confinis* (Naylor, 1930). This maintenance of damp conditions appears to be favorable, also, to the more sensitive young stages of various inhabitants of lower zones too. This is seen in the first year group of the limpet *P. vulgata*. At St. Malo, the density of O-group limpets was 100 to 113 per square meter on wave-exposed rocks, but only 45 to 61 on sheltered ones (Hatton, 1936). The same is true of the barnacles *B. balanoides* and *Chthamalus stellatus* (Fischer-Piette, 1932). Barnacles have much higher growth rates with high wave exposure (Fig. 2–24), but this is probably owing to the increased food supply brought within their reach, since currents produce the same effect, and the growth is particularly high in certain silt-laden waters, despite their shelter from wave action.

The favorable effects of wave exposure on density of spat settlement, vertical distribution, and growth rate of barnacles are indicated by the following calculations of the output of organic material into the sea, by barnacles alone, on a typical wave-exposed and sheltered shore (Moore, 1935). Expressed as kilograms (dry weight) of tissue per kilometer of shore, the values range from 600 to 1600 at high wave exposure and 200 to 320 in shelter. To these must be added the output of larvae which amounts to a hundred million at high wave exposure and a million in shelter; this would about double the tissue production on the exposed shore and raise that on the sheltered one by a third to a half. Thus the wave exposure may have a very marked effect on the organic productivity of a shore.

Wave action is believed to modify the shape of reef corals. It is known to do so in the case of the limpet *P. vulgata*. Orton (1932) showed that limpets growing high on the shore were relatively taller than those lower down. He suggested that the latter were in a damper habitat and so were not forced to contract tightly onto the rock to conserve moisture. As a result the shell, secreted by a more widely expanded mantle, had a flatter shape. This was later confirmed experimentally (Moore, 1934). In the same way, wave action, by keeping the intertidal zone damp, produces the same effect. It has previously been suggested that the flat shape was an adaptation for better withstanding of wave shock. Test (1945), comparing the habitats of various species of the limpet *Acmaea* on the Californian coast, showed that, in general, wave exposure is associated with thinner and more sculptured shells. Thompson (1917) points out that the stresses imposed on the test of a sea urchin by the pull of the tube feet tend to flatten the test, so those exposed to wave action, having to hold more tightly to the substratum, should either be more flattened, or have a stronger shell to resist the pull. Comparison of three populations of *E. esculentus* in the Isle of Man, one from deep water, one from shallower, and one from low watermark, showed little difference in shape but the shells were much thicker in the ones from low water where wave action was strongest (Fig. 2–25).

In sheltered waters, intense temperature and salinity stratification may occur near the surface, and this may impose rapid and extensive environmental fluctuations on attached organisms during the tidal cycle. In such circumstances, the mixing action of waves is of great importance. Although attached organisms are, of necessity, almost absent in the surface waters of the open ocean, this mixing is still important. Waves mix atmospheric gases into the surface waters and so promoting gas exchange. Both the waves themselves and bubbles which they introduce into the water modify the penetration of light. Bubbles tend to diffuse the light and cause added surface loss, but Poole (1936) estimates that this loss will not exceed 10 to 15 per cent. The scattering of the light will tend to change obliquely entering light

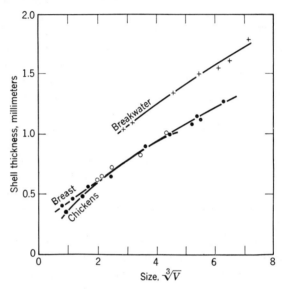

Figure 2–25. The relation of shell thickness to size in three populations of the sea urchin *Echinus esculentus.* The Breakwater habitat is at low water, Breast at 25 to 35 meters, and Chickens at 60 to 70 meters. (After Moore, 1935a.)

to more nearly vertical (Whitney, 1941), and the waves themselves will tend to diffract the light closer to vertical. Moore (1950) estimates that this effect is slight with high solar altitudes, and even with the sun 75 degrees from zenith, the ray path, under extreme conditions, will not be reduced by more than about 13 per cent.

Waves, then, become progressively more important from the ecological standpoint as they approach the shore, and in the neighborhood of the littoral zone they may become a major limiting factor. At present, we lack simple wave-recording apparatus comparable with that for temperature or salinity, nor is it clear just what should be recorded. From the point of view of direct damage, or damage caused by transported hard materials, it is probably the maximum force developed which concerns us. From the point of view of maintaining damp conditions in the intertidal zone, or of keeping food-providing silt in suspension, the average conditions or the duration of conditions of minimum wave action may be more important.

CURRENTS

Although the ecological effects of both currents and waves lie in the resulting movements of the water particles, the relative advantages and disadvantages of the two differ considerably. Currents do not affect penetration of light, except as they lift sediments and so reduce transparency. They do not modify tidal zonation by producing a splash zone, nor do they cause damage by impact, except to the most delicate organisms. Further, their rate of movement is usually much slower than that of the water particles in waves, and this rate does not fluctuate rapidly; its most frequent change is that associated with the tidal cycle. Both tend to transport solid particles, and since currents are more uniform in speed, we can predict more fully how big these particles will be. For example, Johnson (1919) gives the following values. A current of 0.4 knots will shift ordinary sand along the bottom, 1 knot will shift fine gravel, 2.15 knots will move shingle 2.5 cm. in diameter, and 3.5 knots will move angular stones 3.8 cm. in diameter (1 knot = 51.5 cm. per second).

A current may cause some wear on the tissues of an organism growing in it, and particles in suspension may produce abrasion. On soft bottoms, currents result in constant shifting of the sediments and may cause impoverishment of the fauna and flora. On the other hand, a fauna richer both in quantity and in number of species (Remane, 1933) may result. In such a case the fauna consists mainly of solid but active burrowers such as *Cardium edule* and *Mya,* or of a microfauna living in the interstices between the particles. The water-borne sediments are deposited on neighboring surfaces, often resulting in considerable modification of their fauna and flora. Thus, despite otherwise particularly advantageous conditions, young barnacles settle more sparsely on estuarine rocks than they do in clearer water. Those that obtain a foothold there, however, grow much faster than those in the clearer water. The actual flow of water over a surface may prevent or retard settlement of the young; for some older stages a slight current is beneficial, but a stronger one is harmful. Smith (1946) demonstrated this experimentally for barnacles, and Doochin and Smith (1951) give the optimum rate for the growth of *Balanus amphi-*

trite as 0.4 knots. Figure 2–26 shows their results for the bryozoan *Schizoporella unicornis.* Dodgson (1928.) gives an upper limit of 5 miles per hour for the mussel *M. edulis.*

The beneficial action of currents for many organisms lies in the transport of additional food material to these organisms and in the removal of waste materials. For algae, depletion of nutrients and carbon dioxide in the neighborhood of the plant is avoided, and for animals carbon dioxide is removed, along with other products, and oxygen concentration maintained. The barnacle *B. balanoides* shows greatly increased growth in water containing suspended food material and apparently conserves energy when this is presented to it by a current. In still water, this barnacle filters particles from the water by the beating action of its cirri, whereas in a current it has been observed to hold them facing into the current, withdrawing them only at intervals, presumably when sufficient food has accumulated on them.

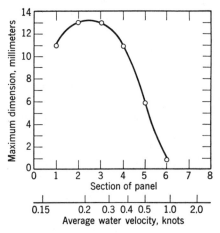

Figure 2–26. Relation of the growth of the bryozoan *Schizoporella unicornis* to water velocity. (After Doochin and Smith, 1951.)

Currents also play a very important role in the distribution of both permanent members of the plankton and planktonic larvae. When the eggs or larvae of a species are planktonic, not only are these removed from competition with the parents for food, but they are given a chance to colonize remote areas when they are ready to settle. This has particular importance for sessile forms, such as an alga or barnacle. Whereas in a steady current such larvae are carried only in one direction, the oscillating tidal currents have the advantage of distributing larvae in different directions from their source. This may be particularly significant in estuarine forms. We have seen that the developing stages frequently have a smaller tolerance range than the adults have for such factors as salinity and temperature. Such forms, carried out of an estuary on the ebb tide, have the opportunity of developing in more normal sea water. When ready to settle, and by then more tolerant of estuarine conditions, some of these larvae will be in a position to be carried again into an estuary on the flood tide and to settle there. The mortality among larvae that fail to find the right type of ground on which to settle, together with the mortality from other causes, is of course tremendous, but it is characteristic of species producing planktonic larvae to produce them in enormous numbers, sometimes over a hundred million per parent. Most larvae, when ready for metamorphosis, are able to postpone this for a time if they do not find suitable conditions, and the currents thus afford them the chance of sampling a much wider area in search of a settling place than they could with their own powers of locomotion. Pyefinch (1950) has made an estimate of the larval mortality of barnacle larvae under optimal conditions. If an adult *B. balanoides* produces 13,000 nauplii, 130 survive to become cyprids, 26 achieve metamorphosis into young barnacles, and 15 of these survive for 2 months.

Ocean currents carrying with them a native plankton often take it to areas where its permanent survival is impossible. The examination of almost any local fauna or flora list bears witness to the ability of currents to carry species, on occasion, far beyond their normal range. On the other hand, the currents may bring with them environmental conditions differing widely from those that would otherwise occur in the area. The Gulf Stream, carrying warm water up the eastern coast of North America, and the Humboldt Current, carrying cold water toward the equator on the west coast of South America, are well-known examples. The distribution and significance of ocean currents are too well described in such oceanographic texts as that by Sverdrup et al. (1946) to need detailed treatment here. It may be noted, however, that not only are the currents ecologically important in carrying plankton to different areas, but the plankton itself is valuable as an indicator of where the current has come from. This aspect will be discussed more fully later.

ABRASION

Abrasion and some related processes form a somewhat heterogeneous group of processes, not always strictly ecological factors but best treated here as such. In the sections on waves and currents we have already considered some aspects of abrasion by water-borne stones and sand. Rocks rising from a sandy beach are frequently denuded of life for a certain distance above the sand surface. The actual abrasion of the sand particles would be sufficient to scour away any inhabitants, and in fact it frequently removes so much of the rock itself that there is strong undercutting at this level. It also, however, scours away the normal film of bacteria, diatoms, and other forms which cover the surface, and work on the fouling of underwater structures has shown that such organisms are normal precursors to the settlement of many larvae. They are also the diet of larger forms such as limpets, which would therefore be discouraged from migrating into such an area.

A similar exclusion of encrusting forms may arise from the activities

Figure 2–27. The vertical surface of a barnacle-covered rock (stippled), showing areas kept clear by the sweep of the brown algae *Ascophyllum* and *Fucus*. (Modified from Yonge, 1949.)

of other encrusting or attached forms. For example, Fig. 2–27 shows how an intertidal rock surface may be kept free from settling barnacles where it is within the radius of such attached larger algae as *Ascophyllum* and *Fucus*. Figures 2–28 and 2–29 show the cleared areas maintained in the neighborhood of two kinds of limpets, and it is interesting to note that, in the areas cleared by the South African *Patella*

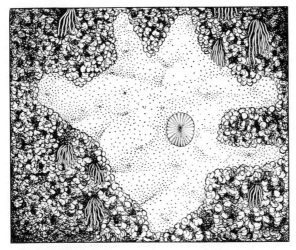

Figure 2–28. Alga-covered rock surface with an area kept bare by the grazing of a limpet *Patella vulgata.* (After Moore, 1938.)

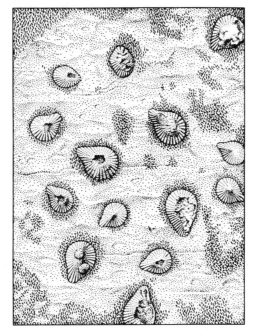

Figure 2–29. Rock surface at False Bay, South Africa. There is a general covering of the alga *Lithothamnion,* but around the limpets, *Patella cochlear,* there is a cleared area covered with the red alga, *Gelidium pristoides.* (After Stephenson et al., 1937.)

cochlear, a new algal flora has developed which is peculiar to such clearings. A further abrasive activity of limpets and some other forms is the wearing of permanent cavities in the rock surface under the edges of their shells.

The weakening of solid structures by boring organisms is another important effect which requires comment here. In some places, wood is so completely riddled by the boring lamellibranch *Teredo* that it is virtually destroyed in a few months. Even chemically treated wood may last only a few years. In the same way, sponges, polychaetes, algae, and other forms are constantly burrowing into shells, rocks, and coral skeletons. On coral reefs, masses of living coral are constantly breaking away because of such weakening of the structures to which they are attached or of their own basal regions. The size of a reef represents a balance between loss by such destruction and accumulation by growth and other means. On a smaller scale, the destruction of many mollusc shells by boring sponges and polychaetes necessitates a high rate of replacement if the strength of the shell is to be maintained. On a still smaller scale, the grinding down of sand grains in the guts of deposit feeders such as holothurians plays an important part in the reduction of the particle size of the deposits.

Such loss of shell from living animals may introduce a problem in the determination of their growth rates. The apex of a barnacle shell is constantly wearing away, and new growth takes place at the base. It is occasionally possible to see annual bands on the shell of the barnacle. However, the space between two such bands must not be taken to be the increase in size of the barnacle during the year, since it represents the sum of the increase and the replacement of apical loss. A similar error arises in the measurement of the height of a gastropod shell, since the apex gradually wears away and new growth occurs at the lip. Some gastropods, *Truncatella* for instance, actually develop an internal septum at a fracture plane and then throw off a considerable section of apical shell. Although wear takes place also in bivalve shells, the same problem is not introduced since measurements are generally made of the length of the shell, terminating at both ends at a growing margin. Among algae, the problem of measuring growth and estimating loss by fragmentation is a serious one, and it has been solved for comparatively few species, as will be shown later.

SUBSTRATUM

Although the planktonic environment offers many advantages to the organisms inhabiting it, there are serious limitations to the size and weight of the protective armor which the organisms can carry. The environment offers no hiding place from predators. On the other hand, it is vastly larger in extent than the solid subsurfaces of the oceans. These, however, though limited in extent, have many obvious advantages. A solid substratum affords a cover to protect from predators and also from adverse environmental conditions. It may itself be edible or it may be the focal point for the concentration of food in quantity. It affords support for both attached and motile forms, allowing these to make use of heavy armor. If the forms are attached, it allows them the benefits associated with life in a current or in water moved by waves, whereas a floating form loses most of these advantages, since it moves with the water. As for marine plants, large size is attained only among the attached forms. Some animals and plants obtain a combination of the benefits of life in a current and of attachment to a solid surface by growing on the hulls of ships, the skin of whales and turtles, etc., but these are comparatively few.

Two main types of substrates may be distinguished. These are solid, including rock, metal, wood, shell, etc., and particulate, such as sand and mud. In general, the greatest amount of solid substratum is to be found between tidemarks, with a progressive change through sand to mud in deeper water. The abyssal bottom consists of only very fine sediments, with occasional solid objects such as shells and bones and rare rock outcrops. Comparatively few algae have developed a holdfast system suitable for growth in soft sediments. The greatest growth of fucoids and similar algae is on rocks in the intertidal zone, and the laminarias and giant Pacific kelp grow only where there is a rock surface for attachment. Such algae require only attachment, and not nourishment, from their root-like holdfasts, and we do not find the differences in flora between, say granite and limestone, that we do on land. Differences are associated more with variations in the roughness and friability of the surface. Thus chalk rarely carries a dense algal growth. The same is true of attached animals, such as barnacles. Figure 2–30 shows a greater abundance of *B. balanoides* and *C. stellatus* on rough surface rock than on smooth. On chalk, the barnacles were practically absent, whereas they were common on flints embedded in the chalk (Moore and Kitching, 1939).

In many attached forms, selection of a suitable surface occurs at the time when the larvae are ready to settle. Thus Hatton (1938) showed that barnacles settled in greater numbers on a scratched surface than on a polished one of the same material. Figure 2–31 shows a group of barnacles, *B. balanoides*, which have settled so densely into a V-shaped groove on the rock surface that competition for food has stunted their growth, compared with isolated individuals on the open rock surface alongside. Hatton (1938) shows that the cypris larvae of barnacles are negatively phototrophic at the time of metamorphosis, and that their tendency to settle in irregularities of the surface is associated with this reaction. Barnacle larvae do not normally wander far after settling, although they do explore the surface by creeping over it for

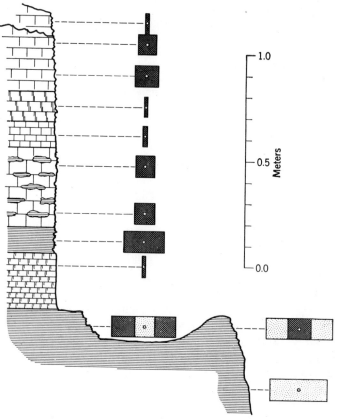

Figure 2–30. The vertical distribution of the barnacle *Chthamalus stellatus* on a varying substrate. Horizontal shading indicates chert, and brick pattern softer limestones. *Chthamalus* abundance is indicated in dotted black and *Balanus balanoides* as light stipple. (After Moore and Kitching, 1939.)

a short distance. On the other hand, the larvae of the shipworm, *Teredo*, alternately settle and swim for some time and thus have a good chance of locating a suitable substratum. It has been shown that there is a chemotactic response to lignin which assists them in locating the wood in which they will later bore.

The surface structure of a hard substrate affects the settlement and survival of forms settling on it, and its consistency may determine their ability to burrow into it. Additional factors become operative in a soft substratum. It is less easy for fine sediments to accumulate where there is much water movement, so sands tend to be associated with wave action and mud with sheltered habitats and deeper water. Particle size is of direct importance to deposit fauna in that small deposit eaters may be unable to swallow large particles. On the other hand, the deposits tend to clog the gills of various burrowing forms, such as crabs, and the filtering mechanism that guards the gills may be effective in keeping out large particles but not sufficient to eliminate fine material. For deposit feeders a coarse particle size may be disadvan-

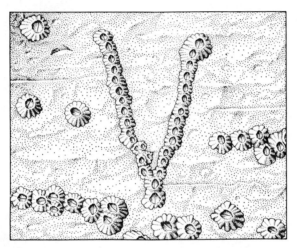

Figure 2–31. Barnacles, *Balanus balanoides,* all of the same age, showing that isolated individuals have grown faster than those crowded together in a crevice. (After Moore, 1935.)

tageous, since, in general, the finer deposits have the higher organic content. Such organic matter is frequently partly colloidal, and both this and the smaller pore spaces make fine deposits less permeable to water. As a result, their interstitial water is less rapidly renewed, and, where the organic content is high, becomes depleted of oxygen. This may result in the presence of free hydrogen sulfide which is toxic. Some burrowing animals can live anaerobically in such an environment, and others can maintain a sufficient water circulation in their immediate neighborhood by keeping open a burrow to the surface, but the combined conditions are beyond the tolerance range of a great many burrowing forms.

The chemical composition of sediments varies in other ways, and not much is known about the specific requirements of particular species.   However, Wilson (1937 etc.) has shown that polychaete larvae actively select the type of bottom on which they will settle and metamorphose.   For example, the adults of *Notomastus* are found in sand or mud.   The larvae are able to delay their metamorphosis for some time, if necessary, and they have been found to settle most rapidly on mud, less so on sand, and least on plain glass.   Wilson has also shown (1952 etc.) that organic substances adsorbed on the particles may determine the favorability of a particular sediment for settlement.   He suggests that such selection of substratum may be rather widespread in polychaetes which have planktonic larvae, and that the possibility of delaying metamorphosis may result in the observed heavy concentration of newly settled young in suitable environments.

The texture of a deposit varies considerably according to its water content, and this may affect an animal's ability to burrow in it.   Chapman (1949) demonstrated this with the burrowing polychaete *Arenicola marina*.   He made a series of mounds of sand of different heights.   The drainage, and as a result the hardness, varied with the height.   He then measured the time taken by an *Arenicola* to burrow into the sand when placed on the surface, with the results shown in Table 2–10.   Burrowing from the surface is, admittedly, a more severe test than burrowing within the sand, but the correlation between ease of burrowing and mound height and hardness of sand is clear.

TABLE 2–10

Correlation between Time Taken by *Arenicola marina* to Burrow into Sand, Height of Mound, and Hardness of Sand

(Chapman, 1949)

Burrowing Time in Minutes and Seconds

Worm	Mound Height—0.0 cm. Hardness—1088	Mound Height—5.0 cm. Hardness—1616	Mound Height—7.5 cm. Hardness—1961	Mound Height—13.0 cm. Hardness—2272
1	2'30''	4'20''	8'00''	6'00''
2	3'15''	4'35''	16'00''+	10'00''
3	4'00''	4'45''	16'00''+	10'00''
4	4'10''	4'50''	16'00''+	
5	4'20''	5'15''		
6	5'00''	5'50''		
7	5'05''	7'20''		
8	5'05''	8'00''		
9	5'10''	8'10''		
10	5'15''	8'30''		

Chapman and Newell (1949) also showed the necessity for a sufficient depth of suitable soil. They studied an area where there was about 15 cm. of muddy sand above thick clay, except for certain strips in which the clay lay at about twice the depth. Numbers of *A. marina* on one side of such a strip, in its center, and on the other, were respectively, 4.4, 47.2, and 7.3 per square meter. Such concentration in the more favorable location may be accounted for in the case of *A. marina* by the ability of the adult worms to migrate readily.

TIDES

The theory of tides and their prediction are sufficiently covered in standard textbooks, and need no description here. We are concerned

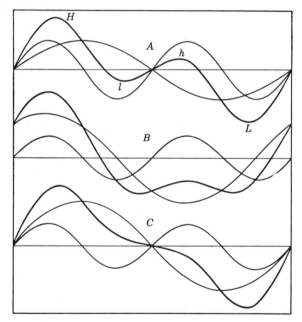

Figure 2–32. Examples of different types of diurnally unequal tides (heavy lines) resulting from different combinations of a diurnal and a semi-diurnal tide (light lines). (After Sverdrup et al., 1946.)

with the effects of the tide in modifying the influence of certain environmental factors, and with how this varies with the different types of tide that can occur. Basically, the tide is the composite result of a semi-diurnal oscillation, with a period of about 12½ hours, and a diurnal oscillation with a period of 24 hours. In some places the diurnal part may predominate, with the result that the tide recurs always at the same time of day. In others, the semi-diurnal component predominates. More usually, the two are mixed, and the progressive change in phase difference between them results in two tides per day, becoming about an hour later each day. Of these two tides,

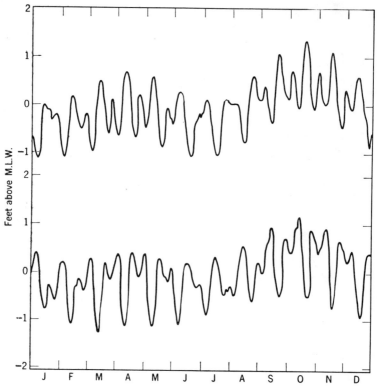

Figure 2–33. Predicted low water for two different years at Mayport, Florida, showing wide difference in seasonal pattern.

there is a progressive change from greater height or amplitude of one through equality, to greater height or amplitude in the other. Figure 2–32 shows three possibilities.

Each full and each new moon is accompanied by larger amplitude, or spring tides, and each quarter by small amplitudes, or neap tides. Spring tides at full moon tend to be larger than those at new moon. Finally, at the equinoxes, spring tides tend to have a larger amplitude and neap tides a smaller one, than at the solstices. These are generalizations, and locally tides may be greatly modified by the natural periodicity of the basins, by the interference of tidal waves from two directions, and by other factors. Only broad generalizations can be made, and there is variation from one locality to another, and often from one year to another. For example, Fig. 2–33 shows the predicted low waters in two different years at Mayport, Florida. In 1945, the lowest tides occurred at the spring equinox, and in 1947 at a midwinter and midsummer low. The chart shows, also, the progressive change in equality of the new- and full-moon spring tides. Tidal range varies widely in different places. In St. Malo Bay, the range at maximum spring tides is 12 meters, and in the Bay of Fundy 15.4 meters. These are extreme cases, but 5- to 7-meter ranges are not unusual. Tides tend to build up to greater ranges on continental coasts than in the open ocean; on oceanic islands they are usually only a meter or less. The Baltic is an example of an enclosed body of water with a tide of less than 1 meter. In some places, where two tidal waves meet and cancel out, there may be almost no tide.

Apart from tidal currents, our main concern is with the alternating conditions of exposure and immersion which they produce in the intertidal zone. The duration of the conditions associated with these two phases is of the greatest importance and has led to the classification of certain intertidal zones in terms of particular tidal levels. Starting at the upper tidal limit, and omitting, for the moment, any effect of wave action, etc., the most significant levels are as follows.

A. High-water level of extreme spring tides. This will be submerged on only one or two successive tides, and at one or two periods in the entire year. It is probably more important as a downward limit for terrestrial and supralittoral organisms than as an upper limit for intertidal ones.

B. Mean high-water level of spring tides. This will be submerged on many of, but not all, the year's spring tides. It is a convenient reference level, but less likely to be ecologically significant than A or C.

C. High-water level of lowest spring tides. Wet at least once in each monthly cycle, this level is likely to be the upper limit for forms for which an occasional wetting suffices, but which cannot go several successive months without water.

D. High-water level of highest neap tides.

E. High-water level of mean neap tides.

F. High-water level of lowest neap tides. Of the last three, F is likely to be the most significant, since it is the highest level on the shore which will be wet on every tide of the year. It will be the upper limit for forms which can withstand several hours, but not several days, of exposure.

G. Mean sea level.

H. Midtide level. Although not always identical, these two may often, for ecological purposes, be treated as the same. Except as a reference point, this is chiefly significant as the level at which certain factors undergo the most rapid change.

I. Highest low-water level of neap tides.

J. Mean low-water level of neap tides.

K. Lowest low-water level of neap tides. It is the highest of these that is most likely to be significant in intertidal zonation, since it is the lowest level that will be exposed on every tide of the year. Just as some organisms cannot tolerate permanent exposure, so others, for a less understood reason, cannot tolerate permanent immersion.

L. Highest low-water level of spring tides.

M. Mean low-water level of spring tides.

N. Lowest low-water level of spring tides. These constitute upper limits for forms that can tolerate only a very brief period of exposure, or, in the case of *N*, no exposure at all. They may also be the lower limit of forms that can tolerate long periods of, but not permanent, immersion.

For those who are accustomed to an area with small tidal ranges, such subdivision of the intertidal zone may appear excessive, since, in such an area, tidal fluctuations caused by winds and waves may far exceed in magnitude those between, say, neap and spring tides. Where tidal ranges are larger, however, these differences are really significant.

In considering the significance of tides, there are two important aspects, namely the duration of exposure or immersion, and, so far as exposure is concerned, the time when this occurs. Below midtide level, the maximum period of exposure, and exposure of the lowest levels occur at spring tides. The lowest spring tide, at a given locality, occurs a certain number of hours after the transit of the moon and two or three days after the full or new moon. Thus it falls always at approximately the same time of day for any one place. If this occurs in the morning and evening, less insolation will be incurred than if the exposure is at midday. Although this effect has not actually been recorded, it seems probable that some sublittoral forms may penetrate above low water of spring tides in the former case but be confined to below the lowest low water in the latter. Diurnal inequality of the tides may introduce some complication here, especially where low water of spring tides occurs near midday and midnight. On the Great Barrier Reef, for example, the lowest ebbs occur at full moon and at night in summer, but in the daytime and at full moon in winter.

The duration of exposure or immersion at a given level controls the duration of adverse factors such as insolation and desiccation, as well as beneficial ones such as feeding.   We have seen that, within limiting lethal values, the duration of a particular condition may be of major importance, and a particular temperature, for example, may be tolerated for 3 hours, where it would be lethal if continued for 9 hours.

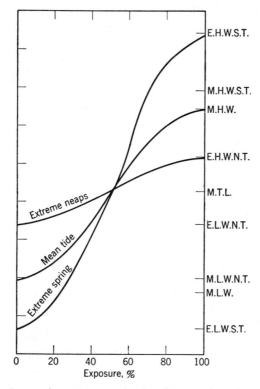

Figure 2–34. Curves for Mayport, Florida, showing the relation between percentage exposure and tidal level. These show also how much percentage exposure at a given level may vary according to the type of tide.

Figure 2–34 shows how, with a simple tide, the duration of exposure, expressed as a percentage of the tidal cycle, varies with level. It shows also the difference that the varying tidal range of spring and neap tides produces.   At the level of low-water neaps, there will be no exposure at all on a neap tide but exposure for about 40 per cent of the cycle on a spring tide.   The maximum period of exposure or immersion that an organism will encounter is likely to be critical in many cases.   Doty (1946) has shown that if the maximum period for a whole year is plotted against level, the curve for a particular locality is not smooth but rather stepped, with sudden increases of two- or threefold in period within a short vertical distance. Figure 2–35 shows his data on duration of immersion for an area on the Pacific coast of North America where diurnal inequality of the tides is pronounced. For some organisms, tolerance of exposure or immersion is to be measured in days or weeks rather than in hours, and similar steps occur when longer periods are considered. The relation of the critical levels indicated by these steps to the inhabitants of the intertidal zone will be described in a later section.

Beside the effects asociated with relative duration of exposure and immersion, there are others associated with changes within one of

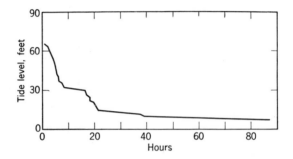

Figure 2–35. The relation between tidal level and the maximum duration of submergence possible at any time during the year. This example is from a part of the Pacific coast of North America where there is marked diurnal inequality of the tides. (After Doty, 1946.)

these periods. Currents of water are beneficial to such forms as barnacles and bryozoa in bringing more food within their reach. They probably benefit some algae in a similar way. On the other hand, they damage delicate organisms, and by transport of sediments they render a soft bottom less stable and thus unsuitable for some of its inhabitants. As will be seen from the shape of the tidal curve, the rate of rise or fall is maximum in the neighborhood of midtide, and least at low and high water. On an open coast, resulting tidal currents will tend to be maximal about midtide, with resulting advantages or disadvantages to particular species around this level. In confined spaces, such as estuaries, the contour of the bottom may be such that, with much wider space available to them, currents are less above midtide level and much greater below when they become concentrated into a narrow channel.

The rate of vertical rise and fall of the tide may be as significant as the rate of resulting horizontal currents. Where there is stratification of salinity or temperature, conditions at a particular level will change during the tidal cycle according to how deeply that level is submerged. It follows that the rate of change of salinity or temperature at that level will be dependent on the rate of rise and fall, so that the midtide section of the shore may undergo more rapid changes than high and low watermark. By one or another of these means, the middle region of the intertidal zone appears to be less generally advantageous than the levels above and below it. This is shown in Fig. 2–36, in which

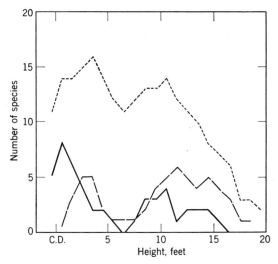

Figure 2–36. Frequency distribution of species limits between low and high water. The solid line shows the number of species with their lower limits at each level, the broken line shows upper limits, and the dotted line shows the total number of species present at the different levels. (C.D. = chart datum). (After Colman, 1933.)

Colman (1933) records, for a rocky shore, the total number of species present at different levels as well as the numbers with upper or lower limits of distribution there. All three show a minimum in the middle of the shore. In the same way, Moore and Sproston (1940) found that colonization of new rocks on the shore proceeded faster near the top and bottom than in the middle zone.

There are many very striking cyclic periodicities of migration, spawning, swarming, etc., which are associated with the phase of the moon, but in which the mechanism is not always understood. In some periodicities the illumination from the moon may be involved, but more generally the correlation appears to be with the resulting tides, and

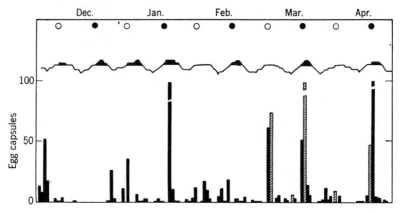

Figure 2–37. The relation between the occurrence of the eggs of the gastropod *Littorina neritoides* in the plankton and the wetting of the high level zone which the adults inhabit. The phase of the moon is shown at the top, below which is a curve for predicted high water. Tides higher than 15 feet above datum are blacked in. The block diagram shows numbers of egg capsules in the plankton. (Modified from Lysaght, 1941.)

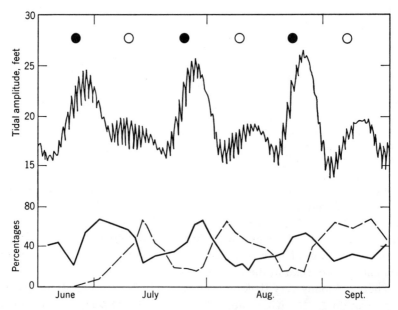

Figure 2–38. The lunar cycle of spawning of the mussel *Mytilus edulis.* The phases of the moon and tidal amplitude are shown above. The lower curves show the percentage of full, mature individuals (solid line) and of spents (broken line). (Modified from Battle, 1932.)

either their pressure, currents, or some other phenomenon. *Littorina neritoides* is a gastropod which lives at the top of the intertidal zone

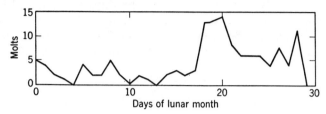

Figure 2–39. Lunar rhythm in the frequency of molting of the shrimp *Anchistioides antiguensis.* (After Wheeler, 1937.)

where it is wet, except by wave action, only at spring tides. Its egg capsules, as shown by Lysaght (1941) are found in the neighboring plankton mainly at the periods of spring tides, and so with a lunar rhythm (Fig. 2–37) Battle (1932) traced the cycle in the mussel *M. edulis* (Fig. 2–38), in which maturation of the gonads takes place during the period of new-moon spring tides, and spawning during the subsequent first-quarter neaps, full-moon springs, and third-quarter neaps. The swarming of the Pacific palolo worm is well known. Huntsman (1948) has described the very precisely timed swarming of the polychaete *Odontosyllis enopla* at Bermuda, the swarming being the time of mating and spawning. Swarming begins three days after full moon and 54 minutes after sunset, recurring at the same time for a day or two. Stormy weather may delay the swarming for a night or

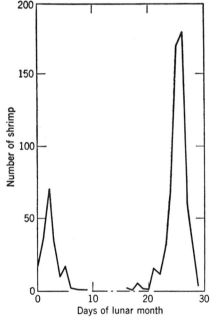

Figure 2–40. Lunar rhythm in the occurrence at the surface at night of the shrimp *Anchistioides antiguensis.* (After Wheeler, 1937.)

two but does not affect the time of day, nor does the degree of cloudiness of the sky. Huntsman (1948) and Herpin (1928, 1929) have reviewed the literature on similar cycles in other polychaetes. Other phenomena also are associated with lunar rhythm. Thus Wheeler (1937) found the shrimp *Anchistiodes antiguensis* at the surface at night only just after new moon and in the third quarter, and in captivity he found a lunar rhythm in their molting (Figs. 2–39, 2–40).

Among commercial fisheries, Savage and Hodgson (1934) describe several examples of lunar rhythms. The autumn herring fishery off

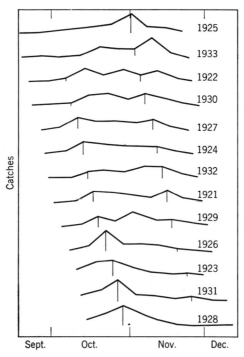

Figure 2–41. Lunar rhythm in the catches of herrings off the east coast of England. The vertical lines indicate the periods of full moon. (After Savage, 1934.)

the east coast of England shows maximum catches at the periods of full moon in October and November (Fig. 2–41). Hake catches also show, in some localities, a peak near full moon. Sea bream, *Pagellus centrodontus,* show peak catches at new moon, and the Californian smelt comes inshore to spawn from March to June on the three nights following full moon. Lunar rhythms then, whether controlled by moonlight or by the tides acting through some other factor, are of widespread occurrence.

3

Chemical Environmental Factors

OXYGEN

A supply of free oxygen is necessary for most forms of life. In the presence of adequate illumination, most plants can provide this. Some bacteria, as well as a few animals, can live completely anaerobically. Other animals, and these are commoner, can survive anaerobic conditions for a time but require access to a supply of oxygen at intervals. Most can survive a considerable lowering of the oxygen concentration but cannot survive any length of time with no oxygen. In some animals, respiratory pigments provide an oxygen reserve to tide them over short periods of anaerobic conditions. Some of those that can survive rather long periods have been shown to make use of glycogen as an oxygen supply, and in one example, the shipworm *Teredo*, glycogen actually comprises half the dry weight of the tissues. Water permanently devoid of oxygen is comparatively rare in the oceans, but where it occurs, as in the deeper parts of the Black Sea, animal life is lacking.

Bottom sediments are frequently devoid of oxygen except at their surface, and may, in fact, take up a considerable amount of oxygen if this
is made available. Blackening of the sediments, and a smell of hydrogen sulfide, are frequently associated with such conditions, although
not always.

The biology and physiology of the inhabitants of such anaerobic
sediments are specially adapted to their environment. In the bottom
muds of the Clyde Sea area, the abundant harpacticoid copepods could
survive for only 24 hours in the absence of oxygen (Moore, 1931).
These were restricted to the extreme surface layer where there was a
little oxygen or where they could readily reach oxygenated water.
Small free-living nematodes, which lived much deeper, were able to
survive anaerobically for a month. The lamellibranch *Syndosmya
alba*, which burrows, but maintains connection with the overlying
water through its siphons, could survive in deoxygenated water for
only $3\frac{1}{2}$ days, but another lamellibranch, *Nucula tenuis*, which burrows but does not have a siphonal connection with the water, could
survive for 5 to 17 days.   The mussel *Mytilus edulis*, which frequently
lives in polluted waters of low oxygen content, can live without oxygen
for several weeks, but during that time remains inactive and does not
feed (Dodgson, 1928).   The clam *Mya arenaria*, which lives in anaerobic muds and sands, can survive for 8 days without oxygen but
during that period suffers a decrease in its glycogen content (Ricketts
and Calvin, 1948).   *Arenicola marina* is a polychaete which forms
U-shaped burrows in sand and mud whose interstitial water is frequently devoid of oxygen.   Wells (1945) points out that if the burrow
drains free of water left by the tide, the worms can make use of aerial
respiration, provided the worm is kept moist.   However, if water remains in the burrow, the worm is unable to circulate this, as it normally does when there is overlying water.   The oxygen therefore
becomes rapidly depleted in the water in the burrow.   When this
happens, the worm repeatedly draws bubbles of air down to cover
several pairs of gills and maintains respiration in this way.   Lindroth
(1938) mentions somewhat similar behavior in two other polychaetes,
Nereis virens and *N. diversicolor*.

Zooplankton may be found in water which is almost, but not quite,
devoid of oxygen, although it is not known whether they remain there
permanently, or only for brief periods.   Sverdrup et al. (1946) record
copepods and other forms in such water which constitutes a layer in
the Gulf of California at a depth of 150–800 meters.   An abundant
zooplankton is also found at a depth of 300 meters in the Gulf of
Panama where the oxygen saturation is only 2 per cent.

Usually, a considerable drop in oxygen concentration can take place before symptoms of anoxia appear and the respiratory rate drops. This is illustrated, in the case of the copepod *Calanus finmarchicus,* in Fig. 3–1. In this species Marshall et al. (1935) found that a greater drop in oxygen concentration was required to produce symptoms of anoxia at low temperature than at high, and that survival of such low concentrations was also better at low temperatures. The latter might be expected, since the respiratory rate itself is lowered at low temperatures (Figs. 2–11, 2–12). In fresh water fish, W. G. Moore (1942) showed, similarly, that much lower oxygen concentrations could be survived at winter temperatures than at summer temperatures. The ability to withstand a considerable drop in oxygen concentration with

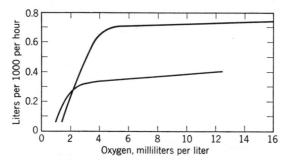

Figure 3–1. The effect of oxygen depletion on the rate of oxygen consumption in the copepod *Calanus finmarchicus.* Upper curve shows mature females, lower curve immatures. (After Marshall et al., 1935.)

little effect on respiratory rate was shown for the Japanese oyster *Ostrea gigas,* by Ishida (1935); the effect began only when the oxygen concentration in the surrounding water fell to 1.5 cc. per liter.

Up to a point, respiratory rates generally increase regularly with temperature, although the curves relating the two do not obey any simple law. The availability of necessary oxygen may be slightly affected by its decreased solubility at higher temperatures. Thus, at a salinity of 34.33°/oo the oxygen content of saturated sea water is 8.08 cc. per liter at 0°C., and only 4.52 at 30°C. However, this effect is unlikely to be serious for any but very sensitive forms or for forms living under conditions of extreme fluctuations of temperature and oxygen concentrations such as may be found in intertidal pools. The increase in respiration resulting from the expenditure of energy in the process of osmoregulation at low salinities has been referred to in the last chapter. Beadle (1931) demonstrated this in various animals, including *Gunda* and *Nereis,* but Marshall et al. (1935) did not find the effect in *Calanus.* Kreps (1929) found it absent in the barnacle *Balanus crenatus* down to $12^0/_{00}$ and only doubtfully present below that. The effect, then, does not appear to be universal. The availability of oxygen is less affected by changes in salinity than by changes in temperature. At 0°C., the solubility is 8.08 cc. per liter at a salinity of $34.33^0/_{00}$ and 10.29 at $0^0/_{00}$, whereas at 30°C, it is 4.52 at $34.33^0/_{00}$ and 5.57 at $0^0/_{00}$. If the differences are large enough to be significant,

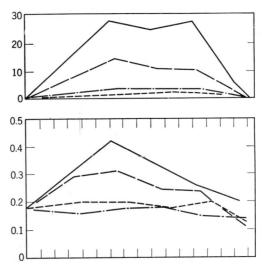

Figure 3–2. The relation between the respiration of the copepod *Calanus finmarchicus* and light. The upper figure shows the diurnal changes in illumination at the surface, 0.5, 5, and 10 meters, and the lower shows the respiration of stage V copepods at the same depths. (After Marshall et al., 1935.)

they tend to provide additional available oxygen where it is needed at low salinities.

Illumination also may have an effect on the respiratory rate of animals, although the reason for this is not, at present, understood. Figure 3–2 shows data obtained by Marshall et al. (1935) for the copepod *C. finmarchicus.* Males, females, and immatures all showed a diurnal rhythm in respiratory rate which paralleled the changes in illumination, both throughout the day and as it varies with depth. They state that the effect could not be accounted for either by changes in temperature or by any marked changes in the activity of the copepods.

Respiration of plants is less understood, except under conditions of darkness. In light, photosynthesis acts in a direction opposite to respiration, and the two effects cannot be separated. In general, plant tissue has a lower oxygen requirement than a similar weight of animal tissue and can probably tolerate greater oxygen deficiency. Where competition for the available oxygen between plants and animal occurs, as in some rock pools, it is generally the animals that succumb first. In such pools there may be such heavy photosynthesis during the daytime that oxygen bubbles may be seen streaming up from the algae, but, if the algal content of the pool is high, oxygen concentration may drop so low at night that fish and other animals may be killed. Nicol (1935) found that, in salt marsh pools, the oxygen saturation ranged from 40 to 80 per cent at night, and from 180 to 200 per cent in the daytime, and that it fell lower at night in pools where the flora was mainly diatoms than where it was mainly larger algae. Orr and Moorhouse (1933) found a diurnal range of 29.7 to 151.3 per cent saturation in water 2 to 5 meters deep on the Great Barrier Reef, and 27.5 to 96.6 per cent in a pool in a mangroove swamp. The low values there were associated with the large amount of decaying organic matter in the swamp. Broekhuysen (1935) found zero oxygen concentration in the water in a *Zostera* bed at 5 a.m., and 260 per cent saturation at 3 p.m. Dahl (unpublished) has observed the migration of amphipods and isopods at night out of such a *Zostera* bed into open water.

Waters polluted by sewage or industrial wastes are another kind of marine habitat where lowered oxygen content is a serious limiting factor. In some waters the low concentration may be directly lethal, but in others forced inactivity may be more important, as it is for other factors already referred to. Oysters, mussels, and other animals may remain closed and cease feeding when conditions are adverse, with poor growth resulting from this inadequate feeding.

CARBON DIOXIDE

Carbon dioxide is produced in the respiration of both animals and plants and is required for the photosynthesis of the plants. The buffering system of sea water is such that it is doubtful whether carbon dioxide concentration ever becomes a limiting factor under natural conditions. Harvey (1945) states that the partial pressure of CO_2 may be reduced to half its normal value during a strong phytoplankton outburst, but that such a value is not limiting. Its importance, ecologically, is greater in connection with the deposition and solution of calcium carbonate. Although the details of the carbonate system in sea water are not yet fully known, it may be said, in general, that calcium precipitation occurs most readily under conditions of high temperature, high salinity, and low carbon dioxide concentration. Such conditions are typical of tropical shallow waters, away from the influence of fresh water, where evaporation raises the salinity and active plant growth reduces the CO_2 content. Such conditions are associated with the direct precipitation of calcium carbonate in the waters of the Bahamas, for instance. They may also be related to the greater proportion of tropical plankton with calcified shells and to the greater abundance of tropical algae with strongly calcified structure.

Although the salinity of deep oceanic waters is not low, the temperature is, and the presence of animal life with no photosynthesizing plants results in high CO_2 content. Solution of calcium carbonate, therefore, is favored by abyssal conditions, and the absence of calcified zooplankton skeletons from deeper-water deposits indicates their solution before they reach the bottom. The deposition of calcium in the skeletons of molluscs, crustacea, and other forms is also more difficult in abyssal conditions and is reflected in the general fragility of such structures, or sometimes by their complete absence of calcification.

HYDROGEN SULFIDE

Hydrogen sulfide, or contaminants associated with it, are toxic to most organisms. Since its presence is correlated with lack of oxygen, it is not always clear which factor is limiting, but at least there is little or no life, other than bacteria, in water in which much H_2S is present. Figure 3–3 shows this clearly for the deeper waters of the Black Sea. Conditions are somewhat different in black sediments in which H_2S is present, since some of the inhabitants maintain temporary or permanent connection with overlying water or air. Thus mangroves and other vegetation may be rooted in black mud, and polychaetes, lamellibranchs, etc., may inhabit it but maintain a circulation of normal water through their burrows or siphons. In the case of the polychaete *A. marina*, which has been referred to in the discussion of oxygen, it has been suggested that the lining of the burrow by mucus may help to prevent the diffusion of H_2S from the mud into the water in the burrow. On the other hand, the blackening of the shells of such forms as *Venus mercenaria* in these habitats indicates that the H_2S must be in contact with the animal.

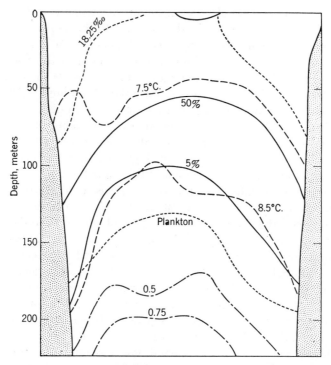

Figure 3–3. Section of the Black Sea showing the absence of plankton and the accumulation of H₂S in the anaerobic deep layers. (After Sverdrup et al., 1946). Isolines show temperature, oxygen saturation, and lower limit of plankton.

HYDROGEN ION CONCENTRATION

It is well known that small *p*H changes can produce marked changes in the physiological reaction of various tissues, as well as in enzyme and other reactions. The significance of *p*H changes in sea water as an ecological factor has been exaggerated in the past, and it seems probable that variations within the observed range in the open sea have comparatively little effect on most whole organisms. Even in fresh water, Welch (1935) considers the *p*H is unlikely to be a limiting factor, and sea water is much more strongly buffered than fresh water and so is liable to much less change. Blinks (in G. M. Smith, 1951) states that a *p*H as high as 9.4 did not injure *Ulva* but killed *Ceramium*. Further, most algae could tolerate as acid a *p*H as 6.0, and several as much as 5.0. Bachrach and Lucciardi (1932) found diatoms able to grow between 6.5 and 9.0, but with an optimum at

8.2. The cell contents of some algae are surprisingly acid, and Wirth and Rigg (1937) have recorded a pH of 1.13 in the brown alga *Desmarestia intermedia,* and 0.78 in *D. latissima.* The ability of *Ulva,* just referred to, to tolerate high pH is reflected in the flora of rock pools where this species is abundant. In such pools the high photosynthetic activity of the *Ulva* may raise the pH as high as 10.0. This is beyond the tolerance range of some of the more delicate red algae, which are thereby excluded from the pools (Atkins, 1922). In the open ocean, surface values range usually from about 8.1 to 8.3; in deep water they may drop to 7.5, and in stagnant basins to about 7.0. For most organisms, this is a comparatively small range. The diurnal change may be greater than this in tide pools with a heavy algal and animal population. In salt marsh pools, where lowering of the salinity reduced the extent of buffering, Nicol (1935) recorded a range of 8.6 to 9.8 in one case, and 7.4 to 8.2 in another. Under tropical conditions on the Great Barrier Reef, Orr and Moorhouse (1933) found a diurnal range of 7.60 to 8.45 in water a few meters deep, and 6.60 to 7.72 in a pool in a mangrove swamp. These are wider ranges than will occur in most habitats. Hoffman (1929) found that the respiratory rate of certain algae rose as the pH was increased, whereas it was little affected by changes in oxygen content.

There is not much experimental information on tolerances, but White (1929) found the wood-boring isopod, *Limnoria lignorum,* apparently unaffected by a range of pH 4.5 to 9.6. It could survive a value of 4.0 for 48 hours but was killed within 24 hours at values below that. Manigault (1932) found the intertidal gastropod *Littorina obtusata* behaving normally within a range of 5.8 to 8.2. From 5.8 to 3.8 it was active but did not behave normally, and it could tolerate as low at 2.2 for 8 hours with subsequent recovery. Although some forms are undoubtedly more sensitive than these to pH changes, this is probably not often an important ecological factor, and the significance of pH measurements lies more in the information they yield on such processes as respiration and photosynthesis.

INORGANIC SALTS

Most of the elements required by both animals and plants are present in sea water in more than adequate quantities, so that their deficiency does not have to be considered as an ecological factor; we are even more rarely concerned with effects due to their excess. In some cases, the concentration of trace elements becomes significant, but as far as we know this happens much more rarely than on land. Regardless of absolute concentration, nitrate and phosphate tend to be present in sea water in a rather constant ratio of fifteen atoms of nitrogen to one of phosphorus. The ratio tends to remain much the same in both phytoplankton and zooplankton, although there are individual variations among different species. Where the supply of both nitrate and phosphate is adequate, the removal from and return to the water are in this ratio, but under special conditions the ratio may be considerably modified.

Phosphorus may be present in the form of either organic or inorganic compounds, and both in particulate form and in solution. Within living tissues it is present mainly in organic compounds, and it is released back into the water by their excretions and decay in either particulate or soluble form. There is evidence that some organic phosphorus compounds can be utilized by algae (Blinks, in G. M. Smith, 1951), but most of it is broken down to phosphate by bacterial action, and then utilized as such by the algae. Organic phosphorus may, perhaps, be used also by some of the nannoplankton, and in view of the increasing realization of the importance of the nannoplankton in the marine flora, this possibility calls for investigation. In general, phosphate depletion affects both photosynthesis and growth about equally. At higher temperatures there is a critical concentration below which the photosynthetic and growth rates show an almost linear relation to phosphate concentration (Fig. 2–1). Above this concentration, further addition of phosphate has little effect, although Chu (1942, 1943, 1946) has shown that there is an optimum concentration of nutrients, above which the rates decrease. At lower temperatures, this critical concentration is less marked, and changes in phosphate concentration affect photosynthetic and growth rates over a wider range of concentrations. In their estimates of the productivity of plankton populations, Riley et al. (1949) assumed the critical level for phosphate to be at a concentration of 0.55 mg.-atoms of phosphorus per cubic meter. Rodhe (1948) found that the optimum concentration of phosphate for growth varied in different species of algae and that a given concentration might be optimal for one, suboptimal for another, and supraoptimal for yet another. There is a continuous cycle of removal of nutrients from the water and their return, and in this cycle inorganic phosphate is regenerated more rapidly than nitrate. However, the difference is partly offset by the greater ability of algae to utilize intermediate breakdown products in the nitrogen cycle than in the phosphorus cycle.

The nitrogen cycle in the sea is very complicated, with the possibility of utilization at various stages. Its details have been discussed by Cooper (1937), among others. Nitrogen, as such, is fixed by various bacteria. It may also be utilized by some higher forms, although there is no evidence that this plays a significant part in the cycle. Drewes (1928) demonstrated such fixation of nitrogen in cultures of *Nostoc pruniformis* and two species of *Anabaena* in nutrient solutions which were devoid of any combined nitrogen. It should be remembered that the ocean receives not only nitrogen but also nitrate from the atmosphere. Allee et al. (1949) give the amount fixed by the action of lightning and falling as nitrate on 1 sq. km. of surface as 175 kg. per year. Andersson (1942) and Kylin (1945) showed that growth could continue in the algae *Ulva* and *Enteromorpha* when their nitrogen requirements were supplied in the form of ammonium salts and esters, nitrate, nitrite, carbamide, and several amino acids. When ammonia is available, it may be utilized in preference to nitrate, as in *Chlorella* (Pratt and Fong, 1940). Some naked dinoflagellates grow better in cultures in which the nitrogen is supplied in the form of amino acids than when it is supplied as nitrate, but it is not certain whether this is always true in bacteria-free conditions. At any rate, this is probably true in the sea where such bacteria are always present. Since much of the regeneration of the nitrogen in the sea takes place in deeper waters where the products are not being withdrawn again into plant tissues, the breakdown proceeds to the stage of nitrate, and it is this, when it re-enters the euphotic zone, which provides the nitrogen fraction of the essential nutrients. This is particularly striking in cooler waters where regeneration proceeds, with little plant growth, during the winter and is followed in the spring by rapid utilization of the resultant nitrate in the spring outburst of phytoplankton. Growth and photosynthesis of both phytoplankton and fixed algae is limited by the concentration of nitrate present, as it is by that of phosphate. Chu (1942, 1943) showed that there was an optimum nutrient concentration, above or below which growth is decreased, but excessive concentrations are unlikely to be met with under natural conditions except in such circumstances as those accompanying heavy pollution.

The possibility of deficiency of other elements affecting plant growth has been less well explored, but the general impression is that they are rarely important. Diatoms remove a large amount of silica from the water, and Hart (1934, 1942) and others have suggested that deficiency of silica may be limiting in some waters. At least, diatoms tend to be thinner walled in some waters where the silica concentration is low. Iron is present in phytoplankton, and its addition to cultures of diatoms may increase their growth rate (Gran, 1931, 1933).

Harvey (1937a) showed that the iron concentration in the water decreased during a period of phytoplankton outburst, but there is no direct evidence of its acting as a limiting factor in the sea. Much the same is true of manganese. Thompson and Wilson (1935) showed that its concentration varies in sea water, and Harvey (1939) obtained improved growth in cultures of the diatom *Ditylium Brightwelli*, to which it was added.

Both plants and animals may accumulate certain elements in much higher concentrations than those found in the surrounding water. There is no evidence in such cases that the external concentration of these elements may be limiting, but the possibility should be considered where such elements are scarce in the water. Thus, in sea water, *Valonia* concentrates potassium 40- to 50-fold, and *Hydrodictyon*, in brackish or fresh water, as much as 4000-fold. Even then, potassium is hardly likely to be limiting. But *Valonia macrophysa*, in sea water, concentrates iodine as much as 10,000-fold, and some algae can concentrate bromine 200-fold (Blinks, in G. M. Smith, 1951). Black and Mitchell (1952) give concentration factors for certain trace elements in several species of brown algae, as shown in Table 3–1.

TABLE 3–1

Concentration Factors for Various Elements in Algae

Species	Nickel	Molyb-denum	Zinc	Vana-dium	Tita-nium	Chro-mium	Stron-tium
Pelvetia canaliculata	700	8	1000	100	2000	300	20
Fucus spiralis	1000	15	—	300	10,000	300	8
Ascophyllum nodosum	600	14	1400	100	1000	500	16
F. vesiculosus	900	4	1100	60	2000	400	18
F. serratus	600	3	600	20	200	100	11
Laminaria digitata							
fronds	200	2	400	10	90	200	90
	200	2	1000	20	100	200	18
stipes	300	3	600	10	200	230	16
	400	2	900	30	90	200	14

Among animals, copper comprises about 0.15–0.25 per cent of the hemocyanin in various invertebrates but is present in sea water in a concentration of only 0.001–0.01 mg. per kilogram. Vanadium, comprising up to 0.05 per cent of the dry weight of ascidians (Goldberg et al., 1951), occurs in sea water at a concentration of 0.0003 mg. per kilogram. Beryllium, which is, no doubt, present in sea water, but whose quantity there has not so far been analyzed, is concentrated in

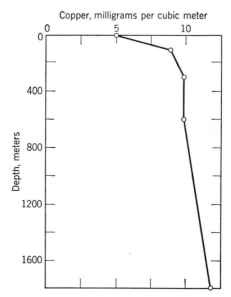

Figure 3–4. Vertical distribution of copper in the open water of the Gulf of Mexico. (After Riley, 1937.)

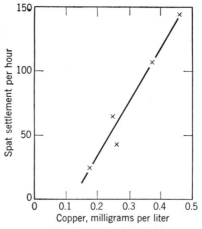

Figure 3–5. The relation of settlement of oyster larvae to the concentration of copper in the water at Milford Harbor, Connecticut. (After Prytherch, 1934; in Allee et al., 1949.)

the ash obtained from certain sponges. The skeleton of the radiolarian *Podecanelius* consists almost entirely of strontium, although sea water contains only 13 mg. per kilogram. In such cases as these, the quantities available may well set a limit to rates of multiplication of the forms requiring them. Harvey (1945) has suggested that both molybdenum and gallium may prove to be limiting factors in diatom growth. Riley (1937) showed that there was a variation with depth in the concentration of copper in the water of the Gulf of Mexico (Fig. 3–4) but considered that there was no evidence of sufficient surface depletion to affect the growth of plankton. On the other hand, Prytherch (1934) brought forward evidence (Fig. 3–5) of a correlation between the intensity of settlement of oyster spat and the concentration of copper in the water.

ORGANIC COMPOUNDS

The possibility of the use of organic compounds in the nutrition of certain algae has already been discussed. It is well known, also, that organic compounds are used by various bacteria and protozoa. There is another aspect of their ecological significance which is that of specific reactions to particular compounds. This field is only now beginning to be explored, and there is no doubt that it will prove to be of very great importance. At present, though, we have little more than an indication of the importance of such organic factors; we also have either no method or at best a biological assay technique for determining the presence or concentration of such factors.

The role of hormones, vitamins, etc., in higher animals and in land plants is well recognized, and our knowledge of the subject is expanding rapidly. In the sea we have, for the most part, only begun to recognize effects typical of such compounds. Although most of these observed effects are concerned with growth, some are related to spawning, swarming, metamorphosis, etc. A review of such effects is, of necessity, a collection of heterogeneous phenomena in the present state of our knowledge.

In controlling the growth of plants, auxins and heteroauxins are known to be of vital importance. It was early found that diatom cultures would not grow successfully on culture media containing only mineral constituents, but that the same cultures would flourish when small amounts of natural sea water, soil extract, urine, and other materials were added. It is highly probable that it was auxins or heteroauxins which were deficient in the original media. Harvey (1939) has discussed the identity of such substances required by diatom cultures and finds that they fall into two types, both of which must be present together for maximum growth. One of these types may be related to cystine, and this substance may, in fact, be used with beneficial results in the culture media. Lucas (1947) has suggested that carotenoids and sterols may also play a part. Certain vitamins, also, as pointed out by Harvey, play an important part in regulating growth in cultures, and these in turn may require adequate supply of certain trace elements. Thus, Fig. 3–6 shows the effects of enriching a culture of *Euglena gracilis* with vitamin B_{12}; from such experiments Hutner et al. (1950) have calculated that a concentration of cobalt of

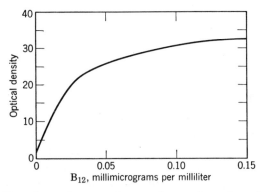

Figure 3–6. The relation between the growth rate (as indicated by the optical density of the culture) of *Euglena gracilis* and the concentration of vitamin B_{12} in the medium. (After Hutner et al., 1950.)

6×10^{-13} gm. per milliliter will be required. However, cobalt is probably never limiting, since approximately 33 times this amount will be supplied in even the purest available form of iron, when this is added in the requisite concentration in the culture. As an example of organic matter affecting higher organisms, Collier et al. (1953) showed a correlation between the activity of oysters and the abundance of an unidentified carbohydrate in the water.

Many animals and plants have been shown to add to the water in which they live organic substances referred to as conditioning agents. Some of them favor future growth of the species whereas others retard it, and still others affect the growth of other species in the medium. Of the selection of instances to be quoted in these paragraphs, some are reviewed by Lucas (1938); individual references are given for others. Among conditioning agents which favor continued growth of the same species, a single *Bacillus coli* will not proliferate when inoculated into a gentian violet broth, whereas twenty together will proliferate. In the same way, there is a population : culture volume ratio effect in *Paramecium;* in the same volumes of medium two will reproduce more than twice as fast as one. *Enchelys farcimen* is killed by a temperature of 30°C. when isolated, but a group can survive this temperature. Goldfish grow better in water in which goldfish have been previously raised (Allee et al., 1940). In some of these species it may be that the combined action of a group is able to remove some toxic material so that its concentration falls below the lethal limit, although one organism alone is incapable of doing this. This has been found to be true when certain poisons are added to the water in which fish are kept. Other control methods are, of course, possible. For instance, flour beetle populations increase fastest at medium densities, the control here being, apparently, low copulation efficiency at small population densities and eating of the eggs by adults at high densities.

Not all conditioning agents favor continued growth of the species. *Chlorella,* for example, produces one which inhibits future growth of the species in the same medium, even when all known nutrient requirements are met (Pratt and Fong, 1940). Levring (1945) obtained similar results with the diatom *Skeletonema.* Agents may condition the medium favorably for the species in question but inhibit the growth of other species. This occurs in *Paramecium* (Sonneborn, 1947). Mysids and copepods live longer in a medium concentration of diatoms than in a high or low concentration. Possibly this is an interaction of inadequate food at low concentrations and inhibition by a conditioning agent at high concentrations. Still other species benefit from the presence of another, as when some species of bacteria do not exhibit their characteristic reactions (such as nitrogen fixation) in pure culture but do so when other species are present. Possibly some symbiotic associations depend on conditioning agents, although other factors are obviously very often present.

Most of these examples refer to laboratory experiments, but there is evidence of their significance under natural conditions also. The killing of great numbers of fish by a conditioning agent produced by naked dinoflagellates such as the "red tide" organism, *Gymdodinium brevis,* is well known. It has been shown that a water-soluble product is responsible in such instances. Similarly, Otterstrøm and Nielsen (1940) showed that the death of fish in certain Danish brackish water lakes was caused by a metabolite produced by the flagellate *Prymnesium parvum.* Hardy (1923, 1926) showed that herring were scarce in areas where *Phaeocystis* was abundant, and in his "exclusion hypothesis," which will be discussed later, he postulated that zooplankton actively avoids areas of dense phytoplankton concentration.

In still other species, the controlling effect of a conditioning agent or other substance may be suspected, largely because no other known factor will account for the observed results. As an example of this, the brown alga *Himanthalea lorea* exhibits a peculiar geographical distribution (Fig. 3–7). On the French coast it occurs only in the neighborhood of deep water, although it is an intertidal form. The distribution cannot be accounted for in terms of salinity, temperature, wave exposure, or similar factors, and it may be that this species either

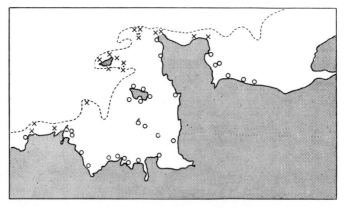

Figure 3–7. The distribution of the brown alga *Himanthalea lorea* along part of the French coast, showing its limitation to regions close to deep water. The dotted line indicates the 50-meter contour; X indicates presence, O absence. (After Fischer-Piette, 1932.)

requires some material present in deep waters or is inhibited by some substance produced in shallow waters or brought down in land drainage.

The effects of organic materials in the water are not restricted to growth or to the killing of particular organisms. They may have equally strong influence on behavior. Chemotactic reactions, such as the attraction of sperm to ova, are well known and widespread. Liberation of eggs only when sperm of the species are already present in the water and mass spawning of whole groups of animals are similar effects. Chemotaxes are also involved in the settlement of many larvae, as in the attraction of *Teredo* larvae to wood under the stimulus of lignin. In his work on the selection of particular types of substratum on which polychaete larvae will metamorphose, Wilson (1952, 1954) finds evidence of attraction to particular types of bottom, as well as of deterrence from unsuitable ones. Although particle size is involved, it appears that a repellent material or microfauna is also responsible, since this may be removed by appropriate treatment of the sediment. The presence of a metabolite in the water may also attract larvae to settle in greater numbers where already metamorphosed individuals, which produce the metabolite, are already present. This has been demonstrated in the barnacle *Elminius modestus* by Knight-Jones and Stevenson (1950). Knight-Jones (1951) showed the same effect in the tubicolous polychaete, *Spirorbis,* and demonstrated that the larvae of two related species were preferentially attracted by the metabolites produced by others of their own species. As another example, Wilson and Armstrong (1954 etc.) have shown that waters of different origins may vary in the success with which larvae can be reared in them. This again may prove to be due to a conditioning agent.

From these scattered examples, it is clear that organic matter in sea water may produce a wide range of effects and is therefore of great ecological importance. However, until appropriate analytical methods are developed, it is difficult to foresee any complete picture of the part they play.

4

Biological Environmental Factors

FOOD

The division of environmental factors into chemical, physical, and biological is, of course, arbitrary and only done for convenience. There is bound to be considerable overlap. In so far as the food of marine plants is mainly inorganic salts and carbon dioxide, these have already been dealt with under the section on chemical factors. The possible use of organic compounds by some plants was referred to in the same chapter. We are, therefore, mainly concerned with the food of animals in the present section.

There is still doubt about the extent of utilization of solutions of organic compounds by nannoplankton (see Jørgensen, 1952). Although this is of importance in the basic understanding of the food cycle, it is, in a way, less important in understanding the needs of such forms. The existing doubts are largely concerned with the question of whether the cultures used were bacteria-free. Under natural conditions there are always bacteria present, and we know that nannoplankton grow particularly rapidly when organic matter is present, regardless of whether they assimilate it directly or through the intermediate step of bacteria. The same is true of many non-planktonic protozoa and probably of some higher forms too.

A large group of marine animals, ranging from the simplest to the highest forms, consists of filter feeders. These remove particulate matter, detritus, or small animals and plants from the water by means of cilia, mucous nets, setae, etc. Our most extensive knowledge of the food requirements of these comes from the copepods. Although there is evidence of a certain amount of selection of particular food items (Lowndes, 1935), in general they filter the water at a uniform rate regardless of its food content. The rate is of course dependent on such factors as temperature. Since the food content of the water does not affect the rate at which the food is passed through the filtering mechanism, when the phytoplankton is very abundant, it will be ingested at a greater rate than it can be digested, and partially digested food will be passed out in the feces. There is thus a limit to the rate at which the food supply can be utilized, but not to the rate at which it can be destroyed. Of course, such destruction is not permanent, unless the feces sink to the bottom and become permanently trapped in the bottom sediments, but it may involve the sinking of the contained nutrients below the photosynthetic zone, so that they will not again be available until such time as water movements bring them to the surface waters. It should be noted that various forms, even those as delicate as planktonic larvae, have been found on occasions to pass alive through the guts of other animals. It is probably true, though, that all but a small fraction of organisms eaten are killed.

It is not known how widespread this principle of steady feeding rate is, but it may well prove to be of rather general application. This is in striking contrast to the carnivorous forms which are adapted to ingest a large quantity of food when they can find it and then pass long periods without any. A good example of this is found in the deep sea fish which inhabit very sparsely populated waters, but which, when they obtain prey, can swallow forms larger than themselves.

In animals that cannot increase their feeding rate to compensate for scarcity of food, the time available for feeding becomes of prime importance. Those filter-feeding zooplankton which execute an extensive diurnal migration must obtain most of their food during the night, when they are in the upper, food-rich waters. The time they spend there is, therefore, important wherever this time fluctuates. This would be true of Hardy's exclusion mechanisms, discussed later, in which zooplankton that lie under a particularly rich patch of phytoplankton either do not ascend as far into it at night, or else remain in it for a shorter time. The time available for feeding is also of importance in forms other than filter feeders. We have already referred to the reaction of lamellibranchs and other protected animals to adverse external conditions—they remain closed until conditions improve. As a result they may be deprived of an important fraction of their normal feeding period, and their resulting poor condition and slow growth reflect this rather than any direct action of toxicity or other adverse conditions in the external medium. Much the same effect is seen in motile forms inhabiting wave-exposed locations. Under such conditions, the gastropod *Purpura lapillus* has access only in calm weather to the open rock surfaces and the barnacles which cover them, whereas heavy wave action drives it into the shelter of crannies where there is little or no food. In another gastropod, *Urosalpinx*, it has been shown that lowering of the temperature results in cessation of feeding before cessation of movement. Many intertidal animals feed only during a part of the tidal cycle; for example, the limpet *Patella vulgata* feeds only when immersed or when in a damp situation (Orton, 1929). Since tidal level determines duration of immersion, it will also determine time available to such forms for feeding. It might be expected that duration of feeding would be a vital factor in intertidal filter feeders, but this appears not to be true of the barnacle *Balanus balanoides*. This form is very sensitive to variations in food supply, growing faster in waters with a large food content and in current- and wave-moved water which brings more food within its reach. Despite this, its growth rate is progressively greater at higher levels on the shore, that is with decreasing time available for feeding. The reason for this is not known, but some other factor correlated with relative immersion and exposure must be involved.

The amount of food available must also be considered. Dawes (1931) showed that in the plaice *Pleuronectes platessa* a certain amount is necessary for maintenance of the body, with surplus food above this amount used for growth. The amount required for maintenance varied seasonally and with the size of fish, and there was a limit to the amount the fish would accept, this amount also varying seasonally. Under natural conditions it is probably unusual for there to be more food available than the plaice can eat, and transplantation of fish from grounds poor in available food to grounds where food was more abundant have been found to result in higher growth rates. Among invertebrates many forms grow faster where the food supply is more abundant, showing that there is not normally more available than they can utilize. In the same way, Stephen (1928, 1929) found that the growth rate of the lamellibranchs *Tellina tenuis* was least under the most crowded conditions, and Ford (1925) found the same thing for *Syndosmya alba*. On the other hand, there are forms for which this factor of food availability is obviously not important. The limpets shown in Figs. 2–28 and 2–29 graze over a limited area of alga-covered rock surface. In the case of *P. vulgata* this area was shown to increase as the limpets grew. Food supply cannot, therefore, have been limiting, although it might be in a place where limpets are more crowded. The same must be true of many other forms which live on, or surrounded by, their food supply. A limit is more likely to be set by the rate at which they can eat and digest their food,

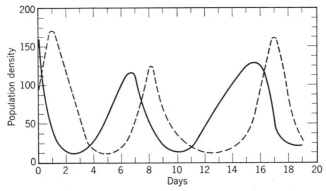

Figure 4–1. Rhythmic fluctuations in population density in a culture which is a mixture of a predator, the protozoan *Paramecium aurelia* (broken line), and its prey, the yeast *Saccharomyces exiguus* (solid line). (After Gause in Allee et al., 1949.)

or by some other factor. Among deposit eaters, the nutritional value of the food they swallow varies, and there must be a limit to the amount of sediment which they can pass through their guts in a given time. Probably some deposits have so high an organic content that their inhabitants are never limited in this way, but for many sediments the organic content is undoubtedly significant.

Unless other factors are involved, animals are most abundant where they can obtain the most food. This may be because of higher survival rate there, or because more animals may move into the neighborhood of the food either as larvae or adults. With increase in the number of animals, more food is eaten, and the food population tends to decrease while the animals eating it are still increasing. An oscillating interrelationship tends to result, of the type shown for a simple, two-species culture, in Fig. 4–1. A similar type of oscillation may be seen, under natural conditions, in phyto–zooplankton relations (Fig. 4–2) and in the barnacle-mussel community referred to in a later section. Overgrowth of a population of a species, with subsequent high mortality, is wasteful to the species, although not to the food cycle as a whole. It need not even be wasteful to the species if the latter has had time to reproduce in large numbers before the high mortality rate sets in, and if the resulting young either differ in diet from their parents or else have a means of dispersal into other areas. Not only is a larger population a potentially greater egg producer than a small one, but a well-fed animal is likely to lay more eggs than a less well-fed one. Figure 4–3 shows this clearly in the case of the copepod

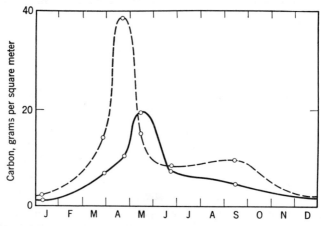

Figure 4–2. The seasonal cycle of phytoplankton (broken line) and zooplankton (solid line) on Georges Bank. (After Riley, 1947.)

Calanus finmarchicus (Harding et al., 1952). It should be noted that, as with growth, there is an optimum food concentration for egg production, and further available food beyond this amount results in little increase in the number of eggs laid. For the adults, however, ability to migrate to other areas which may be better supplied with food, or where the competition for this food is less intense, is of value. Among highly mobile animals intense temporary concentration in the neighborhood of food supplies is often observed. Figure 4–4 shows the concentration of two species of plankton-feeding whales in the Antarctic in a region where their food, *Euphausia superba*, is particularly abundant. The concentration of herring in areas where their copepod food is abundant has led to the development of simple plankton samplers which aid commercial fishermen in deciding where they may most profitably set their nets. Trapping of lobsters and crabs depends on the attraction of these animals by the scent or taste of food in the water. Many more instances could be given, in some of which the animals are directed toward their food by scent or sight, and in others of which shortage of food results in either random movements or movements directed by some external factor. Periodic migrations may thus result from the depletion of the food supply in the immediate neighborhood. For example, some lamellibranchs skim the

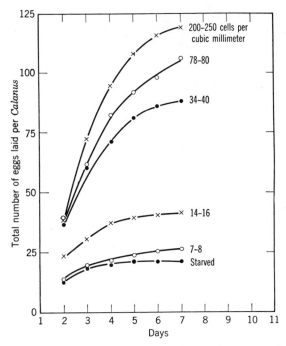

Figure 4–3. The effect of varying food supply on the egg production of the copepod *Calanus finmarchicus*. (After Marshall and Orr, 1952.)

food-rich surface layer from the mud in which they live. This is done with the inhalent siphon, and the animal feeds within the radius of the extended siphon. When this area has become depleted of food, the animal may move on to a fresh area. When such a movement is made, species differ in their ability to pass intervening barriers. Thus the gastropod *Nassa*, which frequently locates food by scent, travels freely across sand in search of it. *Purpura lapillus*, another carnivorous gastropod, which feeds on barnacles and mussels, is restricted to rock surfaces and will rarely cross a sand surface. Both of these species are tolerant of alternate immersion and exposure, but *Buc-*

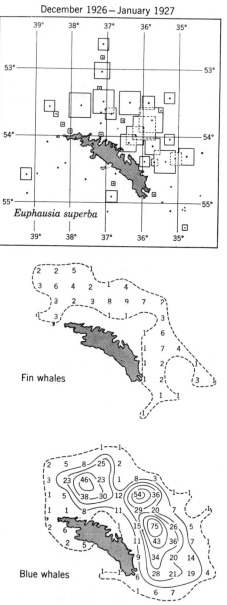

Figure 4-4. The regions of high concentration of *Euphausia superba* in the neighborhood of South Georgia, and the distribution of two species of whales as indicated by numbers of kills. (After Hardy and Gunther, 1935.)

cinum undatum, yet another carnivorous gastropod, cannot tolerate any considerable exposure.

There may be abundant food present, but of a type which only certain forms can utilize. Omnivorous forms may have an advantage here over forms more specific in their requirements. Many groups of animals include species with zooxanthellae in their tissues, but only a few produce a cellulase with which they can digest the zooxanthellae. The mussel *Mytilus californianus* feeds on the smaller particles of material suspended in the water, and these may include large numbers of dinoflagellates with cellulose envelopes, but the mussel possesses no cellulase to allow their digestion. Fox (1950) has discussed the ability of various animals to make use of carotenes and xanthophylls, which are compounds that lend themselves particularly readily to observation. Some sponges are able to accumulate only, or mainly, carotenes. Some ascidians can utilize both equally, and some lamellibranchs only xanthophylls.

Not only the nature of the food, but also its size, must be suitable. A predator will be able to capture prey only up to a certain limiting size or degree of agility. Young lamellibranchs are preyed on by fish and other forms that are unable to crush the heavy shells of older individuals. Small sediment-eating polychaetes are limited in the size of particle they can swallow. This limitation is particularly important among planktonic larvae, many of which cannot swallow anything larger than 5–10 μ in diameter. The small unarmored dinoflagellates are particularly suitable food for these larvae. Finally, the food requirements of an animal usually change as it grows older, and this is particularly true where the larvae are planktonic and the adults are not. Thorson (1950) comments on the apparent absence of a "physiological revolution" when such larvae metamorphose. Marine larvae seem to undergo a rather gradual reorganization.

There is not much known about the effects of changed diet on marine forms although this may prove to be important, as it is in some insects. The small limpet *Helcion pellucidum* occurs in two forms, differing markedly in shell thickness, size, and coloration. One of these is found on the holdfasts and the other on the stipes or blades of *Laminaria.* The difference may, perhaps, be caused by diet. Awerinzew (1911) found that the urchin *Strongylocentrotus droebachiensis* has a yellow-green test when living on sandy gravel, but was colored reddish-purple when living and feeding on the red calcareous alga, *Lithothamnion.* Pigment is probably rather frequently transferred from the food to the eater. Moore (1936) showed that *P. lapillus* laid down certain pigments in its shell only when feeding on a diet of the heavily pigmented *Mytilus edulis,* and not when feeding on barnacles. Furthermore, this pigment may be present in the yolk of the eggs laid by the *Purpura,* and the early shells formed by the larvae which are nourished by this yolk may be pigmented. In the same way, when the young lobsters *Homarus vulgaris* are raised on a diet of the orange-pigmented copepod, *Tigriopus fulvus,* the lobsters themselves become yellow-colored. Outside of pigments, little is known of the effects of food on marine organisms, except in so far as deficiencies are concerned, and even here, mainly among plants. However, it is quite likely that modifications of structure related to diet may be found to occur.

Finally, in the matter of preference for particular types of food, there is some evidence of invertebrates becoming accustomed to one particular diet and refusing any other, until driven to it. Harvey (1937) showed that the copepod *C. finmarchicus,* when fed exclusively for a while on one particular diatom, would select this diatom by preference from a mixture of diatoms thereafter. His experiments are described in more detail in a later chapter. Fischer-Piette (1935) has described how barnacle-fed *P. lapillus,* when faced with a change to a diet of *Mytilus,* continued to eat barnacles as long as any remained, despite the fact that the return for their efforts would have been greater with *Mytilus.* Their first attempts at attacking the *Mytilus* were clumsy; only after some time were the mussels opened in the most efficient way. Wilson (1949) records a case in which the spiny lobster, *Palinurus vulgaris,* learned to attack hermit crabs under the stress of hunger and thereafter continued to attack them, even when plenty of other food was available. The selection of food by at least some invertebrates is, then, influenced by their previous habits, and the acquiring of the necessary skill to cope with a changed diet may be only gradual.

CROWDING

Both inter- and intraspecific competition for space is frequent in marine communities, particularly on those occupying a hard substratum. There may be concurrent competition for available food, light, oxygen, etc., or competition for one and not another. We are concerned here with the causes and effects of crowding, rather than with the mechanisms involved in competition. Crowding may occur whenever there is competition for some necessity such as space, food, light, etc. On the other hand, there may be competition without crowding when the limits to the population density are set by some other factor such as predation, for example. Furthermore, a population density that would be crowded in one set of conditions might be far from crowded in another. In abyssal oceanic waters, an average of one fish or other animal per thousand cubic meters might constitute crowding, since there is too little food to support more. Waters near the surface might support a thousand times this population. An intertidal rock may be so closely packed with algae that they are in actual contact with one another, or it may be covered with touching barnacles with a density of 10,000 or more per square meter. In the plankton communities predation and competition for food may set limits to population growth, whereas on the intertidal rock actual lack of foothold may set the limit. That it is space, and not food, which limits the barnacles is shown by the settlement of young on the shells of older barnacles when no further rock surface is available.

The growth of expanding populations, both of single species and of mixtures, has received much attention and is well reviewed by Allee et al. (1949). We are concerned here with the results when populations have attained their maximum densities, and with the converse effects when they are very sparse. An example of the latter is found in the deep-sea angler fish in which the male is parasitic on the female. It has been suggested that this is an adaptation to the extreme sparsity of their populations, insuring that a male will always be present, when needed, to fertilize the eggs of the female. The complicated luminous displays of many abyssal animals may also, in some species, serve as recognition signals, and so facilitate mating. Deep-sea barnacles occur on the rare solid fragments lying on the soft ooze covering the bottom. The same problem appears to have been met in many of them by the evolution of complementary males which live within the mantle cavity of the females. Intertidal barnacles can extend the penis far enough to copulate with another barnacle which is not more than two or three times their diameter distant. Barnacles settled further apart than this are unable to breed.

Crowding may also afford a measure of both inter- and intraspecific protection from various adverse environmental factors. Young plants of the "sea grasses" *Cymodocea* and *Zostera,* before they become deeply rooted, are easily washed away by water movement if isolated. When settled among older, well-rooted plants, the roots of the latter bind the sand so that there is less shifting of the surface layers. In a bed of intertidal algae, such as *Fucus* or *Ascopyllum,* the parts of the plants that are at the surface of the algal layer, when exposed at low tide, protect the lower layers from insolation and desiccation. Even if this damages them, the lower layers provide a reservoir for the growth of replacements. Young plants which settle among the older ones are protected until they reach a larger size and have developed greater resistance. In a group of sea urchins, young ones, less well protected by spines, would gain protection from the proximity of older and better-armored neighbors. Similarly, many interspecific advantages in crowding could be cited. To name only a few, the crowded growth of more robust corals on a reef gives shelter to many more delicate forms. The crowded conditions in a bed of mussels or oysters similarly shelters many smaller forms.

Crowding may also be important in connection with conditioning agents and similar substances in the water. In Hardy's exclusion hypothesis, zooplankton actively avoid particularly rich concentrations of phytoplankton; and if a conditioning agent is responsible, the crowding has permitted, in this case, a sufficient concentration of the agent to deter herbivores and so reduce a major source of mortality. In the same way, various species referred to in an earlier section are able to tolerate adverse conditions of temperature, certain poisons, etc., when the species are present in numbers but not when only one or two are present. Similarly, reproductive rates may be accelerated under more crowded conditions; and, of course, among species in which fertilization takes place in the water more efficient fertilization is achieved when the organisms are crowded together at the time of spawning.

Disadvantages of crowding are often more apparent than the advantages. Where space is limited, as on a rock surface, settlement of young may be so heavy that there is not room for all to survive as they grow, and a heavy mortality may result. This applies to sedentary forms, since motile ones can usually diffuse out to less crowded areas as the demand arises. Not infrequently crowding results in overgrowth of the original specimens, with a final catastrophic mortality which leaves the area completely denuded. This happens in a bed of mussels when later arrivals settle on top of earlier arrivals and finally smother them. A storm may then peel off the whole colony in a sheet, leaving the surface to which they had been attached bare. With a less dense settlement, the death of individuals would not have affected their neighbors. In the same way, epiphytic and epizoic growth on algae, corals, sea rods, etc., may so increase their area that they are carried away by wave action.

Competition for available food may also become severe under crowded conditions, with resulting reduction in growth rate. Figure 2–31 shows barnacles of the same age which have attained a much greater size when isolated than when crowded together. Isham et al. (1951) showed a similar effect in the shipworm *Teredo pedicellata*. In wooden test panels, crowding was found not to be serious in 2 months but to have a pronounced effect in 4. The ratio of growth attained in 4-month panels to that attained in 2-month panels gave, therefore, a measure of the effect of crowding on growth. A measure of the degree of crowding was obtained from the number of burrows occurring in unit area, weighted in proportion to the time the young shipworms had had to grow (Table 4–1).

TABLE 4–1

Effect of Crowding on Growth Rate of *Teredo pedicellata*

(Isham et al., 1951)

Month	Crowding Index	Growth Index
December	(102)	205
November	(152)	149
February	183	857
July	376	4
October	(535)	227
September	(616)	12
August	689	20
June	909	8
May	938	5

Crowding may similarly affect the growth of sand-burrowing forms. The lamellibranch *Tellina tenuis* picks up food particles with its siphon, and, if not overcrowded, tends to keep a definite distance away from its nearest neighbor; this spacing reaction is probably initiated by contact of the siphons if two approach one another (Holme, 1950). The density of spat fall of this species fluctuates very greatly from one year to another, and Stephen (1929) states that in a year of heavy settlement, when crowding occurs, growth is correspondingly reduced. Oysters, as well as barnacles, tend to settle too closely to allow subsequent growth of all of them, and the results in both of them may be not only high mortality and reduced growth rate but also distorted growth in the individuals that do survive.

In a culture of protozoa or diatoms, reproduction is so rapid that growth of the population to its maximum possible size occurs rapidly. Among higher forms, growth is frequently much slower, and, in addition, there may be reproduction at only one limited period of the year. If depopulation of a considerable area of, say, barnacle-covered rock surface occurs as a result of overcrowding, it may be almost a year before a fresh supply of spat is available to recolonize the area. In the meantime, of course, other forms may have settled there and may have rendered the surface unsuitable for future settlement by barnacles. This may result in a more or less rhythmic fluctuation in the constitution of the population, or in a slow process of adjustment to a permanent condition.

There is a rather general impression that any vacant space is rapidly occupied by the young of whatever algae or animals are available at the particular time. This is very often true, but the extent and rapidity of recolonization varies widely in different circumstances. Moore and Sproston (1940) found that a newly made intertidal rocky shore at Plymouth did not attain its normal flora and fauna for several years, and in general this was not because of overcrowding by early settlers since much of the surface was not occupied. Herpin (1935) found a similar situation in a newly made intertidal sandy beach in France.

DISPERSAL

The mobility and means of dispersal of organisms are more biological than strictly ecological problems, but their understanding is vital to any ecological study. Although there are various relative advantages and disadvantages in a fixed, as compared with a motile, type of life, the former carries with it the necessity of some means of dispersal. This affects practically all the larger plants, as well as many of the smaller ones, and a considerable fraction of the marine animals also. Vegetative growth provides only a very limited degree of dispersal, and an ability to float, swim, or otherwise move about is necessary at some stage in the life history. Usually this stage is an early developmental one, although in some it occurs only in the adults and in others it represents one of two alternating generations. Spores, eggs, and larvae, which are temporary members of the plankton, constitute the most important dispersal units. Water movements provide an ideal means of scattering such forms over a wide area, affording the maximum opportunity of colonizing all suitable localities. The degree to which this mechanism is utilized is indicated by the high proportion of such young stages in the inshore plankton; on occasions they may constitute practically the whole of it.

Young so liberated into the plankton suffer a much higher mortality rate than do those protected by the parent or in egg capsules, or in other ways, until they are well developed. It is necessary, therefore, that they be produced in correspondingly larger numbers. In those dogfish which are viviparous, or whose yolk-nourished young are large and active when they leave, the egg capsule, only about a dozen eggs are produced per year, or the female may even lay only every second year. At the other extreme, the oyster produces 55,000,000 to 114,000,000 eggs at a time (Galtsoff, 1930), and the blue crab 1,750,000 (Pearse, 1939). This huge difference in numbers is offset by a corresponding difference in size, planktonic eggs being much smaller than non-planktonic eggs, and usually supplied with little or no yolk, so the energy expended by the female in egg production is probably about the same in the two cases. On the other hand, gonad production of either type is a heavy drain on the resources of the organism and is usually postponed until considerable growth has been achieved. At sexual maturity, growth frequently decreases markedly and sometimes ceases completely. Thorson (personal communication) has pointed out that egg production usually involves more energy drain on the parent than does sperm production. Perhaps because of this, males of many marine invertebrates mature 2 or 3 months earlier than the females. In the high Arctic, where production of yolky eggs is the rule, the animals that are adapted to the poor food conditions are usually protandrous hermaphrodites (e.g., *Modiolaria laevigata, Cardium groenlandicum, C. ciliatum*). Growth is very slow, but more energy is available for it in the male than in the later female phase. The warm-water relations of such forms (*Modiolaria marmorata, Cardium edule, C. fasciatum*) produce small eggs and have the sexes separate. Thorson has found it to be generally true among the lower invertebrates that large egg size (which is often associated with viviparity or broad protection) tends to be associated with protandrous hermphroditism.

There are obvious advantages in the possession of planktonic larvae. In addition to being widely dispersed, the young are carried into an environment in which, they do not usually compete with the parents for food. This may also be a more favorable environment so far as various environmental factors such as salinity and temperature are concerned. On the other hand, the planktonic larvae suffer certain disadvantages. The high mortality rate is not important, since it is probable that more are usually available at the time of settling than could be accommodated in the available space. However, these may not be available over the right type of habitat; and although, as we have seen, most larvae are able to delay metamorphosis for some time until they locate a suitable environment, they are still subject to a risk of not finding it. Evidence of this is given by Thorson (1946) who

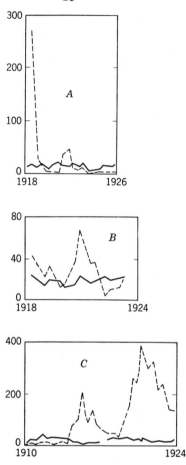

Figure 4–5. Annual fluctuations in the population density of Danish bottom invertebrates, comparing, in each case, ecologically similar species. A, *Cultellus pellucidus* (broken line—long pelagic larval life), *Nucula nitida* (solid line—very short pelagic life). B, *Abra alba* (broken line—long pelagic larval life), *Macoma calcarea* (solid line—non-pelagic development). C, *Corbula gibba* (broken line—long pelagic larval life), *Nucula nitida* (solid line—very short pelagic life). (Thorson, 1946.)

has shown that fluctuation in intensity of spat fall from one year to another is related to duration of planktonic life. Those species with a long planktonic life tend to have widely differing good and bad years for settlement of young, and those with a short or no planktonic life maintain a much more uniform population (Fig. 4–5).

Seasonal availability of food for the planktonic larvae may be another problem. In tropical waters, the phytoplankton production is more or less uniform throughout the year, whereas in colder waters it is much more cyclic. The colder waters have, typically, a small winter plankton population, a heavy spring outburst, and a fluctuating but much smaller summer population. Sometimes there is a smaller outburst in the autumn. Planktonic larvae will have a better chance of finding adequate food supplies if they are liberated early in the period of the spring outburst and if they can leave the plankton before the food supply has declined too seriously. The period available to them decreases poleward, and the danger of their mistiming the release of the eggs becomes, therefore, progressively greater. It is presumed that this lies behind the steady increase with warmer waters in the proportion of species having planktonic larvae. This is illustrated, in the case of prosobranch gastropods, in Table 4–2.

TABLE 4–2

Percentage of Prosobranch Gastropods Having Planktonic Larvae

(Thorson, 1940)

East Greenland	0	British Isles	64
East Iceland	10	Danish waters	65
South Iceland	30	Iranian Gulf	75
Faroe Islands	40	New Caledonia	57

PREDATION

There are few, if any, organisms which are not regularly or occasionally preyed on by some animal. Some, by reason of protective armor, poisonous characteristics, speed, or similar safety measures are relatively immune, whereas being eaten by a predator is the most likely cause of death in others. The most detailed information on rates of predation comes from studies of plankton communities, and the equations developed in Riley et al. (1949) make use of expressions of these rates. For phytoplankton, their basic formula is

$$\frac{dP}{dt} = P(P_h - R_p - G)$$

where P is the phytoplankton population, P_h a coefficient of photosynthesis, R_p a coefficient of repiration, and G an expression of the rate of grazing by herbivores. In the same way, for the herbivore population, the formula is

$$\frac{dH}{dt} = H(A_H - R_H - C - D)$$

where H is the herbivore population, A_H the rate of assimilation of food, R_H the respiratory rate, C the rate of consumption by carnivores, and D the mortality rate by accident, old age, and other causes. A similar formula was developed for the carnivore population.

The expansion of these equations to accommodate varying environmental conditions will be treated in a later chapter, but the assumption with regard to predation rates will be considered here. For the phytoplankton-eating herbivores, it is assumed that feeding is a continuous process which is not dependent on the concentration of the food; if an excess is ingested, this is only partly assimilated. In general, the rate of removal of the phytoplankton will be a function of the concentration of the phytoplankton and of the herbivores. Temperature and other factors may also modify this rate, and Fuller (1937) has shown that there is an optimum temperature for feeding of the copepod *C. finmarchicus*. Filtration rates at 3, 8 and 13°C. were, respectively, 0.35, 2.83, and 1.09 cc. per copepod per day. A similar temperature effect has already been referred to in connection with the rate of beat of the cirri of barnacles, and it may be assumed that this rate of beat reflects the rate at which they filter food particles from the water. There is less information on the feeding rates of deposit eaters, but for those which are non-selective it may well prove that, as with the copepods, food is swallowed at a uniform rate, other things being equal, and the rate at which the food organisms are removed from the deposit are a function of their concentration and that of the eaters.

When we come to forms such as the limpet *Helcion pellucidum* which live permanently on the large alga comprising their food, or ones like the *P. vulgata* which live under conditions such as those shown in Figs. 2–28 and 2–29, food supply is always present in excess, the rate of removal of algae is, presumably, only a function of the number of feeders present and their size and activity. In the case of the latter, the area grazed was a more or less linear function of the volume of the limpet, with the exception that the very smallest animals take relatively more food, probably on account of their high growth rate (Fig. 4–6).

There is even less information on the rate of predation of carnivores From the work of Dawes (1930, 1931) on the plaice, it is clear that there is a limit to the amount of food which will be accepted and that this limit varies seasonally and with the size of the fish. No doubt such excess of food is sometimes met in nature, but it may be deduced from known growth rates that less than maximum food is normally available, and in such cases the rate of predation is no doubt a function of the abundance, size, and activity of the predators. On the other hand, the carnivorous gastropod *P. lapillus*, living on a dense sheet of barnacles, has no appreciable distance to travel in search of food and no doubt feeds at a rate which is a function only of its activity. This activity may be curtailed by such factors as low temperature and heavy wave action. Unless there is storm damage, the mortality among barnacles may be almost entirely due to *Purpura*. The empty barnacle shells persist for some time and provide a measure of the predation. Mortality rates ranged from 3 to 35 per cent per annum in *B. balanoides* in the Isle of Man (Moore, 1934a) and from

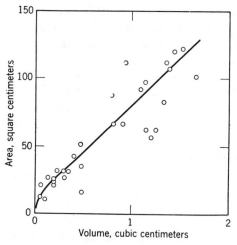

Figure 4–6. The relation between the area grazed by a limpet, *Patella vulgata*, and the size of the animal. (Modified from Moore, 1938.)

3.3 to 46.5 per cent for *Chthamalus stellatus* at Plymouth (Moore and Kitching, 1939). The lower figures were from the upper zones into which *Purpura* hardly ranges. The activity of the *Purpura* is limited in wave-exposed situations, and Hatton (1938) found correspondingly higher mortality rates in *Chthamalus* in sheltered localities than in exposed ones. Similar information could be obtained from lamellibranch shells bored by carnivorous gastropods, with the particular advantage that the shape of the bored hole is frequently characteristic of a particular species of gastropod, and its size is some indication of the size of the borer.

Tides are particularly important in controlling the duration of predation in the intertidal zone. Many predators feed only when the tide is in or out, as the case may be. Thus non-aquatic predators such as gulls, rats, and raccoons operate only when the tide is out, whereas fish and various invertebrates feed only when it is in. Tidal level therefore affects the duration of exposure to such predation, as we saw in the case of the low mortality rate in high-level barnacles. Some predators—gulls for instance—hunt mainly by sight, and their prey may be aided in avoiding them by nocturnal habits. It has also been suggested, although there are alternative explanations, that the significance of the diurnal migration of plankton lies in the avoidance of predators that hunt by sight in the well-lit upper waters in the daytime.

As pointed out in the discussion of food, the interaction of predator and prey tends to produce an unstable and oscillating population. Although this is best illustrated by various culture experiments, it may occasionally be seen under natural conditions, and the account by Fischer-Piette (1935) of the cycle on an intertidal rocky shore in France is worth considering in detail. From 1925 to 1929, the rocks on this shore were covered with the two barnacles *B. balanoides* and *C. stellatus*. *Purpura lapillus* was abundant and fed solely on the barnacles. *Mytilus edulis* was scarce and restricted to crevices except for one patch on open rock and was apparently not preyed on at all by the *Purpura*. About the end of 1929 the *Mytilus* began to spread over the open rocks of the area. This spread continued rapidly in 1930 and 1931 and did not cease until 1933, by which time some local regression had taken place. As the *Mytilus* covered the rocks, the barnacles were killed, although at a later stage they colonized the shells of the *Mytilus*. Up to the end of 1931, although the *Mytilus* were by then abundant, the *Purpura* were still feeding solely on the remaining barnacles and did not attack the mussels, but thereafter they changed over steadily to a *Mytilus* diet. It is interesting to note that, for the first few months on this new diet, they made numerous errors, boring into already emptied shells and even getting inside empty shells and boring out, but after a few months they appeared to have learned the technique and such errors were not made. The *Purpura* population did not show any appreciable increase in numbers until the end of 1952, but about then it began to increase very greatly. With the change in diet, many *Mytilus* were killed and many more became detached. The *Mytilus* had by then formed a thick layer more than one shell deep. If a mussel in the underlying layers was killed by a *Purpura*, it soon became detached, and with it those in the upper layers which had attached to it instead of to the rock. Thus the eating of a single *Mytilus* might cause the loss of a whole cluster. As such clusters were detached, areas of bare rock became available for recolonization by barnacles, and when these were big enough, after about 6-months growth, the *Purpura* began to feed on them again. When last examined, in the summer of 1934, the area had practically returned to its original condition. *Mytilus* was restricted again to crevices except for the one area of open rock which it had originally occupied. The rest of the rock surface was again occupied by *Balanus* and *Chthamalus*, and these constituted the sole diet of the *Purpura*.

This example has been given in some detail since, except for the original cause of increase of the *Mytilus*, the other mechanisms involved in the interactions can be clearly seen. It is particularly interesting to observe the delay in reaction of the more slowly reproducing and growing predator. In this instance the initial observed change in the community was in the nature and amount of the prey. A case in which the initial change was in the predator is given by Delphy (1917). Here an unusually cold winter at Île Tatihou caused a great mortality in the *Octopus* population. For some time thereafter crabs and other crustacea which were the normal food of the *Octopus* increased greatly in numbers. In both examples it appears that there must have been sufficient food available to support a larger population of the prey and that the predators were exercising a marked control on their numbers. Many other examples of predator control might be given, such as the effects of *Urosalpinx* and *Asterias* on oysters, of *Limulus* and *Polynices* on clams, and, for that matter, of human predation on many marine forms.

Where predation involves the removal of whole organisms, its estimation is considerably easier than when only a part of the organisms is removed and the rest survives and possibly regenerates. This happens in certain burrowing lamellibranchs whose siphons are frequently bitten off, as they project above the surface, and the rest of the animal remains untouched. It is even more frequent among algae, hydroid colonies, and other vegetatively reproducing forms. Much the same problem is present in the determination of the growth rate of algae which constantly lose material by fragmentation; so far, the method of measuring this growth rate has been determined in only a few special cases.

INTERACTION OF MULTIPLE FACTORS

In laboratory experiments it is usually possible to hold all but one environmental factor constant and then study the effects of variations of this one factor. In this first section we have, in general, considered the various factors individually, with only occasional reference to the effects of varying more than one at once. Unfortunately, many ecological problems do not lend themselves to solution under laboratory conditions. In fact we are frequently unable to duplicate in the laboratory even those conditions necessary for survival of an organism. We are therefore driven, to a considerable extent, to studying the effects of varying environments in the fields where there is little or no opportunity to modify conditions at will and where all the variations imposed by natural conditions have to be accepted. In effect, this means that we are dealing with simultaneous variations of a large number of factors, and we are faced with the problem of whether their combined effects can be expressed as the sum of the individual effects, or to what extent they interact with one another.

If a large series of observations can be obtained, correlation coefficients may be calculated which will suggest connections between particular factors and observed effects. The method, as applicable to ecological work, is discussed in a paper by Riley (1939). As an example, he took the phytoplankton productivity in Linsley Pond and its relation to temperature, solar radiation, etc. After correlation coefficients had indicated where significant relationships lay, regression curves were prepared and, as a test of the goodness of these, a prediction was prepared of the seasonal fluctuations of productivity, assuming the various equations which had been developed. In Fig. 4–7, the predicted and observed values are superimposed, and it will be seen that, although the fit is not perfect, it is good and justifies the methods used.

Under natural conditions it often happens that two different factors tend to vary together. Thus the salinity is low under estuarine conditions, and the silt content is usually high. From examination of populations from a number of localities it may be difficult to tell whether observed differences in, say growth rate, are due to salinity differences or differences in food supply. Sometimes the problem may be solved by selecting abnormal circumstances. Thus, in work already referred to, various organisms were found to penetrate further up an estuary in summer than in winter, but there was a question whether this was associated with higher summer salinities or higher summer temperatures, either of which might, theoretically, produce such an effect. The problem was solved by studying the distribution of the organisms in years when the salinities were abnormal, but the temperatures normal, and vice versa. In another case, purple or brown coloration of the shell of *P. lapillus* was shown to be associated with high wave exposure and also with the preponderance of *Mytilus* over *Balanus* in the diet. *Mytilus,* in the area studied, is most abundant in wave-exposed localities, so there was doubt about which of the two factors was responsible for the coloration, and the solution lay in finding the occasional wave-exposed locality that had a colony of *Purpura* but not *Mytilus,* and the sheltered one with both species. In yet other cases field observations will establish which factors are significant and will define the effect of some; laboratory experiments can be devised to separate any confused effects.

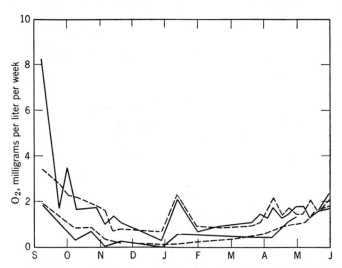

Figure 4–7. Comparison between calculated (solid line) and observed (broken line) productivity in Lindsey Pond in 1937–1938. The upper pair shows surface conditions, and the lower, mean conditions. (After Riley, 1939.)

There remains the problem of the joint effect of two or more variables, and there is very little information on the subject, since an attempt is nearly always made to treat the variables separately. The growth of an organism, for example, may be a function of temperature and of food supply. The curve relating growth to food may be different at different temperatures, and that relating growth to temperature may differ with the food supply. Figure 2–10 shows how the curves relating growth and photosynthesis of phytoplankton to the available phosphate vary at different temperatures and illuminations.

Another example of interaction of factors is taken from the effects of temperature and pressure on the luminescense of bacteria (Brown et al., 1942). The bioluminescence involves two processes, the excitation of luciferase by the oxidation of luciferin and a process of rever-

sible thermal inactivation. Both processes are slowed by increased
pressure, but the relative effects of pressure on the two is dependent
on the temperature. As a result, increased pressure increases bioluminescence above a critical temperature but decreases it below that
temperature (Fig. 4–8). Further, since this critical temperature
varies in different species, at a given temperature increased pressure
may increase the bioluminescence of one species, have little effect on

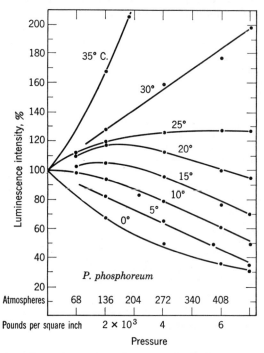

Figure 4–8. The effect of varying pressure on the bioluminescence of a marine
bacterium at different temperatures. (After Brown et al., 1942.)

a second, and decrease it in a third (Fig. 4–9). In the field we find
low salinity tolerated by an organism in one locality but not in another,
the difference obviously lying in variations in some other factor.
There are two abundant intertidal barnacles in the English Channel,
of which one, *C. stellatus,* is dominant toward the west, and the other,
B. balanoides, toward the east (Moore and Kitching, 1939). The
factor responsible for this distribution is not certainly known, but it
may be air temperature. The relative ability of the two species to
penetrate into estuarine waters varies according to the locality,
Chthamalus entering the estuaries in the west and *Balanus* those in

the east. Tolerance of estuarine conditions is therefore dependent on the factor responsible for the geographic distribution. From this and similar examples, it has been postulated that "departure from optimal conditions for one environmental factor may reduce the tolerance range of a species for another factor." Although this generalization appears to be valid, and of wide application, it gives no numerical assessment of the modification of the effects of one factor by another.

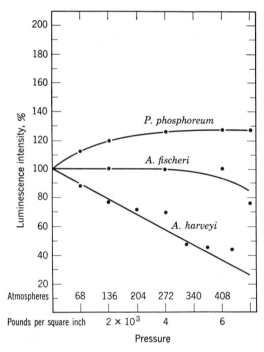

Figure 4–9. The effect of varying pressure on three species of marine bacteria at a constant temperature (25°C.), showing specific differences in response. (After Brown et al., 1942.)

The reaction of an organism to environmental factors could presumably, if fully understood, be reduced to a series of chemical and physical reactions. Then, if the reaction is a function of one variable, and another function of a second independent variable, the reaction may be expressed as the product of these two functions. If the two factors are interdependent, the reaction may be expressed as a function of the product of the partial derivatives of the two factors with respect to each other. It may be assumed that the same principles hold true with regard to the relation between an organism and its environment.

A very much simplified treatment of such a problem is given by Moore (1952) for a diurnally migrating member of the plankton which oscillates between differing day and night temperatures. The "prosperity" of the species—a deliberately vague term—is rated from 0 to 100. It is equal to the percentage of the particular species in the total population of that and other competing species. A relation between the prosperity or survival index and temperature is assumed to have a definable form, which is a part of a sine curve in the simplest case and modifications of this in others. If the animal alternates diurnally between depths with two external temperatures for which the survival index is, say, 75 per cent and 50 per cent, the over-all index for that locality will be the product of the two, or 37.5 per cent. In other words, the joint effect of two factors is assumed to be the product of their individual effects. Although obviously oversimplified, the method gives results which are in reasonable agreement with observations. In a more elaborate formulation, Riley has produced equations expressing the relation of plankton productivity to environmental conditions in which he makes use of the products in a similar way. His equation (Riley, 1946), which will be discussed in more detail later, includes the following expression for the rate of photosynthesis:

$$P_h = \frac{pI_0}{kz_1} (1 - e^{-kz_1})(1 - N)(1 - V)$$

in which P_h is the photosynthetic rate, p a photosynthetic constant, I_0 the surface illumination, k the extinction coefficient of the water, z_1 the depth, N the depression in rate due to phosphate deficiency, and V the reduction by vertical water turbulence; N and V are both derived, in separate equations, from measurable environmental conditions.

Similar examples can be found in the dynamics of fish populations. It is surprising that such methods have not been more widely used in marine ecology. Riley's work brings out another advantage also. When equations have been developed, and predicted results are compared with those observed, a perfect fit is very unlikely to occur. The distribution of the misfit may, however, prove a valuable pointer to some previously neglected factor. The misfit may, for example, be greatest at one particular season or locality, and the determination of the peculiarities of that time or place may lead to an improved set of equations which yield a better over-all fit.

5

Habitats

ABYSSAL

No classification of habitats can be altogether natural, and a series graded in order of depth would differ from one graded in order of varying substratum, and this again from one based on distance from land or other characters. It seems easiest to start with the simplest habitat, in which environmental factors exhibit the least variation, and use this as an introduction to more complex conditions. With this in mind, the abyssal sea floor is the logical starting place.

In abyssal waters there is no light other than that of bioluminescent origin, no photosynthesis, and very little plant growth. It is improbable that even dead plant tissues of marine origin ever sink into the region, although waterlogged tree trunks must do so regularly. There is no wave action, and any currents are so slow that, although they may serve to transport planktonic larvae, they impose no significant strain on attached organisms. Diurnal, seasonal, and year-to-year variations in temperature, salinity, and similar conditions are either absent or so minute as to be negligible from the ecological standpoint. In the section on the effects of temperature we have discussed the possible advantages of a fluctuating temperature rather than a fixed one. We do not at present know whether such advantages are real,

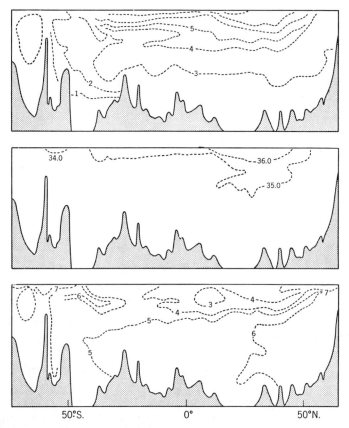

Figure 5–1. South to north vertical section of the west Atlantic showing the general pattern of distribution of temperature (upper—°C.), salinity (middle—⁰/₀₀), and oxygen (lower—milliliters per liter). The original figures have been considerably simplified by omission of some shallow and intermediate contours. (Modified from Wüst, in Sverdrup et al., 1946.)

or of general application, and in the past it has been generally believed that the unvarying nature of the abyssal environment was ideal. Not only is there very little periodic fluctuation in external conditions, but also these conditions remain the same over very wide geographic areas. Figures 5–1 and 5–2 show, in transects of the Atlantic and Pacific oceans, how little difference there is in the salinity, temperature, and oxygen content of the bottom waters from the equator to the polar regions.

Although some conditions are peculiar to abyssal waters, many factors differ from surface conditions by amounts well within the

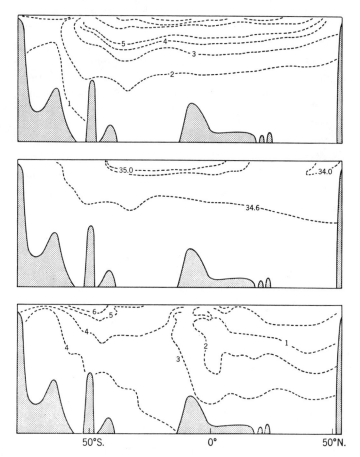

Figure 5–2. South to north section of the Pacific Ocean with details as in Fig. 5–1. (Modified from Sverdrup et al., 1946.)

range of individual species. Both salinity and oxygen differ to only a small extent from surface conditions. Temperature is always within a few degrees of 0°C., below the lower limit for many warmer-water animals, but there are plenty of cold-water animals for which such temperatures are permissible or even optimal. The carbon dioxide content of the water is high, and the principle effect of this appears to be the greater solubility of calcium carbonate which is reflected in the generally weaker calcification of shells and skeletons. On the other hand, the stillness of the waters reduces the need for the support of strong skeletons, so the only loss will be in the skeleton's value as armor.

Pressures are extremely high and, as we have discussed in the section on this factor, we deduce that modified types of tissues must be employed to meet its effects. These include changed viscosity of fats and of protoplasm itself, possible denaturization of proteins, lowered flotation value of gases, and probably other phenomena. It is likely that the most important effect of very high pressures will prove to lie in their modification of the rate of various chemical reactions. This in turn is closely linked to a temperature effect (Zobell and Johnson, 1949; Zobell and Oppenheimer, 1950). It is to be hoped that means will be found to bring abyssal animals to the surface under pressure for study of their biology.

Apart from these pressure effects, it is probable that the most significant characteristic of abyssal waters is the paucity of the food supply there. All food has, ultimately, to be obtained from that which rains down out of shallower waters, originating in the first place in the photosynthetic zone. The sinking rate of dead copepods has been determined to be about 500 meters per day (Seiwell and Seiwell, 1938), and at this rate they would take a week or more to reach bottom in deep water. The probability that they would be eaten en route is therefore high, and even if they were not, considerable loss by protozoan and bacterial action might be expected. It may, then, be assumed that very little particulate organic matter of surface planktonic origin reaches the bottom. Most of it either is eaten or passes into solution in the water first. At each step in the food chain, still more of it passes into solution. Sinking then stops until the soluble material is again built up into particulate organic matter by bacteria or possibly some nannoplankton, or until circulation carries it again into the photosynthetic zone. With this steady removal of falling particulate matter, it is not surprising that very little reaches the bottom in deep water. Sverdrup et al. (1946) give the rate of accumulation of typical abyssal sediments as follows:

Blue mud:	1.78 cm. per 1000 years
Globigerina ooze:	1.2 cm. per 1000 years
Red clay:	<0.86 cm. per 1000 years

If we assume an organic content of 1 per cent, this indicates a deposition of only about half a gram of organic matter per square meter per year. The material which settles has a higher content than this but is being trapped and eaten as it arrives at the bottom, and the 1 per cent represents the amount that remains. Much of the raining sediment undoubtedly has a high mineral content by the time it reaches the bottom; but even if its organic content were large, it is obvious that there is sufficient food supply for only a very sparse bottom community.

Krogh (1934a) has approached the question of food supply from another aspect. Whales are so large that if they die at sea they are likely to sink to the bottom more or less intact. We know of no animal that could swallow one whole, so all that is likely to be lost is what can be bitten from the whales by passing sharks, squid, and similar forms. A sinking rate as low as 100 meters per hour would take a whale to the bottom in about 2 days, and it would probably sink much faster than this. From estimates of the total population and the mortality rate of whales, Krogh estimates that one sinks each year, on the average, onto each 50 square miles of bottom. Although it is difficult to assess the weight of an average whale, it may be assumed that whales contribute something less than a gram of food per year per square meter. Smaller bodies not only sink more slowly, and for this reason are more likely to be intercepted in falling, but also stand a greater chance of being eaten by an animal which can swallow them whole. Nevertheless, the absence of knowledge about the abyssal conditions justifies an attempt to establish a similar figure for the sinking of fishes. If the commercial fish landings for North America were spread over the whole of its continental shelf, they would be equivalent to about 10 gm. per square meter per year. For many reasons this is a minimum estimate of the fish productivity of the area, but it is probably not a hundredfold too small. From the estimate by Riley (1941) of a phytoplankton productivity of 600–1000 gm. of carbon per square meter per year, and allowing for loss at two stages in the food chain, this would even appear to be too high. Further, Riley's own estimate may be too high. Since the productivity of oceanic waters is not very much less than that of coastal waters, we may apply the same figure to oceanic fish production; and, since far fewer fish than whales can reach the bottom uneaten, their bodies can hardly contribute more than the whales to the bottom food supply. Such vague calculations are justified only in making it clear how serious a limiting factor food supply is in abyssal waters.

The bottom itself resembles, in many ways, the muds of shallower waters and may be assumed to present similar problems to its inhabitants. To begin with solid objects to which sessile animals can attach are very scarce. Mollusc and other shells are usually thin and pass rather rapidly back into solution when the animals are dead. In the rain of dead planktonic organisms from the upper waters, most of the calcareous matter has been dissolved before the bottom is reached, except in the case of the shallower abyssal deposits. Apart from mineral concretions such as manganese, the two common solid objects in these muds are the ear bones of whales and the teeth of sharks, both of which are particularly resistant to solutions. One dredge haul taken at a depth of 4300 meters in the Pacific is reported to have brought up 50 ear bones and thousands of shark teeth. Nevertheless, such objects are relatively scarce on the abyssal bottom. Recent exploration has shown the existence of rocky bottom and steep cliffs in some places at abyssal depths, and Fig. 5–3 shows a stalked crinoid and sea rods growing on such a rock at a depth of 1200 fathoms in the Gulf of Mexico. At present we do not known how common such submarine structures may be, but it is improbable that they constitute more than a very small fraction of the abyssal bottom.

The sediment itself seems to be fairly soft at the surface, presenting some problem to animals which move over it. At least this has been offered as an explanation of the slender, spider-like legs of some bottom livers and of the extended creeping surfaces of others. On the other hand, the very large holothurian shown in Fig. 7–3 has left only slight disturbance of the surface showing where it has passed, so the bottom cannot have been very soft.

Burrowing animals must be faced with problems similar to those of animals inhabiting muds in shallower water, one of the chief of which is oxygen supply. There is but little circulation of the interstitial water in such sediments, and the reducing power of the organic matter present usually removes all oxygen from such water. Animals inhabiting the muds are therefore faced with the necessity of either utilizing glycogen or respiratory pigments as a temporary oxygen source, or else maintaining contact with the oxygenated overlying water by means of a burrow. Adaptations to such conditions will be discussed more fully in later sections. By comparison with shallower muds it is probable that the extreme surface layer is somewhat richer in organic matter, and also, because of its proximity to a source of oxygen, less reducing in character. It is therefore a more rewarding feeding ground than the more deeply buried mud, as well as being a habitat suited to those animals which do not possess special mechanisms for coping with deficiency of oxygen. Some bottom photographs taken at these depths show an area of different color in the immediate neighborhood of burrows. This is typical, in shallower water, of the removal of the surface film by the siphons or other mechanisms of some burrowing form, and the exposure of the underlying, less oxidized sediment.

We know so little about the characteristics of the abyssal fauna

Figure 5–3. A stalked crinoid photographed at a depth of 2200 meters' in the Gulf of Mexico. The rocky nature of the bottom is clearly shown. The crossbar and dark shadow in the foreground are part of the camera. (Photograph by D. M. Owen, Woods Hole Oceanographic Institution.)

that we can only guess at certain modifications which would be necessary if shallow forms were to be able to live much deeper. We have therefore no direct evidence about what environmental factors are most important for the abyssal forms, and it should be borne in mind that attempted extrapolations of this type may prove highly misleading.

THE PELAGIC ENVIRONMENT AT MID-DEPTHS

We have considered the abyssal environment in so far as it influences animals living either in or on the bottom, or swimming close to the bottom. Since the bottom is, in many ways, a more complex environment than the pelagic, it is best to consider next the various types of pelagic habitat. Ultimately, the life in the oceans is almost entirely dependent on the plankton, and the original organic production takes place in the phytoplankton. It is logical, therefore, to separate the zone in or near which active plant production takes place from the depths below it. There is an upper zone in which photosynthesis is sufficiently active for the oxygen produced by the phytoplankton to excede that utilized by the plants in their own respiration. The depth at which the two are equal is known as the compensation depth, and although plants may live at greater depths, they do so with a resulting loss, instead of a gain, in the total amount of fixed organic matter. Although production is confined to levels above the compensation depth, and maximum production to comparatively shallow depths, the rain of dead and dying phytoplankton provides a source of plant food much deeper. Figures given by Riley and Georgy (1948) for the plant pigment content in the Sargasso Sea waters are probably typical of the distribution in other oceanic waters. The values were as follows:

Surface	140 Harvey units
100 meters	220 Harvey units
200 meters	120 Harvey units
300 meters	60 Harvey units

The compensation depth may be as far down as 100 meters, and in inshore waters it is much shallower. Below, say, 500 meters, the plant pigment content of even oceanic waters is slight. However, the depth to which this plant food is effective is considerably extended by the diurnal migration of the zooplankton. Many species at these depths perform an extensive migration at night to or toward the surface, presumably obtaining the bulk of their food while at the shallower levels. Such diurnal migration has been shown to take place down to a depth which is believed to be about the limit of illumination at which vision by daylight is possible. Below this depth there is insufficient solar energy to produce vision, and all that remains is light of bioluminescent origin. From Fig. 5–4 it will be seen that a natural division of the plankton may conveniently be made, at least in the Atlantic, at about 1000–1200 meters, which will separate the peak concentration of these migratory animals, at about 800 meters, from a deeper concentration at about 1600 meters. It is assumed that the latter exhibit no diurnal migration since they receive no diurnal change in illumination to stimulate it.

Conditions in these mid-depths, extending from about 1000 meters to the bottom waters, are in most ways comparable with those just above the bottom. They undergo little or no diurnal or seasonal changes in temperature, salinity, etc., and conditions are relatively constant over wide areas. As can be seen from the sections in Figs. 5–1 and 5–2, below 1000 meters, only a few degrees difference in temperature are involved at any depth from polar to equatorial waters. Oxygen is rather more variable, there being a minimum oxygen layer at about the upper limit of the zone under consideration (Fig. 5–5). In parts of the equatorial Pacific oxygen saturation may drop as low as 1 per cent in this layer, but in most other parts of the oceans it does not drop much below 50 per cent, which is probably within the tolerance range of most species. It is from this zone that we have tentative evidence of the control of distribution of planktonic organisms by the specific gravity

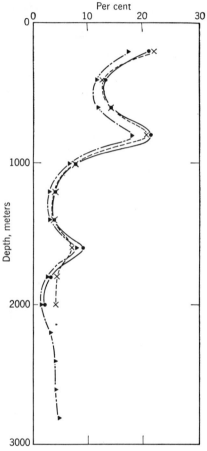

Figure 5–4. Quantitative vertical distribution of macroplankton at three groups of stations in the North Atlantic. (After Leavitt, 1938.)

of the water. Both eggs and adults of the cephalopod *Vampyroteuthes infernalis* are more limited in the range of densities at which they occur than they are for either temperature or salinity, and the eggs occur at somewhat lower and denser levels than the adults (Fig. 2–14).

What has been said about the effects of both pressure and food supply on the abyssal bottom may be applied also at mid-depths. Pressures will be less and food supply greater than in deeper water, but both are probably highly important factors. The nature and abundance of the plankton of the upper waters are undoubtedly reflected in the food reaching animals at deeper levels; in shallower waters, as will be shown later, the abundance of bottom fauna also may closely

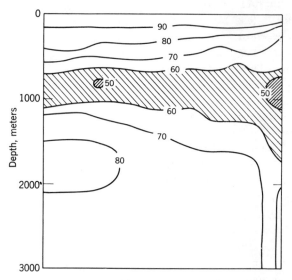

Figure 5–5. East to west section in the North Atlantic at 20°–25°N., showing the vertical distribution of oxygen (percentage saturation). (After Seiwell, 1934.)

reflect the productivity of the surface waters, and this in turn follows the local hydrographic conditions which lead to varying supplies of inorganic nutrients.

THE UPPER OCEANIC ZONE

The upper oceanic zone may be considered under three subdivisions. At and close to the surface there is a zone where the daytime illumination is above optimal or is even lethal for phytoplankton. It is also too high for most zooplankton. Below this is the zone in which active plant growth takes place, including the water somewhat deeper where phytoplankton, although not actively reproducing, is still relatively abundant. The third zone includes, in the daytime, those zooplankton which, at night, migrate up into the phytoplankton-rich upper waters.

Leavitt's data on the vertical distribution of the larger zooplankton, which are shown in Fig. 5–4, indicate a marked concentration in the neighborhood of 800 meters. The reason for this concentration is not known, nor is there information whether a similar distribution occurs in oceans other than the North Atlantic. This concentration is not limited to one particular group but includes decapods, euphausids, mysids, amphipods, chaetognaths, and others. Species of these groups that do not execute a diurnal migration live under conditions similar to those encountered in the mid-depths already discussed. They will usually be in or near the minimum oxygen layer, and they will be too

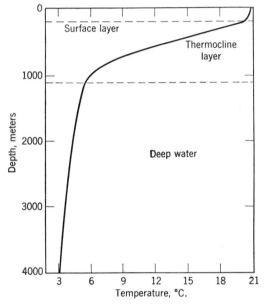

Figure 5–6. The vertical subdivisions of ocean water. (After Iselin, 1936.)

deep to be appreciably affected by seasonal temperature changes. Figure 5–6 shows typical vertical distribution of temperature in this and the upper zones, and Fig. 5–7 the decrease in the seasonal temperature range with increasing depth. Waterman et al. (1939) found an extensive diurnal migration among many forms from these depths. It was definite at depths of 200–400 meters and may have occurred even down to 1200 meters, which was the deepest level sampled. More recently (Moore, 1950) sonic methods have demonstrated diurnal migration in zooplankton lying as deep as 1000 meters in the daytime, although there is still doubt about the identity of the organisms concerned. Diurnal migration implies ability to perceive diurnal changes in illumination, since no other diurnally varying factor is known at these depths. It is true that an inherent rhythm might motivate animals living below the light zone, but it would be necessary for them to be in the light zone at least at intervals for the rhythm to keep in phase with the daylight. A theoretical limit to the light sensitivity of an eye is set by a certain minimum number of photons stimulating the photoreceptors per second. Physiologists apparently differ rather widely about the value at this limit, but it is at least clear that there is a depth below which no eye could be expected to perceive changes in daylight. From the sensitivity of the eye of the shallow-

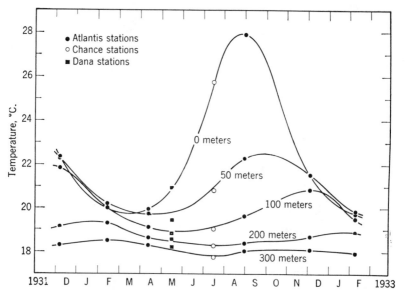

Figure 5–7. The variation in seasonal change in temperature with depth in the North Atlantic. (After Iselin, 1936.)

living fish *Lepomis,* Clarke (1936) has calculated that a comparable eye in a deep-sea fish could perceive daylight at a depth of 750 meters in the very clear waters of the Sargasso Sea. However, Waterman (1937) has pointed out that arthropods are, in general, more sensitive to blue than to green light. The calculations based on *Lepomis* allowed for greatest sensitivity to green light, and as blue-green light penetrates further than green into clear water, crustacea might be expected to see daylight at a greater depth than fish. Waterman et al. (1939) suggest that this might be as deep as 1500 meters. Unfortunately no photocell that can be used at sea can measure light as weak as this, and there is some uncertainty with regard to the transparency of the subsurface waters, so we cannot calculate the exact illumination at such depths. If, as seems possible, the transparency is greater in deep water than near the surface, light may penetrate further than we have previously supposed. Recently measurements of illumination have been made with an improved type of photocell down to about 600 meters (Clarke and Wertheim, 1956; Clarke and Backus, 1956).

Light and temperature appear to be the two major physical factors affecting the distribution and behavior of zooplankton at these levels, so it is necessary to consider the distribution of these two factors in some detail. Furthermore, diurnal migration involves a very rapid change in habitat, and it is necessary to take into account the range and rate of such change. For example, Table 5–1 shows the difference

TABLE 5–1

Temperature Differences Encountered in the Course of Diurnal Migration in Relation to Latitude at a Series of Positions in the Atlantic

	Temperature, °C.	
Latitude	800 Meters to Surface	800 to 100 Meters
60°N.	0	0
50	1.7	1.2
40	9.5	9.0
30	13.0	11.0
20	17.5	16.5
10	22.9	20.9
0	23.2	15.2
10°S.	21.0	16.0
20	24.0	13.0
30	10.0	9.0
40	8.5	7.5
50	8.1	7.6

in temperatures which will be encountered in a typical series of Atlantic stations, by an animal migrating from a day level of 800 meters up to a night level of either the surface or 100 meters. Such a migration is made by a number of kinds of animals within a few hours. Welsh (1933) found that the copepod *Centropages* could, under laboratory conditions, swim at a rate of 82 meters per hour. Moore (1949a) recorded rates of ascent under natural conditions of more than a meter a minute among various animals including copepods. Hardy and Gunther (1935) found that two species of *Euphausia* ascended in the evening at 100–200 meters per hour. A rapid temperature change must therefore be involved.

The range is, naturally, much greater near the equator than in polar waters. Furthermore, the range is only very slightly smaller if the animal stops short of the surface by as much as 100 meters. If it remains much deeper than this, it will fail to enter the rich feeding ground of the upper waters.

The level of illumination concerned in the diurnal migration of these deep forms, and in fact of a large fraction of the zooplankton, is of a different order of magnitude from that concerned in photosynthesis, and for this reason certain sources of fluctuation must be considered from one point of view which may be neglected for the other. At the

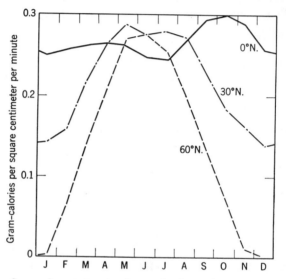

Figure 5–8. Seasonal variation in the total solar radiation incident at the sea surface, and the relation of this to latitude. Each graph is a mean of two localities. (After Kimball, 1928.)

day level of these deep-living migratory forms we can calculate the illumination to be of the order of 10^{-10} to 10^{-20} of full sunlight, if we make certain assumptions which are described later. Factors reducing surface illumination by 50 per cent or even 90 per cent may be disregarded, whereas they are important to the shallower living plants. To begin with, the radiation incident at the surface in summer is of about the same order, regardless of latitude, but the latitude has an enormous effect on the extent of the seasonal variation in incident radiation. This is clearly seen in Fig. 5–8. This radiation suffers certain losses at, or close to, the surface. There is loss by reflection which, from a smooth surface, ranges from 40 per cent when the sun has an altitude of only 5°, to 3 per cent at 50° or over (Sverdrup,

1943). In general, the presence of waves increases this loss. Waves also mix air bubbles into the water, and reflection from these contributes a further loss which Poole (1936) estimates as not exceeding 10–15 per cent. Before entering the water at all, the illumination may have been reduced by clouds, the maximum loss from this cause being 80 per cent (Haurwitz, 1946). Table 5–2 shows the depth of water required to produce a hundredfold reduction in illumination, and it will be seen that even a 90 per cent change in surface illumination corresponds to only a comparatively small depth shift. Thus, in clear ocean water with an extinction coefficient of 0.05, complete clouding over might raise the limiting depth at which vision was possible by about 50 meters, and in inshore waters the distance might be a tenth of this.

Table 5–2 makes it clear that the transparency of the water is of first

TABLE 5–2

Depth of Water Required to Reduce Vertical Illumination to 1 Per Cent in Relation to Extinction Coefficient of Water

Extinction Coefficient	Depth, meters
0.03	83
0.04	63
0.05	50
0.06	42
0.08	31
0.10	25
0.20	13
0.30	8.5
0.40	6.3

importance in controlling the penetration of light. Transparency can, at present, be measured only near the surface, and calculations of deep illumination are based on the assumption that the transparency does not change with depth. This has been found to be true as deep as photocell measurements have been made, but there are indications that the deeper waters may be clearer than those near the surface.

The extinction of light during its passage through water is due partly to particles in the water and partly to molecular action of the water and its dissolved content. The extinction from both causes includes both absorption and scattering, the former removing light and the latter changing its direction. From data given by Jenkins and Bowen (1946) it appears that scattering and absorption are of about the same order of magnitude in coastal waters, where there is a high content of particulate matter. They believe that, in clear oceanic water, the scattering fraction is relatively insignificant, except, perhaps, in the top hundred meters. When light from an oblique source is scattered, that part whose direction is vertically downward has a shorter path to travel to reach a given depth than the parts that are scattered more obliquely. The latter, therefore, suffer a higher percentage of extinction in their longer path than does the more vertical

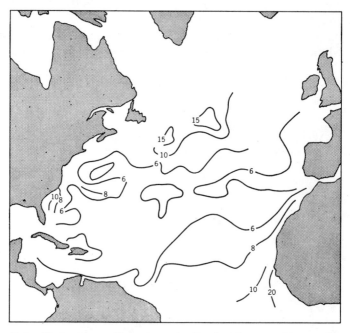

Figure 5–9. Extinction coefficients in the North Atlantic. (Figures have been multiplied by 100.)

fraction. A selective action results whereby a light ray, whatever its incident angle, tends toward the vertical with increasing depth. As an example, Whitney (1941), working in water whose extinction coefficient was probably as high as 0.10, showed that light whose angle was 30° from the vertical at a depth of 10 meters was shifted to 25° from the vertical at 40 meters. Present calculations of the penetration of light to the depths we are considering have assumed that such an angular shift may be neglected in clear ocean waters, although this still remains to be proved. In coastal waters, with their higher content of suspended matter, it is clear that the effect is marked, that all light tends rather rapidly to approach vertical.

Along with attenuation there is a marked selective change in the constitution of the light with increasing depth. Figure 5–10 shows the extinction coefficients of different types of water at different wavelengths. Ultraviolet and infrared are very rapidly absorbed and are effectively absent except at the extreme surface. Red, and to a lesser extent blue, are absorbed more rapidly than the central region of the spectrum, so that the light reaching deep water is mainly blue-green in oceanic water and yellow-green in coastal waters. The significance

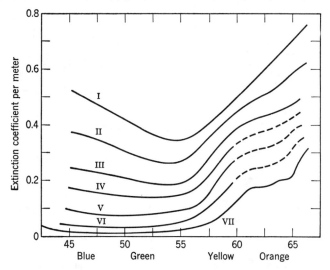

Figure 5–10. The relation of extinction coefficient to wavelength in various types of sea water: I, II, III, maximum, mean, and minimum for coastal waters; IV, V, and VI, maximum, mean, and minimum for oceanic waters; VII, distilled water. (After Sverdrup et al., 1946.)

of the color of this light in connection with the sensitivity of the eye has already been referred to.

When its reactions are not modified by other factors such as temperature, much zooplankton migrates vertically at such a rate as to maintain itself at a more or less constant illumination. Figure 5–11 shows the very close agreement occurring under certain conditions between the level of the deep scattering layer and calculated isolumes. The layer is detected by ultrasonic methods, and there is still question about the nature of the organisms which constitute it, but its behavior is, at least, typical of zooplankton. Although the calculation of such isolumes is based on certain doubtful assumptions already referred to, these would not seriously modify certain important conclusions which can be drawn with regard to light conditions in deep water. The statement is made in various works that the day becomes progressively shorter in deeper water. For an animal capable of diurnal migration, the reverse of this is actually true. Figure 5–12 shows calculated isolumes for a station in the Atlantic, on an occasion when there was moonlight for more than half the night. An animal living in the day-time at about 30 meters would at night, even if it came right to the surface, find only about a thousandth of its day illumination there. On the other hand, one living at 300 meters in the daytime could, by

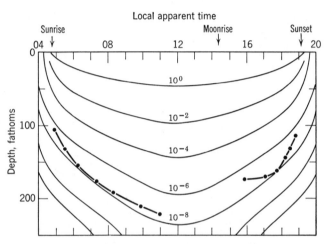

Figure 5–11. Diurnal movements of the scattering layer on an occasion when light appeared to be the only factor controlling its depth. The break in the record is instrumental. Isolumes are drawn at intervals a hundredfold apart. (After Moore, 1950.)

ascending about 150 meters at night, maintain constant conditions of illumination until moonset, which in this instance is throughout all but a few hours out of the 24. Its day would, in effect, be much longer than that of the animal living in shallower waters. Another approach, which is considered in a later section, is that of the stimulus inducing vertical movement in the animal. This may be proportional to the rate of change of the factor—in this case illumination—and Fig. 5–12 shows how the rate of change of illumination varies diurnally and vertically. If we consider an arbitrary threshold value of 30, it will be seen that values exceeding this are present almost throughout the 24 hours at depths of 200 meters or more, but are present for only a brief period around sunrise and sunset near the surface. Another peculiar condition of deep illumination has been suggested by Moore (1950),

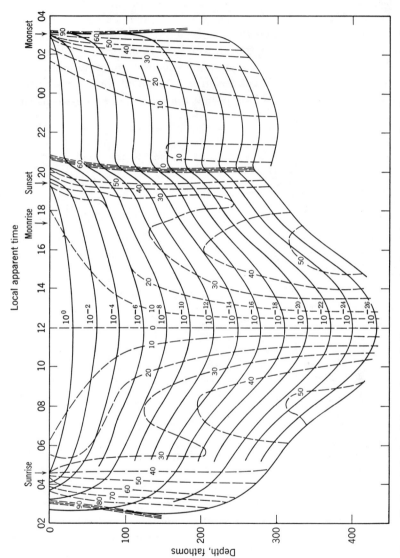

Figure 5-12. Calculated lines of equal illumination (isolumes) on an occasion when the moon set about midnight. These isolumes are drawn at intervals a hundredfold apart. The broken curves join points of equal rate of change of illumination and are numbered in arbitrary units. (After Moore, 1950.)

its validity depending on the extent to which a vertical beam of light
is modified toward the vertical in oceanic water. In the Northern
Hemisphere, in winter and at full moon, when there is the maximum
difference in declination between the sun and moon, light from the
sun enters the water much more obliquely than that from the moon.
The sun's rays have a longer path to follow in order to reach a given
depth than do the moon's rays and suffer correspondingly more rapid
extinction per unit of vertical distance. Although the solar illumination at the surface may be nearly half a million times as great as that

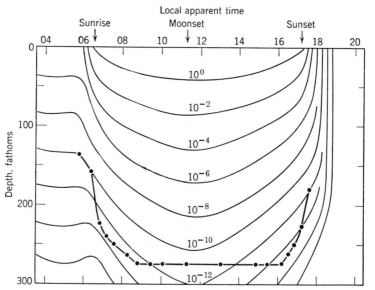

Figure 5–13. Diurnal movements of the scattering layer on an occasion when
the morning descent and the evening ascent were controlled by illumination,
but during the middle of the day movement was arrested at a low-temperature
barrier. Isolumes are a hundredfold apart. (After Moore, 1950.)

from the moon, there must be a depth at which their different extinction rates bring them to equality; below this depth moonlight at midnight will be stronger than sunlight at midday. The effect will be
greater at high latitudes and with high extinction coefficients. If the
trend of light toward the vertical may be neglected, and this is at present doubtful, then at 60° north latitude, and with an extinction coefficient of 0.20, equality of sun and moonlight would be reached at levels
as shallow as 200 meters in midwinter. If the effect actually exists,
and it would appear that it must, at least in high latitudes, the curious
situation must arise of shallow-living forms moving upward at night

in response to decreasing illumination while, simultaneously, deep-living forms below them are descending in response to increasing illumination. Although some of the points raised here will probably have to await verification until better instruments are produced for measurement of illumination, it is clear that where light is concerned, deep conditions are quite different from those near the surface. The deep illumination cycle cannot be considered as just a diluted version of that of the upper waters.

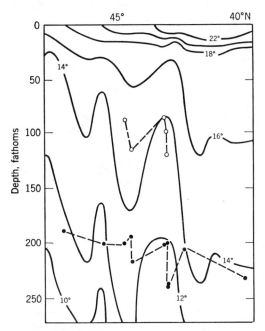

Figure 5–14. Vertical distribution of temperature along a north-south transect in the North Atlantic near the Azores. The noon levels of two different scattering layers are shown for a series of stations, and these tend to lie deeper towards the south where the water temperature, at their depth, is higher. (After Moore, 1950.)

Temperature, at these depths, may play ,as important a part as illumination in controlling diurnal migration. Figure 5–13 shows another example of the movement of the scattering layer; this movement is interpreted as indicating a period of morning descent which more or less follows constant illumination, followed by an arrest of descent at a low temperature barrier. Evening ascent then begins when the illumination has decreased again to a certain value. In support of this interpretation, Fig. 5–14 shows how the depth at which this descent is arrested increases as the warm water extends deeper to the southward end of an Atlantic transect. The example, shown in Fig. 5–11, of a scattering layer which followed closely on an isolume throughout the day, with no trace of such noon flattening, was obtained in the Mediterranean, where there is very little thermal stratification. In a later section, a theory will be presented of the particular temperature and illumination requirements of different species, and

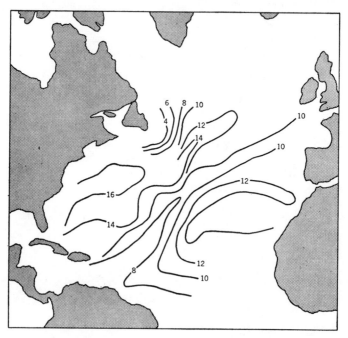

Figure 5–15. Distribution in part of the North Atlantic of the temperature at that depth at which the midsummer, noon illumination has a value of 10^{-12} arbitrary units. (After Moore, 1952.)

of how this may control their geographical distribution. In this section we are concerned more with the temperature and illumination conditions which a diurnally migrating animal will encounter during the course of the day and with the geographical distribution of these variations.

It is becoming apparent that, at their daytime level, these diurnally migrating animals may be forced to compromise between going deeper, and thereby entering water too cold for them, or remaining shallower and undergoing too high illumination. The extent to which they would have to tolerate one or the other condition may define the suitability of a particular locality for a species. In an attempt to com-

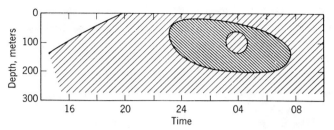

Figure 5–16. Diurnal migration of the total zooplankton of the top 250 meters in the neighborhood of Bermuda. The heavy shading indicates more than 20 ml. per standard tow and the lighter shading 10–20 ml. (After Moore, 1949.)

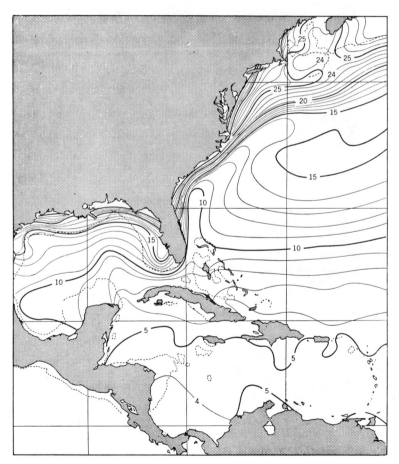

Figure 5–17. The seasonal range of temperature (°F.) of the surface waters of the western North Atlantic. (After Fuglister, 1947.)

bine the two factors, Moore (1952) produced a chart for the North
Atlantic area of the temperature at the depth of 10^{-12} illumination.
Based on a summer surface illumination value of 100 arbitrary units,
this corresponds to the average conditions at the depth where the deep
scattering layer is found in the warmer waters south of the Gulf
Stream. The contours so produced (Fig. 5–15) have proved more
valuable for explaining geographic distribution than either factor by
itself, but the method requires extention to a wider area.

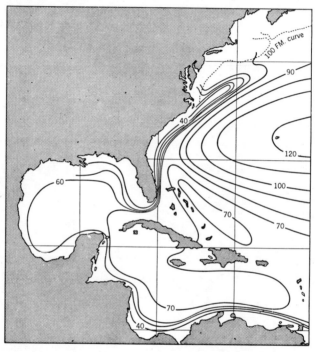

Figure 5–18. The average depth (meters) of the virtually isothermal layer in
winter in the western North Atlantic. (After Fuglister, 1947.)

The night migration carries these deep-living forms into the upper
zones which we are to examine next. Figure 5–16 shows the enrichment of the shallow plankton which occurs at night as the deeper
forms move up. Within this next zone we are concerned with a daytime illumination sufficient to allow significant photosynthesis; and
in considering conditions affecting plant growth, we have to take into
account such additional factors as nutrient salts. To begin with, seasonal fluctuations in temperature extend down 100 meters or more into
this zone (Fig. 5–7). At the surface the seasonal range may be 15°C.

or more, decreasing, in general with depth. Figure 5–17 shows the seasonal surface range for a part of the western North Atlantic. Mixing produces a surface layer which is more or less isothermal, and the thickness of this mixed layer is greatest in winter and least in summer. These conditions are shown, for the same area, in Figs. 5–18 and 5–19. Since both seasonal and horizontal temperature changes are more pronounced here than at greater depths, they may be expected to have a

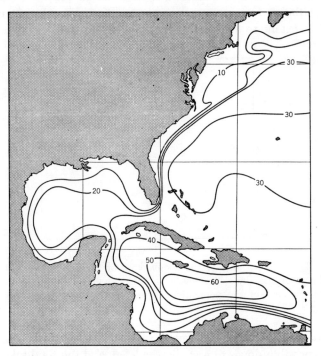

Figure 5–19. The average depth (meters) of the virtually isothermal layer in summer in the western North Atlantic. (After Fuglister, 1947.)

more marked influence on the distribution of both shallow-living plankton and the deep-living forms that move toward the surface at night.

Where the behavior of zooplankton is concerned, changes in surface illumination that can be neglected in so far as they affect deep levels become important nearer the surface. This will be discussed in more detail later, but, as an example, Fig. 5–20 shows how the average level of the zooplankton of these upper waters may vary in relation to the cloudiness of the sky. Similar marked differences may be found between summer and winter, and, in fact, diurnal migration may cease under conditions of polar winter darkness, the zooplankton becoming at the same time more vertically diffuse.

For phytoplankton, the illumination is of the first importance. Up to a limiting value, the rate of photosynthesis and growth is a linear function of the available radiant energy. Not only is there a seasonal variation in the energy reaching the surface of the water and an increase in this variation with increased distance from the equator (Fig. 5–8), but there is also a poleward decrease in the total energy received at the surface during the year. This is brought out in Table 5–3. The extent to which this light penetrates is dependent on the

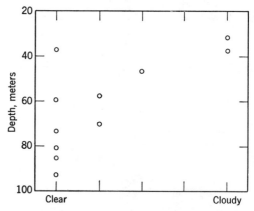

Figure 5–20. The response of the zooplankton of the Bermuda area to changes in cloudiness of the sky. The levels on the various occasions are those above which 75 per cent of the population of the upper waters lay. (After Moore, 1949.)

extinction coefficient of the water, so in less clear waters, photosynthesis is possible down to a shallower level, and the total taking place under 1 square meter of surface is correspondingly less. This in turn means, other things being equal, that the food production is less per unit area.

Working in the English Channel, with the diatom *Coscinodiscus excentricus*, Jenkin (1937) found that, for a 24-hour period, the maximum photosynthesis occurred at a depth of 5 meters, and the compensation depth at 45 meters. The latter is the depth at which the photosynthesis of the diatom just balances its respiration. Since other workers are in relatively good agreement with Jenkins on the energy present at the compensation depth, her results may be considered to be fairly typical of phytoplankton in general, and the estimates in Table 5–4 may be made for other types of water.

TABLE 5–3

Total Annual Incident Radiation in Gram-Calories × 10⁴ per Square Centimeter*

Latitude	Radiation	Latitude	Radiation
60°N.	7.2	0°N.	11.8
60	7.1	0	16.2
52	8.1	10°S.	15.0
52	7.7	10	15.5
42	11.2	30	15.9
42	11.6	30	13.5
30	12.2	42	11.1
30	10.7	52	8.8
10	14.5	60	5.7
10	12.9		

* Data taken from a series of stations at different latitudes, and modified from Kimball (1928).

TABLE 5–4

Depths of Maximum Photosynthesis and Compensation Depths in Relation to Clarity of Water

Locality	Extinction Coefficient	Maximum Photosynthesis, meters	Compensation Depth, meters
English Channel	0.13	5	45
Oceanic	0.10	6.5	58
Oceanic	0.05	13	117
Oceanic	0.03	22	195

It must be realized that these figures are only an approximation intended to show that a much greater water column is available for plant production in clear water than is available in less transparent waters. The actual values must depend to some extent on the species concerned, and, furthermore, the balance between respiration and photosynthesis is itself dependent on such factors as temperature. Thus both temperature and solar altitude may contribute to seasonal changes in the compensation depth. Riley et al. (1949) state that the following formula of Baly appears to hold good, at least at low values of illumination.

$$\log \frac{P_h}{K'I - P_h} = \log \frac{K''}{I} - \frac{Q'}{T'}$$

where P_h is the photosynthetic coefficient, I the light intensity, T' the absolute temperature, and K', K'', and Q' are constants.

Both these relationships and the effects of varying nutrient supplies will be described more fully in connection with the organisms in inshore waters, where most of the work has been done. Briefly, there is a linear relation between both photosynthesis and growth and the concentration of phosphate present in the water up to a value of about 0.55 mg.-atoms per cubic meter. Above this value additional phosphate has little effect. Both temperature and illumination modify the relationship. Growth and photosynthesis are also dependent on the nitrogen available, but, since nitrate and phosphate tend to be present in a fairly constant ratio in the water, it is often, for an approximation, sufficient to consider the distribution of only one of them. Nutrients are removed from the water by the phytoplankton and are therefore depleted in the surface waters. Dying organisms, phytoplankton and others, sink and pass back into solution, with accompanying breakdown from organic matter to simple salts. The deeper waters, below the level where phytoplankton is active, are therefore being constantly enriched. Figure 5–21 shows typical vertical distributions of phosphate in the Atlantic, Pacific, and Indian oceans. Although the type of distribution is the same, absolute values in the Atlantic differ from those elsewhere. In areas of convergence, phosphate-poor surface waters are carried down to greater depths, and in areas of divergence the richer deep waters are carried toward the surface. This is well shown in a section of the Pacific Ocean in Fig. 5–22. Such areas of upwelling are highly productive of phytoplankton, and this, followed through the food chain, results in high productivity of fishes, whales, and birds. Figure 5–22 covers only a comparatively small range of latitude; toward the poles, nutrient-rich water comes closer to the

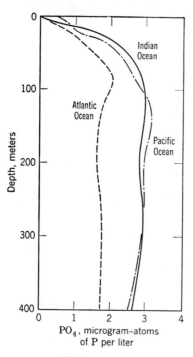

Figure 5–21. The vertical distribution of phosphate in the Atlantic, Pacific, and Indian Oceans. (After Sverdrup et al., 1946.)

surface, and there is much less intense stratification. The possibility of other salts essential to plant growth being reduced to a point where they may become limiting has already been covered in an earlier section. It was pointed out that, although addition of some elements to culture media may result in improved growth, there is little evidence of deficiency of these elements under natural conditions. Silicon is a possible exception, at least under conditions of particularly heavy phytoplankton production, and Fig. 5–23 shows that its vertical and horizontal distribution may closely parallel that of phosphate, indicating a similar cycle of depletion and enrichment.

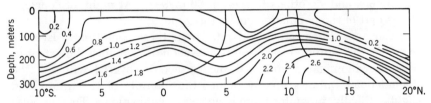

Figure 5–22. The vertical distribution of phosphate (microgram-atoms per liter) in a south to north section of the Pacific Ocean. (After Sverdrup et al., 1946.)

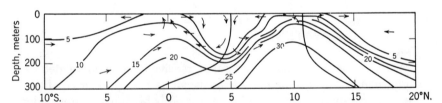

Figure 5–23. The vertical distribution of silicate (microgram-atoms per liter) in a south to north section of the Pacific Ocean. (After Sverdrup et al., 1946.)

The characteristic that necessitates the separate consideration of the extreme surface layers is the high intensity of illumination there. It is true that surface layers are subject to wave action, but the effects of this decrease rapidly with depth, and except where waves are actually breaking, they are unlikely to have a serious effect on plankton or pelagic fish. Except in high latitudes, midday illumination close to the surface is too intense for most marine plankton. In the diatom *C. excentricus*, systrophe occurs at about 9.6 gm.-calories per square centimeter per hour. With zenith sun, this would correspond to a depth of perhaps 10 meters in average oceanic water and 20 meters in very clear water. Whether or not the effect is lethal, a diatom undergoing systrophe will increase in specific gravity and tend to sink. An illumination less than that just given may still be considerably greater than optimal, and Clarke (1936a), in experiments conducted in the Sargasso Sea, found that the maximum rate of photosynthesis occurred as deep as 80 meters. The one plant that is apparently well adapted to surface illumination is the floating sargasso weed.

Most zooplankton actively avoids strong illumination, and if exposed to sunlight is injured or killed. Of the zooplankton inhabiting the upper 300 meters in Bermuda waters, 75 per cent on a sunny day lay below 80 meters deep, and 50 per cent below 100 meters (Moore, 1949). Of the 68 species studied, only one copepod and one chaetognath were found to have their maximum, in the daytime, in the top 25 meters, and six others in the top 50 meters. At night, of course, a large part of the population enters this zone.

Polar seas differ rather markedly from these conditions. Even in summer the altitude of the sun is low enough to reduce the extent of this over-illuminated zone. If the surface is covered with ice, the included air bubbles greatly reduce the intensity of the transmitted light. Finally, in winter there is no solar illumination. Thus in polar seas disadvantageous surface conditions are seasonal in character, and at their strongest are less severe and extensive than in lower latitudes.

COASTAL WATERS

Waters near shore have, naturally, received much more detailed study than less accessible oceanic areas, and although their conditions are more complex, coastal conditions are probably much better understood than those offshore. In general, the range of variation of the various factors, both seasonal and geographical, is greater in shallow water. This is in part associated with the lesser depth and in part with proximity to land drainage. Among the depth effects are increased sediment content from disturbance of the bottom by wave action and the absence of the population of deep-water zooplankton which enters oceanic surface waters at night. On the other hand this zooplankton is, in part, replaced by a population of animals which live on or in the bottom in the daytime. Land influence is associated with such differences as lower salinity, increased sediment with resulting decrease in light penetration, and a great increase in the ratio of larvae to adults in the plankton. This increase results from the large fraction of attached and bottom-living forms, both animals and plants, whose eggs, larvae, etc., are temporarily planktonic.

The Loch Striven area, in Scotland, has perhaps received more detailed study than any other and may be taken as an example of temperate inshore conditions. It is peculiarly suitable, since it includes deep water close to land, has relatively little land drainage, and is sufficiently far from the sea for the same body of water to remain for a long period without much interchange with neighboring water masses (Marshall and Orr, 1927, etc.). During the winter, despite some lowering of surface salinities, there is sufficient surface cooling to maintain mixing of the whole water column. Although this brings nutrient-rich water to the surface, it also results in the carrying of phytoplankton down below the compensation depth. This, combined with the low winter illumination and low temperature, results in reduced phytoplankton growth, and the surface population is only 10 to

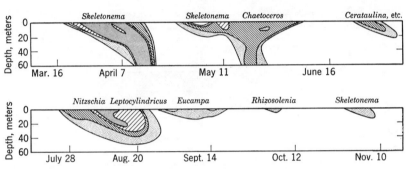

Figure 5–24. Seasonal changes in the abundance and vertical distribution of the more important phytoplankton species in Loch Striven. (After Marshall and Orr, 1927.)

100 diatom chains per 20 cc. About mid-March rising surface temperatures result in stabilization of the water column, and concurrently there is a spectacular phytoplankton outburst. Surface values rise to over 10,000 chains per 20 cc., and the concentration spreads progressively deeper. Figure 5–24 shows the progress of this and later outbursts. Accompanying the spring outburst there is a rise in surface pH from 8.0 to between 8.3 and 8.4, a rise in the oxygen content to supersaturation, and a decrease in phosphate to about half the previous value. Evidence that the outburst is not simply a response to increasing illumination is found in the fact that, in successive years, the earliest outbursts did not occur in those years when spring illumination was highest (Fig. 5–25). During the summer, successive minor phytoplankton outbursts occur, and there are considerable fluctuations in phosphate, oxygen, and pH. In August there is a second major outburst, although less pronounced than that in the spring; finally, in mid-October, surface cooling brings the water to an unstable condition

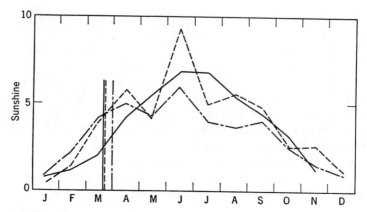

Figure 5–25. The mean monthly sunshine in 3 successive years in Loch Striven and the times of onset of the spring diatom increases. (After Marshall and Orr, 1927.)

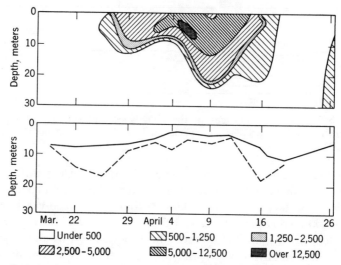

Figure 5–26. The progress of the spring diatom increase in Loch Striven in 1928 (upper figure). The lower figure shows, for the same period, the transparency of the water, as indicated by Secchi disk readings (solid line) and the calculated compensation depths (broken line). (After Marshall and Orr, 1930.)

again, and the plant population drops to its winter value. Soon after the phytoplankton outburst in the spring, there is a corresponding zooplankton outburst, delayed because the rate of reproduction of zooplankton is slower than that of phytoplankton. These phyto- and zooplankton cycles will be discussed more fully in a later section.

Although some of these cyclic changes are due to the control of the organisms by environmental factors, others are direct modification of the environment by the organisms. These include the changes in *p*H, oxygen content, and nutrient salt content. Similarly, although illumination plays an important part in regulating the rate of photosynthesis, the spring outburst of phytoplankton may be sufficient to reduce markedly the transparency of the water, and so raise the compensation depth, as shown in Fig. 5–26. In this case, the extinction coefficient was 0.24 immediately before the outburst, 0.67 during it, and 0.15 afterward (Marshall and Orr, 1930). This is probably an extreme

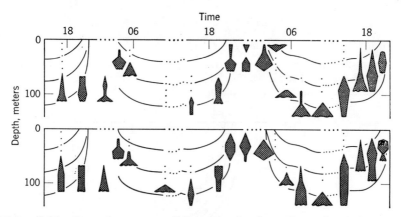

Figure 5–27. Diurnal migration of the copepod *Calanus finmarchicus*, the upper figure adult males and the lower figure stage IV copepodites. Curves join points of equal illumination, and the breaks in the top margin indicate shortening of the time scale. (After Clarke, 1933.)

example, since the spring outburst is particularly pronounced in Loch Striven.

Seasonal and diurnal changes in illumination affect not only the phytoplankton but also much of the zooplankton. Diurnal migration, as in deeper water, may be closely associated with the changing illumination. Figure 5–27 shows this in the case of the copepod *Calanus finmarchicus*. Less is known of the effects of seasonal changes of illumination on zooplankton, and the situation is complicated by the frequent occurrence of successive broods during the year, each with a differing light tolerance. Seasonal changes in temperature may similarly limit vertical distribution, some forms at least changing their vertical distribution in close parallelism to the seasonal shift of the isotherms (Figs. 5–28, 5–29). The cycle initiated by the spring stabilization of the water mass, resulting in the spring phytoplankton out-

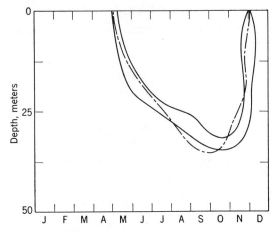

Figure 5–28. Seasonal changes in the depth of the lower limit of distribution of the cladoceran *Evadne nordmanni* (broken line) and of the 12 and 13°C. isotherms (solid lines). (After Nikitine, 1929.)

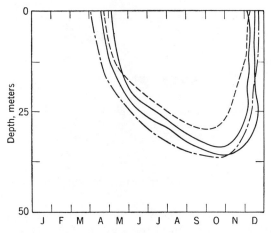

Figure 5–29. Seasonal changes in the depth of the upper limit of distribution of the ctenophore *Pleurobrachia pileus* (upper broken line) and the chaetognath, *Sagitta euxina* (lower broken line), and of the 11 and 12°C. isotherms. (After Nikitine, 1929.)

burst, is followed through in those forms for which, directly or indirectly, the phytoplankton forms a food source. We have seen the succeeding increase in the copepod population, and the same increase can be traced in other planktonic forms such as planktonic larvae. Plankton-feeding fish may in turn be affected, as well as bottom-living animals onto which the plankton rains. The pronounced spring outburst in Loch Striven was shown (Moore, 1931) to be followed a few weeks later by a rain of diatoms onto the bottom muds, and this in turn was followed by a rain of the feces of copepod and other fecal masses from the zooplankton (Fig. 5–30). The seasonal character of this sedimentation was sufficient to produce a visible banding of the sediments and could hardly have failed to affect the fauna eating these sediments.

This seasonal cycle has been found, with modifications, in various other temperate waters. For example, Fig. 5–31 shows the illumina-

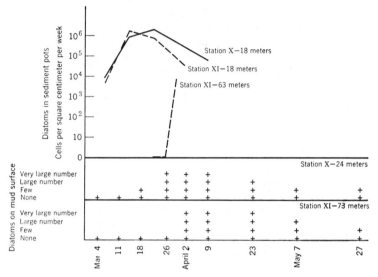

Figure 5-30. The settling of diatoms from the upper waters to the bottom in Loch Striven. The upper figure shows the numbers settling into collecting jars at different locations and depths, and the lower figures show their estimated abundance on the surface of the bottom mud. (After Moore, 1931.)

tion, phosphate, and temperature changes during the year in the less sheltered waters of the English Channel. Figure 5–32 shows the corresponding cycles in the phyto- and zooplankton with the content of the entire water column considered. Figure 5–33 shows similar data for Husan Harbor, in Korea. Here there is considerable variation in different years, but the autumn phytoplankton outburst appears to be stronger than that in the spring.

Because of the difficulties in working in polar seas, we have less information from these regions. It is clear, however, that a similar or even more pronounced plankton cycle occurs there. Figure 5–34 shows the seasonal cycle in the phytoplankton in the neighborhood of

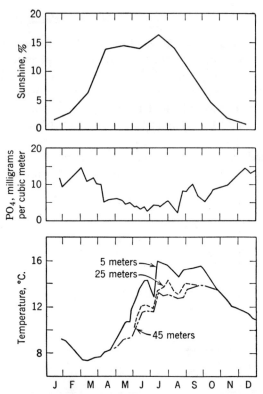

Figure 5–31. Seasonal changes in hydrographic conditions in the English Channel. The upper figure shows the monthly percentage of the year's sunshine, the middle figure shows the phosphate, and the lower figure shows the temperature at 5, 25, and 45 meters. (After Harvey et al., 1935.)

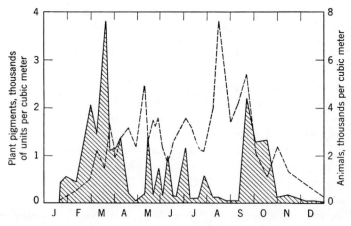

Figure 5–32. The seasonal cycle of phytoplankton (shaded) and zooplankton (broken line) in the English Channel. (After Harvey et al., 1935.)

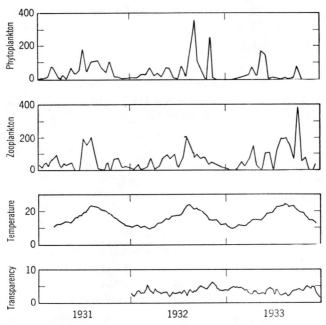

Figure 5–33. The seasonal cycle of phytoplankton (top), zooplankton, temperature, and transparency (bottom) in 3 successive years in Husan Harbor, Korea. (After Riley and Von Arx, 1949.)

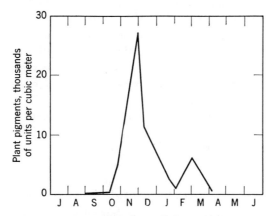

Figure 5–34. The seasonal cycle of phytoplankton in the South Georgia section of the Antarctic. (After Hart, 1942.)

South Georgia, with pronounced peaks in the southern spring and autumn. Table 5-5 shows the seasonal character of the zooplankton there as represented by certain copepods.

TABLE 5-5

Number of Copepods per Standard Net Haul through the Top 250 Meters off South Georgia

(Hardy and Gunther, 1935)

Species	November 1926	December 1926	March 1926	May 1927
Calanus propinguus	5	105	143	69
C. acutus	64	112	232	5
Rhincalanus gigas	18	57	71	20
Ctenocalanus vanus	310	194	1069	175
Drepanopus pectinatus	298	477	1681	0
Metridia lucens	0	14	202	198
Oithona frigida	1426	1954	3933	2619

Illumination variation is of course a major factor in polar areas with the period of continuous winter darkness. In addition, when ice is present on the surface, this greatly reduces the light penetration. The phytoplankton cycle is therefore particularly pronounced, with corresponding modifications of the food chains dependent on it. Very few arctic bottom invertebrates produce planktonic larvae; this has been attributed to the shortness of the season during which phytoplankton would be available to them for food and the hazard of mistiming spawning so that sufficient food would not be available throughout the larval life. Another characteristic of arctic inshore waters is the extreme lowering of the surface salinity when the snow and ice are melting. This may result in an impassable barrier to upward migration of much of the zooplankton.

In tropical inshore waters, some of the environmental factors show as wide a seasonal range as in temperate waters, but the plankton cycle is much less marked. For the waters of the Great Barrier Reef, we have a study of the chemical and physical conditions by Orr (1933), of the phytoplankton by Marshall (1933), and of the zooplankton by Russell and Colman (1934). Mixing of the water occurred throughout most of the year but was intermittent only from November to January. The average water temperature was 25.6°C. and the range 8.6°C. Salinities ranged from 31 to over 35⁰/₀₀ at the surface and from 33 to 35⁰/₀₀ at a depth of 28 meters. Phosphate and

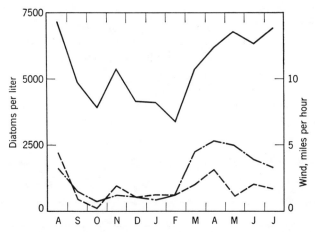

Figure 5–35. Seasonal changes in the wind force (solid line) and of the pennate (dash-dot line) and other diatoms (broken line) in the waters of the Great Barrier Reef. (After Marshall, 1933.)

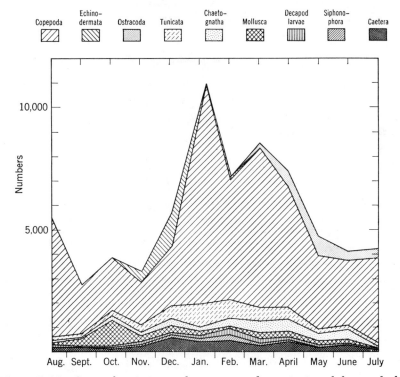

Figure 5–36. Seasonal variation in the amount and constitution of the zooplankton in the waters of the Great Barrier Reef. (After Russell and Colman, 1934.)

nitrate concentrations were both very low and showed no definite seasonal variation.   Extinction coefficients ranged from 0.07 to 0.34 with an average value of 0.14.   There was some seasonal cycle in the quantities of phyto- and zooplankton, but with a much smaller range than in cooler waters (Figs. 5–35, 5–36).   The fluctuations observed in the

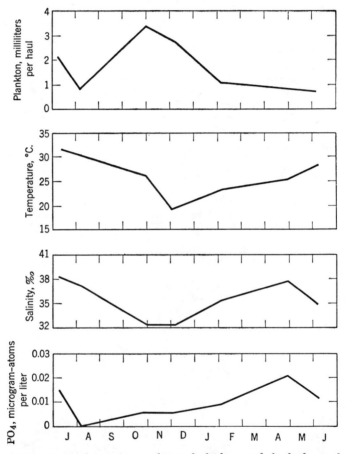

Figure 5–37.   Seasonal variation in the total plankton and the hydrographic conditions in the inshore waters of Biscayne Bay, Florida. (After Smith et al., 1950.)

phytoplankton appeared to be correlated most closely with the winds and the resultant changes in water masses.

The very low nutrient salt concentration and the small seasonal variation in plankton appears to be typical of tropical waters.   Figure 5–37 shows conditions in Biscayne Bay, Florida, in water considerably

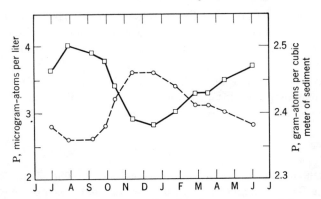

Figure 5–38. Seasonal variations in the phosphorus content of the surface layers of the bottom (broken line) and in the overlying water (solid line) in Hurricane Harbor, Florida. (After Miller, 1952.)

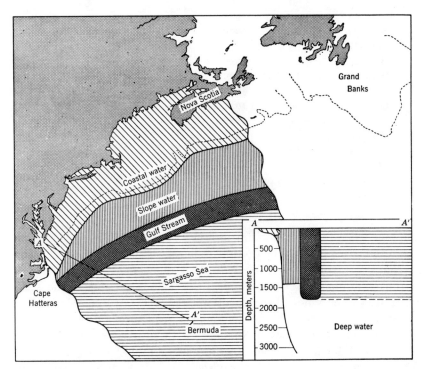

Figure 5–39. Schematic distribution of the water masses along the east coast of North America. (After Iselin, 1936.)

shallower than that on the Great Barrier Reef. Here the extreme range of the plankton concentration was only about fourfold.

In these waters, at least, it has been shown that some of the regeneration of nutrients takes place not in the water itself but in the bottom sediments, with subsequent diffusion back into the water. Miller (1952) demonstrated this in a part of the same Biscayne Bay area. The phosphate content of the water drops to a minimum in winter, at

TABLE 5–6

Annual Differences in the English Channel in the Phosphate Content, Percentage Ratio of *Sagitta elegans* to *S. setosa*, and Catch of Young Fish

(Modified from Russell, 1936)

Winter	Phosphate, % deviation from mean	Year	S. elegans, %	Young fish, number per standard haul
1923–24	+20	1924	—*	696
1924–25	+ 2	1925	—	140
1925–26	+29	1926	—	909
1926–27	− 3	1927	—	170
1927–28	+17	1928	—	—
1928–29	+17	1929	—	321
1929–30	—*	1930	75	403
1930–31	− 6	1931	42	230
1931–32	−21	1932	11	197
1932–33	− 9	1933	15	117
1933–34	−18	1934	6	79
1934–35	−26	1935	8†	37

* Dash indicates absence of data.
† First 2 months only.

the time when that in the sediment is at a maximum (Fig. 5–38), rising again in the summer as the phosphate in the sediment decreases. The mechanism involved appears to be that of a change from ferric to ferrous phosphate. The insoluble ferric salt is present in the sediment in winter when, because of mixing of the water column, the water and the surface of the sediment is well supplied with oxygen. More stagnant conditions in summer result in oxygen depletion and reduction of ferric phosphate to the more soluble ferrous salt. This diffuses into the water, and, if hydrogen sulfide is present, reprecipitates as ferrous sulfide, with liberation of the phosphate ions. Alternatively, the ferrous phosphate may diffuse up into a better oxygenated zone where it is again converted into the ferric salt and precipitated.

The break between oceanic and coastal water varies locally in complexity. Frequently there is a characteristic body of "slope" water be-

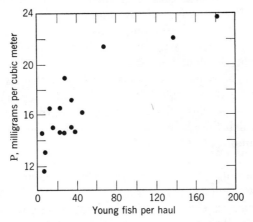

Figure 5–40. The relation between the numbers of young fish caught in the English Channel and the phosphorus content of the water which occupied the area the previous winter. (After Harvey, 1950.)

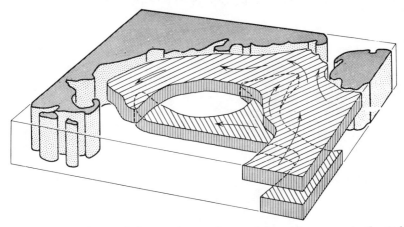

Figure 5–41. Scheme of the circulation of two of the water masses in the Gulf of Maine. (Modified from Bigelow, 1926.)

tween the two, similar to that shown diagrammatically for the east coast of North America in Fig. 5–39. Interchange between the various water masses is of the greatest importance, and periodic influxes of oceanic or slope water into the coastal region may have widespread effects there. Deeper oceanic water brings with it characteristic temperature and salinity which may have a temporary effect, but it may also bring enriched nutrient supplies with a more lasting effect on the productivity of the inshore areas which it invades. As an example of this, the years between 1923 and 1926 were characterized, in the mouth of the English Channel, by unusually heavy enrichment with outside water. In the succeeding years the reverse was true. Evidence of this enrichment was found in the total phosphate content of the water during its winter maximum. It was also found in the ratio of the two indicator species of plankton, *Sagitta elegans* and *S. setosa*, the former being the oceanic form and the latter the coastal. Figure 5–40 and Table 5–6 show the changes in these from year to year and the way in which the changes were reflected in the lowering of commercial fish landings in the area.

Bigelow (1926) has traced the influx of outside water into the Gulf of Maine, with its contained characteristic plankton. The drift of two of the three typical levels is shown in Fig. 5–41. This intrusive water may retain its characteristics for long enough for some, at least, of its inhabitants to travel considerable distances, and sometimes even to breed. Since some of the intrusive water is of cold northern origin, and some is from the warm Gulf Stream, they must have considerable effect on the conditions in the Gulf of Maine area.

6

Sea Bottom—Continental Shelf

For those organisms living in, on, or close to the bottom, there are two separate entities in the environment to be considered, namely the substratum and the water close to it. Neither is completely independent of the other, since the water contributes by exchange to the interstitial water and receives material from it. Bottom sediments also become dispersed to a varying extent in the overlying water, thereby modifying its characteristics. Nevertheless, there is one group of organisms living in the substratum and almost wholly conditioned by its character, and another group living in the water and comparatively little influenced by the substratum. Intermediate between these are such forms as molluscs and polychaetes which live in burrows but draw in water through siphons or extend tentacle nets into the water. Attached forms, such as most algae, gorgonids, and many sponges, are dependent on finding a suitable surface for attachment but beyond this are little influenced by the substratum. Finally, there are animals, such as various crustacea, part of whose time is spent buried in the sediment and part swimming in the overlying water.

The characteristics of inshore waters have, to a large extent, been considered in an earlier section. Seasonal changes in temperature and salinity are generally less in bottom waters than in surface waters, this difference becoming less pronounced at shallower depths where mixing is more complete and endures for longer periods. Wave action is less near the bottom, although it will be remembered that its effects have been demonstrated at 40 meters in the English Channel and at 200 meters in the open ocean. Since the influence of long-period ocean swell extends deeper than that of shallow-water, short-period waves, the degree of shelter from ocean swell is important in determining the degree of stability of the bottom. Since the size of particle moved is also dependent on the rate of movement of the water, it may be said that finer sediments tend to occur in deeper water and coarser ones near land in shallower water. There are, of course, many factors that can modify this generalization. The nature of the substratum, i.e., sand, gravel, etc., reflects the external conditions, such as water movement, that determine its deposition. Particle size may, therefore, be a useful index of conditions limiting the nature of the bottom-living communities but not affecting them directly through the substratum itself.

The particle size of the sediments is of considerable significance to the animals living in them. For many of the smaller forms of deposit feeders there is a limit to the size of particle which can be swallowed. Too many large particles, such as pebbles, may also obstruct the movement of burrowing forms. Many animals are adapted for movement only on a limited range of substrates. Thus *Purpura lapillus* requires a hard surface and rarely crosses sand. The particle size of the sediment is also significant in determining the content of interstitial water and the degree of interchange between this and the overlying water. If interchange is restricted, oxygen becomes depleted and hydrogen sulfide appears. Such conditions are limiting to many burrowing forms.

The organic content also plays a part in determining the oxygenation of the interstitial water, anaerobic conditions being most prevalent where there is the most oxidizable matter present. Since much of this organic matter is produced in the inshore algal beds or else carried into the sea by river drainage, and since, also, it has more chance of reaching the bottom without decomposition when the water is shallow, there is a general trend towards higher organic contents in sediments near shore.   Trask (1939) gives average values of 1–8 per cent organic content near shore, and 0.3–1.5 per cent offshore.

For one reason or another, the nature of the sediment plays a major part in determining the bottom fauna.   Petersen (1914a,b, 1918) and other Danish workers have made a very extensive study of the communities associated with different bottom conditions, and Figs. 6–1 and 6–2 show the close parallelism between the distribution of three

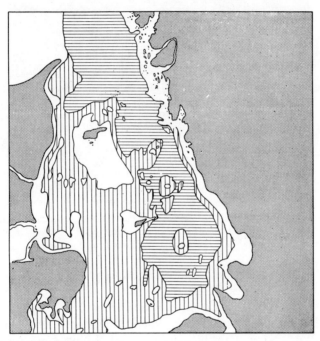

Figure 6–1.   The distribution of two typical bottom communities of the Cattegat. Horizontal shading, *Brissopsis lyrifera;* vertical shading, *Echinocardium cordatum.* (Modified from Petersen, 1914b.)

typical communities and the type of sediment in the Cattegat.   The constitution of these communities will be discussed later.

The rate of supply of organic matter to the bottom is a major determinant of the amount of life which can be supported there.   Such food supply may come from the phytoplankton, from attached algae or grasses, and from detritus of land origin.   Brotskaja and Zenkevich (1939) have endeavored to show the relation of rich bottom communities to areas of rich surface phytoplankton production associated with the meeting of different water masses in the North Atlantic.

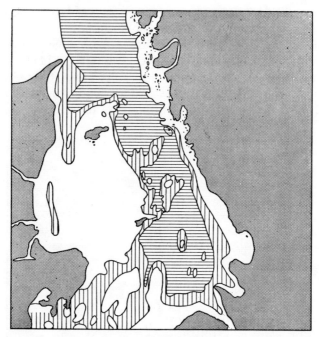

Figure 6–2. The distribution of types of bottom in the Cattegat. Blank, sand, gravel, stones; horizontal shading, soft bottom—blue clay and black mud; vertical shading, mixed hard and soft bottom. (Modified from Petersen, 1914b.)

Tressler (1940) gives the extent of certain beds of giant kelps on the Pacific coast of America (Table 6–1).

The estimated potential yield, which is probably too high, is equivalent to 161 tons wet weight per square mile, or 275 gm. per square meter. We can compare this with the annual phytoplankton production in Long Island Sound, as estimated by Riley (1941). He esti-

TABLE 6–1

Estimated Area of Some Pacific Beds of Giant Kelps, and Their Standing Crop if Harvested

Region	Area, square miles	Standing Crop in Tons, wet weight
Cedros Island to San Diego	91.36	16,979,800
San Diego to Pt. Conception	97.92	18,195,300
Pt. Conception to Cape Flattery	36.24	4,377,400
Puget Sound	5.00	520,000
Southeast Alaska	70.78	7,833,000
Western Alaska	17.86	3,567,000

mates that 600–1000 gm. of carbon are produced per annum under 1 square meter of surface. If about 0.5 per cent of the wet weight of the kelp is carbon, then the annual production of the kelp is far less than that of the phytoplankton. However, Riley's figures may be too high.

Even if we assume that the productivity of beds of larger algae and that of the phytoplankton are about the same, the difference in particle size of the products is important in determining their future. Phytoplankton sinks slowly and has a relatively very large surface. Considerable loss by solution therefore occurs before it reaches the bottom, and additional loss occurs as it lies on the surface of the substratum. Large algae, when detached, sink rapidly and may be buried in the substratum in comparatively large masses or are cast ashore. After a storm, banks of algae a meter or more high may accumulate above high watermark. Large concentrations of food are thereby made available to the forms which feed on them, and comparatively little energy need be expended in searching for such food. While still attached, the algae also afford both a substratum and a food supply for many forms, which therefore obtain their food in a highly economical manner from the point of view of energy expenditure. Phytoplankton is never concentrated to this extent, and an energy-consuming filtering mechanism is necessary in the animals that utilize it for food.

Shallow waters maintain a large population of filter feeders whose situation differs considerably from that of filter-feeding plankton. These are attached animals which characteristically can grow to a larger size than most plankton, and which, being attached, filter the water which passes them instead of swimming actively through the water and thus relying solely on their own energy for producing water currents. Although more liable to mechanical damage from such water movement as wave action, they are generally benefited by a more or less steady movement of water past them. This not only ensures their food supply but also provides the oxygen supply and removes waste products. Many species flourish only where water movement is strong but apparently receive the same beneficial effect from either waves or currents. Thus, in Bermuda inshore waters, various gorgonids are restricted to the more wave-exposed parts of the reef area except in channels with strong tidal currents. Here they may penetrate into very sheltered regions.

For such filter-feeding animals, the inshore waters provide food in the form not only of permanent plankton and detritus but also of the larvae of many of the inshore forms. Attached algae liberate immense quantities of spores. Barnacles liberate so many larvae that there are, at certain times, the major item in the diet of such animals as young herring. Thorson (1946) found that, in the Isefjord, at the height of the larval season, there are about 3000 larvae, of one kind or another, per liter of water. A single adult *Mytilus*, filtering 1.4 liters of water per hour, would catch 100,000 larvae in 24 hours. The food supply is large but the filtering mechanism is correspondingly efficient. A coral reef or a gorgonid bed, with their various filter-feeding inhabitants, or a bed of *Mytilus* or sponges can remove the food material very rapidly from the water. Evidence of this is found where offshore water is swept through a reef area. The outside species of zooplankton are usually different from those characteristic of the water inside the reefs, and it is surprising how few individuals survive to appear in plankton catches made across the reef from their normal habitat.

Despite the heavy mortality involved, dispersal by water movement is essential for those forms with attached adults but planktonic larvae. Such mortality arises not only from predation but also from the carrying of larvae by the currents to regions unsuitable for growth of the adults. A large proportion of the coastal currents is tidal and is of an oscillatory nature. This movement is largely backward and forward alongshore, or in and out of estuaries, rather than on and offshore. Loss by being carried offshore is probably not serious. Johnson (1939) has provided evidence of the slowness of offshore drift for the anomuran *Emerita analoga*. This has a limited vertical distribution in the intertidal sands of the Pacific coasts of the United States, and settlement of postlarvae will be unsuccessful unless it occurs reasonably close to this zone. The first zoea stage may persist up to 4 weeks after hatching, and the maximum distance offshore that this stage was found was 20 miles. The fourth zoea stage, perhaps 4 months old, was found up to 130 miles offshore. If these represent maximum offshore movements, it appears that a considerable proportion of the larvae must remain close to shore throughout their planktonic existence.

CORAL REEFS

The organisms are as essential a part of the environment as the water, substratum, etc., and it would not be proper to consider the environmental conditions with the organisms excluded. Conditions in a coral reef are, however, so dominated by the characteristics of the living corals and calcareous algae themselves that it is more convenient

to defer detailed discussion of these conditions until the reef inhabitants have been described. It is sufficient at this stage to mention
certain external conditions which limit the existence of reef corals. To
begin with, the vertical range is limited. Pacific reefs extend up
slightly into the intertidal zone, but Atlantic reefs appear to be limited
to below extreme low watermark. The depth to which reefs extend
varies, probably being controlled largely by the transparency of the
water, and rarely exceeds 40–60 meters.

Coral reefs are restricted to the warmer seas, not occurring where
the water temperature drops much below 21°C. in winter. In Bermuda, the northern limit of Atlantic reefs, the winter minimum is
about 18°C., whereas off Miami, the northern limit on the American
mainland, the winter minimum is probably about 20°C. At Miami
Beach, where conditions are probably more extreme, the average winter minimum is 18.7°C. and the recorded minimum 16.7°C.

THE INTERTIDAL ZONE

Because of its accessibility, the intertidal zone has been explored in
much more detail than any other. It has the advantage that, when
the tide is out, it can be examined directly, instead of by remotely controlled instruments such as dredges. To offset these advantages, conditions there are highly complex and vary rapidly both in time and
within small distances. So we probably have a fairly detailed picture
of the ecology and general biology of more individual species in this
zone than elsewhere, but the picture of the ecology of the zone as a
whole is no more complete. Although the number and range of limiting factors in the intertidal zone complicate the situation, the wide
range of conditions available facilitates the isolation of effects attributable to each particular factor. An example of this, brown or purple
coloration in the shell of the gastropod *P. lapillus,* has already been
quoted. In this and similar instances, choice of suitable localities for
comparison has made it possible to trace the effects of a particular
ecological factor, and the choice is particularly easy in the wide range
of intertidal conditions.

Intertidal habitats can be classified in many ways, but probably the
most convenient initial subdivision is in terms of the substratum. This
is a region where a high proportion of the organisms are attached and
are therefore very dependent on the nature of the substratum, or else
are closely dependent on its character for shelter, burrowing, and other
processes. Omitting for the moment the special conditions in estu-

aries, we may consider shores under the headings of rocky, sandy, etc. For all these there is one predominant factor, namely the tides.

The intertidal zone is essentially the meeting place of air and water, and the vertical zonation observed within it reflects the relative periods of aerial and aquatic conditions. In the simplest possible example, where there was no tidal change, a zonation would still occur, with conditions limiting certain forms to a zone close below the water surface and others to a zone close above it. The effects may be seen on a small scale at the edge of pools near high watermark. On a larger scale, the effects of proximity to the sea water are reflected in the varying closeness of approach of different land plants to the edge of the water. Below low water a similar series of algae reflects the varying thickness of water separating them from the air with its high level of illumination. As a natural entity, then, it would be more logical to consider a region extending from the sublittoral to the supralittoral, with the intertidal zone as its central part. So, although the tides determine at a given level the relative proportion of the periods of immersion and emersion, other factors complicate this; some of the conditions associated with the aqueous phase extend above high watermark, and some of those associated with the aerial phase extend below low watermark.

Rocky Shores. During the low-tide period, the inhabitants of the rocky shore are subject to the conditions of temperature, etc., existing in the surrounding air, except in so far as the organisms can isolate themselves from the aerial conditions by possessing thick shells, living in pools, burrowing, and other methods. Such factors as temperature, salinity, and insolation, which limit or modify the well-being of the organisms, are present here with a generally wider range than in the sea and with more rapid fluctuations. For example, the temperature range in the air is usually much greater than in the water. The salinity of the interstitial fluid within the organism tends to rise with evaporation and to fall when rain floods it with fresh water. There is less protection from insolation, and particularly from ultraviolet radiation, than below the surface of the water. Different species vary in their ability to insulate themselves from such changes, and different habitats, even as close together as one in a crevice and one on the neighboring rock surface, have widely divergent external conditions. Finally, the much more rapid changes in conditions introduce the factor of duration of particular conditions. An elevated temperature or salinity may, for example, be tolerated by a particular alga for a period of 6 hours without ill effect but may prove lethal after 18 hours.

Doty and Archer (1950) have worked on this last phase in connection with the theory of critical levels in which, at certain levels on the shore, a very small increase in height results in a two- or threefold increase in the maximum period of aerial exposure. Broekhuysen (1940) has shown that the period over which certain South African intertidal gastropods can tolerate conditions associated with aerial exposure is related to the level they normally inhabit and thus to the period of exposure they normally undergo. On the whole, though, we have very little information on the relation between conditions and the period over which they can be tolerated. Most intertidal surveys give information only on average or extreme conditions, and not on their time relations. It is becoming increasingly apparent that only a gross picture can be obtained by considering average or extreme conditions, and some form of time-condition study is called for. At this stage, however, it is not at all clear how such measurements should be made or expressed.

Temperatures on the rocky shore, in general, range between those of the sea and air, although, of course, an object in the sun may become hotter than the surrounding air. The rock and the organism itself act as heat reservoirs and help to reduce the temperature range. Evaporation of neighboring water, as well as that in the tissues, may help also to reduce temperatures. Few measurements of temperature *in situ* in the tissues have been made, but most of these, made on a hot day and during the low-tide period, showed temperatures well below that of the air. Hutchins (1947) has shown the importance of maximum and minimum temperature in limiting the geographic range of a species, limits being set either to survival or to breeding. Such correlations between geographical distribution and temperature are well known. In the intertidal zone it is necessary to consider not only the sea temperatures but also those of the air, since the latter are likely to be the more extreme. For example, Fig. 6–3 shows the distribution of the barnacle *Chthamalus stellatus* round the British Isles. Its limits, as shown, approximate the distribution of a winter minimum isotherm for 40°F. air temperature but are a much poorer fit with a water isotherm. Incidentally, the region of poor fit in the Irish Sea is a region where a marked extension of range appears to have taken place in the last few years. Isotherms such as this do not, of course, represent the true minimum temperatures that would be encountered in the intertidal zone; data on such minimum temperatures are usually unavailable at present. In the same way, available observations on sea temperatures do not usually refer to the actual intertidal zone, often being made in somewhat deeper water. Charts of ocean isotherms are even more misleading, since offshore and intertidal waters may differ markedly in temperature. This is particularly true when the incoming tide floods over large shallow areas. Stephenson (1947), reviewing the faunal zones of the South African coast, says "There is every sign, if the arrangement of populations is any guide, that the main currents do, as one would expect, affect the coast directly, in a

Figure 6–3. The distribution of the barnacle *Chthamalus stellatus* (stippled area) around the British Isles, and the winter minimum 40°F. air isotherm. (Modified from Moore and Kitching, 1939; Bartholomew, 1950.)

broad sense. There is also evidence, however, that when we come down to details there are complicating inshore factors which, although they do not neutralize the broad effects, modify them and may even affect them quite decidedly locally."

Except under estuarine conditions, which will be considered later, the salinity changes suffered on the rocky shore during the high-tide period are generally much less than those during the aerial phase. Where the tide floods over extensive shallow areas, particularly in the tropics, there may be elevation of salinity owing to evaporation.

Rainfall may produce a low-salinity layer at the surface of the water, and in polar regions melting ice may do the same. On the rock surface, small shallow pockets of water may evaporate during the low-tide period until salt crystals form. Evaporation of water from intertidal organisms must result in increase in the salinity of their remaining fluids, but it is difficult to say how far this progresses. Broekhuysen (1940) found that the gastropod *Littorina knysnäensis*, which may live above high water of equinoctial spring tides on the South African coast, could tolerate an external salinity of $50^0/_{00}$ for 2 days when immersed in concentrated sea water. He also found that the animal could tolerate desiccation to a point where its wet-tissue weight had decreased about 14 per cent and the resulting increase in internal salinity would appear to be up to about $100^0/_{00}$. Under natural conditions it is possible that some of this water loss is made up at night by hygroscopic absorption of atmospheric moisture. Forms living lower in the intertidal zone could tolerate, in general, successively less desiccation and less elevation of external salinity. Doty and Archer (1950) assumed that an increase of salinity to one and a half times its normal value approximated the change in the tissues of algae growing intertidally at the levels with which they were concerned. The duration of desiccation, and hence the amount of resulting salinity increases, will depend on tidal level, and the vertical distribution of the different intertidal species reflects, at least in part, their ability to tolerate such changes.

Oxygen availability and, for plants, carbon dioxide availability are probably rarely limiting on intertidal rocky shores. Both gases are present in ample supply in the air, and the action of waves and currents is sufficient to keep both well mixed into the surface waters which flood the intertidal zone during the high-water period. When rocks are bedded on sand or mud, the restricted water interchange under them may result in anaerobic conditions; special conditions may exist in rock pools also.

Insolation is a major factor in the intertidal zone and is probably responsible for the apparent barrenness of this zone in the tropics when compared with the heavily clothed shores of many cooler areas. Its effect is seen also in marked differences in the inhabitants of the north and south sides of upstanding rocks and of rock surfaces facing upward and overhangs. Damage from insolation may be directly due to actinic action, or it may arise through desiccation or overheating. Shells, or similar covering, afford a measure of protection from the actinic action and from desiccation and are probably more highly developed in this zone than below low water. Groups in which such protective mechanisms have not been developed, for instance coelenterates, cephalopods, etc., are therefore poorly represented in the intertidal rocky shore except in permanently wet habitats such as pools. The red algae, also, have adapted themselves less well to these conditions than the other groups of algae. Mobile animals may avoid the effects of insolation by adopting nocturnal habits, hiding in crevices and pools during the daytime.

Wave action profoundly modifies the effects of most of the environmental factors in this zone. Tidal levels are effectively raised, often far above their normal position, so that, in an extremely wave-exposed locality, algae which are otherwise intertidal may extend above high watermark by a distance greater than the tidal range. Spray from waves breaking on the rocks may be carried great distances beyond the actual reach of the waves. Despite various attempts at classifying wave action, there is still no satisfactory method of assessing it. Here, as with other factors, the time element enters, and we are in doubt what exactly should be measured. One effect of waves lies in direct damage caused by the water movement or by movement of solid objects carried by the waves, making the maximum wave action in the locality the most significant. However, heavy wave action may be most common in winter but rare in summer, and forms with a short life period can colonize the shore, under those conditions, only during the summer. For them, then, maximum wave action at a definite season should be measured. Other effects of wave action are beneficial— the wetting of marine forms at high levels, for instance. For organisms occupying such situations, frequency of wave action is more important than intensity. Winter wave action would benefit only short-lived winter forms, and long-lived ones would be left dry in just those summer months when insolation and similar adverse effects are most serious. Duration of wave action may also be important from an adverse aspect. Various animals, such as *P. lapillus*, shelter in crevices in stormy weather, moving out to feed on the open rock surfaces only in calmer weather. Duration of wave action is therefore important for them in determining the time available for feeding. Finally, wave action has a direct effect on the ecologist himself, for on many coasts open to oceanic swell waves are almost never completely absent and exploration of the lower levels of such shores may be possible only at rare intervals.

We have so far considered rocky shores in general, with little reference to geographical differences in conditions. On the shores in polar regions, not only the cold may be limiting, but the ice itself may be especially so. This immobilizes the organisms for a large part of the year, cuts them off from their supply of light and oxygen, and by its mechanical action scrapes most of their attached growth from the rocks. Life on such shores, then, tends to be restricted to forms which can migrate to deeper water in winter, or which can regenerate each spring from the small parts that survive the action of the ice. The melting of the ice is often accompanied by the formation of a layer of very low-salinity surface water which floods the intertidal zone and still further restricts the forms that can colonize it. On tropical intertidal rocks, insolation, with resulting high temperatures and desiccation, is probably the most serious limiting factor, and growth on exposed rocks on such shores is typically sparse. Heavy algal growth is largely restricted to below low watermark, and much of the intertidal fauna is either nocturnal or burrowing. On all shores, the coincidence of low tides with periods of extreme insolation, etc., is important. If, for example, the lowest spring tides in a given place fall in the morning or evening, conditions there will be less severe in the lowest zones than if these are exposed to the midday sun. Similarly, in some places wave action tends to be least in summer when insolation is greatest. In others, such as parts of the South African coast, storms may be more prevalent in summer and so keep damp the intertidal zone at the time when desiccation would otherwise be its most severe.

Rock pools form a very distinct habitat on the rocky shore, one that differs considerably from both the exposed rock and the neighboring sea water. Except for those lying above high watermark, all suffer a complete interchange of water with the sea at every high tide. For those lying higher, such interchange is only sporadic. Two main types can be distinguished—those that are shallow and suffer marked changes in temperature and salinity during the low-water period and those that are deep and large enough for such changes to be small. The extent of the changes taking place in a pool is of course widely variable; the general characteristics are as follows. Under insolation, the temperature rises, often above the maximum that many organisms can tolerate. Such temperature may also be strongly stratified. Evaporation is likely to take place, particularly in the pools that are high enough on the shore to be reached only by splash or by occasional spring high tides. The increase in salinity may be so great that salt actually crystallizes out round the margins. Some forms, such as the harpacticold copepod, *Tigriopus fulvus*, can survive even these conditions provided the pool does not dry out completely. If there is rain, or where there is land drainage, the salinity in the pool may be greatly lowered. In deeper pools there may be strong salinity stratification, so that the bottom water is still comparatively saline, but in very shallow pools there is often almost complete mixing. Any organisms living in such pools must be able to withstand wide and rapid salinity fluctuations. Where there is much algal growth in the pool, the oxygen saturation varies greatly during the course of the day. During the hours of sunlight, the water is usually saturated or supersaturated with oxygen, and we can frequently see streams of bubbles ascending from the algae. At night, with the respiration of both the algae and the animal population, the oxygen, content decreases and may fall below the minimum requirements of certain animals. This is a condition that rarely occurs in the sea itself. Corresponding wide fluctuations in *p*H occur, the value often dropping markedly at night. Another characteristic of intertidal pools is that, although the changes associated with insolation, evaporation, etc., build up comparatively slowly, there is usually a sudden return to sea conditions as the pool floods on the rising tide. Drastic changes in temperature, salinity, *p*H, and other factors may thus occur almost instantaneously.

An example of fairly extreme variation for an intertidal pool is given by Orr and Moorhouse (1933) for a pool in the Great Barrier Reef. The data cover a period of spring tides when the duration of isolation from the sea was maximum, and when low water fell in the middle of the day and night. They record that the oxygen fell as low as 18 per cent saturation, which would be sufficient to cause distress in some fishes even at a lower temperature but would not be dangerously low for the corals. The salinity in this case did not vary greatly. The same area was examined at other seasons, and the oxygen saturation was found to drop to zero under exceptional circumstances. The highest temperature which they recorded in a shallow pool was 37.8°C., but Gardiner (1903) recorded values as high as 56°C. in pools at Minikoi, with no apparent harm to the coral fauna. It is interesting to note that temperatures as high as 44.8°C. were recorded in oysters living on the open beach rock on the Barrier Reef.

Loose Rocks and Stones. Loose rocks provide another type of habitat which differs in various ways from that of the rocky shore in general and which grades through to the sandy type of shore. Large boulders may be virtually immovable on many shores, and very often they differ little from solid rock. They share with some areas of rock the fact that they are usually bedded in a loose substratum of sand or small stones, and their lower zones are therefore subject to abrasion. As a result there tends to be a zone close to the substratum in which attached forms such as algae, barnacles, limpets, etc., are absent. In part this is directly due to the abrasive action of particles washed by wave action over the surface of the rock, and in part it is due to the varying level of the substratum. From time to time, particularly on a sandy shore, this may build up to smother attached forms which are not able to move up as it advances. At other times the sand surface may recede, often leaving a scoured pool at the foot of the rock. The extent of such shift in level may be considerable, often a meter or more. Naturally both this effect and abrasion tend to be greatest where there is most wave action, and in a really sheltered locality, the rock may be inhabited down to the surface of the substratum.

On smaller rocks there is reflected the effect of occasional movement by wave action. Naturally the size of rock in which this occurs is related to the degree of wave action in the locality in question. Rocks that are not bedded in mud and have a circulation of water under them develop a special fauna on their undersides. It consists of organisms requiring shelter from sunlight, desiccation, water movement, and other conditions they would encounter on exposed rock surfaces. If the rock is likely to be turned over at intervals by wave action, such fauna will risk being left on the exposed upper surface where most of it will die. The stability of the rock is therefore a very important factor for such forms and its significance increases with the life span of the animal. Thus, if the risk of overturning is present only in winter, when wave action may be greatest, attached summer annuals may have a chance to populate the underside, recolonizing each spring the rocks that have been disturbed during the winter. On the other hand forms taking a year or more to mature will have less chance to survive there. There are, of course, some animals which normally inhabit this habitat and which are able to migrate to another stone if disturbed.

With stones of smaller sizes, approaching gravel in dimensions, the stability is very slight except in the most sheltered localities; not only is there the risk of the stones being turned over, but there is the added abrasive action of one stone against another. For this reason, a wave-exposed pebble beach tends to be extremely barren of life.

It will be seen from this discussion that wave exposure is of prime importance. Level is of considerably less significance since, despite statements to the contrary, wave action is probably just about as effective in overturning stones at high water as at low. Further, some of the zoned effects of factors, exhibited on open rock surface, are largely masked under stones. Thus desiccation on an open surface is likely to show a close correlation with duration of emersion, and hence with tidal level. The undersides of stones normally constitute a damp habitat, even long after the tide has left them, and so can be tolerated by forms that could survive only a brief period of emersion on the open rock. Comparatively unprotected forms may therefore be found under stones right up to the level of high-water neap tides, that is to say to the level at which they will be wet by the sea twice every day. Above this point there is a break in conditions, as there is on the open rocks, although the change in conditions is somewhat less extreme.

Usually the illumination under stones and rocks is insufficient to allow much algal growth. The food of forms living there is mainly what is carried in suspension by the water. Those forms with adequate powers of locomotion can, of course, use the rocks simply as a shelter in the daytime and explore the open rock surfaces at night, finding there whatever is their normal food.

One factor of major importance for this understone fauna is the extent of circulation of water under the stone. On a pebble beach, where there is no intermingled fine material, normal sea water is able to circulate to a considerable distance below the surface of the ground. However, if a rock is bedded on mud, there tends to be a very little chance for water to circulate under it, and there is frequently a condition of depleted oxygen supply. Those who have collected on a rocky shore will be familiar with the difference in fauna under a rock bedded on mud and under one that is more or less elevated so that water can run freely under it. Animals living under the mud-bedded rock are those that can survive low oxygen values or maintain a burrow out to the surrounding water and so insure an oxygen supply. The fact that hydrogen sulfide is often present when free oxygen is absent in the interstitial water of muds provides an added deterrent to the survival of many animals.

Intertidal Sand. It is rather surprising that more actual measurements appear to have been made on environmental conditions in sand and mud than on open rocks. This is perhaps due in part to the fact that the conditions within the sand are obviously different from those in the overlying water or air, whereas it has often been assumed that conditions on the rock surface may be characterized from those measurements which are often available, such as those of local sea and air temperature. It is unfortunate that so few actual measurements have been recorded for rocky shore conditions.

A sandy shore presents a comparatively uniform gradation of topography. It is frequently somewhat steeper at or above high water, and there may be minor gulleys or pools, but on the whole it shows a very uniform slope. There are none of the sharp irregularities of the rocky shore. Such factors as insolation, desiccation, wave action, etc., operate more or less uniformly all over the beach except in so far as they are modified by tidal level. The sand is usually a mixture of particles of various sizes, and there is usually a gradation of these in different parts of the beach. In a sheltered area there is a tendency for an accumulation of finer material. Toward high watermark the beach is often coarser in texture than toward low watermark. These are of course generalizations to which there are many local exceptions.

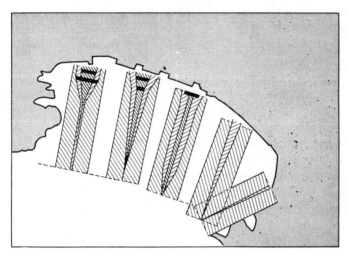

Figure 6–4. Variation in particle size on a sandy beach at Port Erin, Isle of Man. The larger particles (heavy shading) tend to accumulate at the higher levels and at the less sheltered (upper) end of the bay. (After Pirrie et al., 1932.)

Figure 6–4 shows the size distribution on a beach in the Isle of Man illustrating both of these points.

There are very few organisms which permanently inhabit the surface of the sandy beach. These are restricted to a few algae and grasses capable of "rooting" themselves there, certain diatoms and dinoflagellates that bloom on the sand surface, and the forms that inhabit the surface only during the low- or high-water periods. We are, thus, almost entirely concerned with conditions within the sand. Bruce (1928) points out that, in a perfectly packed assemblage of spherical particles of uniform size, there is about 25 per cent pore space. With graded natural sand, owing to irregular shape and imperfect packing, there is about 35–45 per cent pore space. However, natural sands are a mixture of different particle sizes, and with the resulting closer packing, pore space is about 20 per cent. In the upper part of the sandy beach this usually allows good drainage, with the result that there is a water table at a depth below the surface depending on such factors as height above tide level, distance from the sea, and nature of the sand. Capillary action raises the water to a considerable height above sea level, and the amount of this rise is greatest in the finest sediments. From this level up to almost the sand surface the interstitial air is still saturated with water vapor, and there is a film of moisture on the particles. It may, then, be assumed that animals inhabiting sand below high watermark will be able to keep permanently damp, and deep-burrowing forms may reach standing water. Even above high watermark, deep burrows will reach damp sand and may reach water.

In earlier sections we have discussed the nature of the interstitial water in sands and its effects on the fauna, as well as the results of variations in some characteristics of the sand itself on the burrowing abilities, feeding, and other activities of the fauna. We are concerned here with the distribution of these factors and effects on the shore. With regard to particle size, the tendency to concentration of larger particles in the upper part of the beach may deter some animals from burrowing or feeding there. On the other hand, the added proportion of silt in the sand of the lower beach will be deterrent to forms whose gills might be clogged, or which might suffer in other ways from the presence of too much silt. The animals that are deposit feeders will be favored near low water by the generally higher organic content there. The higher organic content tends to be correlated with lower oxygen content in the interstitial water, and this again makes them unsuitable for forms not specially adapted to meet such a situation. In extreme cases of black subsurface muds, the oxygen content is very greatly reduced, although even there Bruce (1928) records as much as 25 per cent saturation.

The sand acts as a buffer against marked changes in several other factors against which there is less protection on the rocky shore. For example, even in extreme cases there is much less fluctuation in salinity in the interstitial water than might be expected. Reid (1930) gives a section (Fig. 6–5) through a sand beach which had a considerable stream of fresh water flowing down it at low tide. Even though the samples were taken at about the time of low water, and on a spring tide, it will be seen that the salinity drop at a depth of 6 inches is comparatively little at all levels on the beach, and as shallow as 2 inches below the surface the drop does not become marked until well above midtide level. Figure 6–6 shows the salinity distribution at a depth of 20 cm. on another sandy shore onto which two small streams of fresh water discharge, and on only a comparatively small area does the value drop to below $24°/_{00}$.

In the same way, sand is a barrier to the harmful effects of insolation, even a few millimeters being sufficient for this purpose. It is also a considerable barrier to temperature changes. Studies on tropical beaches have shown a very sharp gradient in the top inch or two,

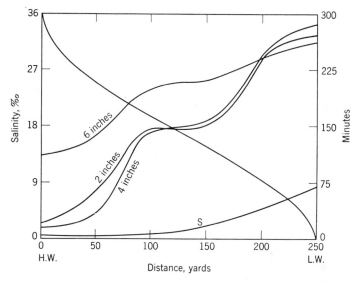

Figure 6–5. The distribution, between high and low watermark, of the salinity in a stream flowing over a sandy beach, and of the interstitial water at depths of 2, 4, and 6 inches. These samples were not taken simultaneously but over a period from 1 hour and 41 minutes to 26 minutes before low water. The curve crossing these shows the change in tide level with time during the period studied. (After Reid, 1930.)

with only a very slow change below that. Similarly, in records of the effects on the fauna of unusually severe winters, very often the forms that could not burrow far below the surface of the sand were killed by freezing, but the forms burrowing deeper were protected. Sometimes it appeared that they might have been killed by the cutting off of their oxygen supply by the frozen surface, rather than by the low temperature itself (Blegvad, 1929).

Sand, being unstable, does not provide the shelter from wave action that rocks do. Its inhabitants must either be able to burrow very deep or else be able to burrow rapidly if washed out. For many active forms the latter is not difficult, and there is a series of forms whose habitat is just at the edge of the shore where the waves are constantly stirring up the sand. For many others, however, excessive wave action is a serious danger, and after a storm great numbers may be cast up to a level where they will die. Since there is wide variation

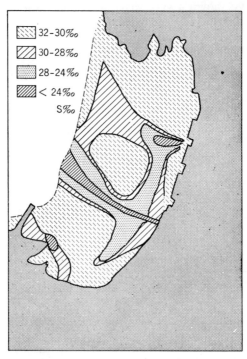

32-30‰
30-28‰
28-24‰
< 24‰
S‰

Figure 6–6. The distribution of salinity of the interstitial water 20 cm. below the surface of a sandy beach at Port Erin, in the Isle of Man. (After Pirrie et al., 1932.)

in ability to tolerate or avoid such wave action, there is a gradation in population from sheltered to wave-exposed sandy beaches. In general the latter support a smaller fauna, and the very exposed ones are comparatively barren between tidemarks. In addition to the stirring up of the sand by waves, the sand is subject to bulk transport which may produce large and rapid changes in the tidal level of the surface. Cornish (1934) records waves on the surface of intertidal sand that were up to 24 cm. inches high and progressed about a meter a day. This change in level is small compared with the result of a storm on some beaches where the whole intertidal sand may be carried away, changing the level by as much as the whole intertidal range or more. Of course such a shift would probably carry any fauna away with it, but where the surface was moving up or down slowly enough for the inhabitants to keep pace with it, they might soon find themselves at a level beyond their tolerance range.

Although the faunas of sandy beaches have been rather intensively studied in parts of the European and American coasts, they have received less world-wide study than have rocky shores. Generalizations about their geographic variations are therefore difficult to make. Intertidal sands in the Arctic will suffer sealing-off from any oxygen supply for long periods, and it is unlikely that they will be able to support a fauna that cannot migrate into deeper water for the winter (Madsen, 1936). Such migration is known to take place in some intertidal forms. Accounts of intertidal sands on the Great Barrier Reef and in other areas show that a considerable burrowing population may be supported. There is little information, though, on the conditions under which they live.

Intertidal Muds. Since intertidal muds cannot exist where there is much wave action, the habitat is limited in the extent of certain of its environmental factors. Muds are normally deposited only where there is little water movement or where the water movement is offset by a heavy supply of silt, as in an estuary. Because of their finer texture and often high colloidal content, there is less circulation of interstitial water than in sands. The usually high organic content provides a rich food supply, but the lack of circulation, together with the organic content, frequently results in anaerobic conditions with consequent limitations on the fauna able to inhabit them.

Muds tend to accumulate in comparatively sheltered areas, and frequently these are associated with a rich supply of organic material. To begin with, organic detritus is usually considerably less dense than inorganic mineral particles so that a selective sorting action takes place on coasts that are partly sandy and partly muddy. In addition, very often the shelter is correlated with the presence of heavy plant growth as, for example, in salt marshes and mangrove swamps, which results in a larger-than-usual supply of vegetable matter. On the other hand, there are shores composed almost entirely of inorganic clay or marl. Here the texture may be extremely fine and the organic content low. Such shores are often composed of sediments which were not deposited recently and under present conditions, although in certain parts of the tropics such calcareous marl deposition may be

occurring actively at the present time. Clays of this type are sometimes so firm that, when exposed, they can survive comparatively
strong wave action.

The slowness of interchange of the interstitial water is one of the
most important characteristic of muddy habitat. As an indication of
this, we have data on salinity given by Alexander et al. (1932). They
dug a hole 15 cm. deep into the mud, 1 meter from the water's edge.
These data were obtained in the Tees estuary where there were wide
fluctuations in salinity. As will be seen from Table 6–1, this near-
surface water showed only a partial salt interchange with the neighboring water.

TABLE 6–1

Interstitial Salinities in the Tees Estuary

(Alexander et al., 1932)

Distance from Sea, miles	Salinity of Water in Mud at Low Tide, $^0/_{00}$	Salinity of Water Offshore at Low Tide, $^0/_{00}$	Average Salinity of Water at High Tide, $^0/_{00}$
6	28.4	12.6	30.0
6	22.3	14.2	30.0
10	11.5	0	25.0
$11\frac{1}{4}$	5.0	0	21.0

Temperatures are similarly buffered. Linke (1939) gives the
following figures for a more sandy beach at low tide in summer: temperature in surface puddles, 26.2°C.; at a depth of 10 cm., 21.3°C.;
at 30 cm., 19.4°C. Finally, the shortage of oxygen in many muds is
indicated by the presence of a black layer a short distance below the
surface. Hydrogen sulfide is usually present in this layer and free
oxygen absent.

Since muds can be transported by slower currents than sands and
their angle of repose is smaller, muddy intertidal areas tend to be
even flatter than sandy shores. This may result in poor drainage and,
with the greater water retention, the formation of shallow pools.
Finally, such drainage as takes place is more likely to cut channels in
muddy shores than in sandy ones.

The fauna and flora of muddy shores have then to tolerate rather
markedly different conditions from those found in any other habitat.
The substrate is soft, and unless shell or other hard material is mixed
into it, there is poor holdfast for attached forms. Exception are mangroves and grasses, which have a good rooting system. The softness

of the surface also eliminates those forms requiring a hard substratum on which to crawl. On the other hand the texture makes burrowing easy, and the proportion of burrowing to surface forms is high. The frequent shortage of oxygen necessitates that the fauna either be capable of tolerating anaerobic conditions for a considerable time, as many nematodes and other forms can, that it be able to maintain an oxygen supply from the surface, as many burrowing forms do, or that it be limited in its vertical distribution to the extreme surface layers. The mechanisms employed will be discussed more fully in a later section. The rich organic supply affords food for a large population of deposit eaters, although, since there is frequently an associated high silt content in the overlying water, there may also be a large population of suspension feeders. Muddy shores are frequently associated with conditions of widely varying salinity, which provides some limitation on the species that can inhabit them, but this is offset to some extent by the comparative impermeability of the mud and the protection that it affords to burrowing forms from rapid salinity fluctuations.

ESTUARIES

The peculiar conditions in an estuary are usually associated with the variations in salinity found there, but there are a number of other important factors operative which include currents, silt, and frequently pollution. Day (1951) gives a valuable review of the conditions in various kinds of estuaries. A tidal estuary is an area in which there is an influx of fresh water at the upper end, and both an influx of saline water and an outpouring of diluted sea water at the lower end. The extent of the fresh influx typically varies seasonally and is also liable to vary rapidly and sporadically with different climatic conditions. Owing to the shallowness of many estuaries, the low-tide volume may be only a small fraction of the high-tide volume, which results in much greater longitudinal movement of the water than is found on most open shores. Since these movements are tidal, the differences between spring and neap tides are liable to produce corresponding exaggerated differences in dependent factors such as salinity, exposure, etc.

Considering a typical, temperate, shallow estuary, there is firstly a horizontal salinity gradation from the head to the mouth. In some cases the isohalines are closer together in the middle, in others at the two ends. They also tend to slant or curve across the estuary. The last two characters are well shown for Chesapeake Bay in Fig. 6–7.

Sometimes the direction of slant is dependent on the direction in which the tide is flowing, as illustrated in the tidal cycle series for the Tamar estuary shown in Fig. 6–8. This figure also brings out the tendency for the tidal flow to lag at the edges relative to the center of the estuary so that, at a given depth, marginal water tends to have a lower salinity than the center on a rising tide and a higher salinity on a falling tide. The same figures also show well the typical sectional contour of an estuary with a central deep channel and wide shallow margins, which result in much greater volume at high tide. The degree of stratification varies, but water is usually fresher at the surface and more saline at the bottom, so that water of a given salinity penetrates further up the estuary near the bottom than near the surface. This is an important fact in considering the salinity range to which organisms will be exposed at different tidal levels and the variations of these with position in the estuary. Let us consider (Fig. 6–9) a longitudinal section of a hypothetical tidal estuary, taken at full tide, half tide, and low tide. The isohalines have moved progressively down the estuary during the period. Four positions are considered, of which A is near the sea, and B, C, and D are progressively higher up the estuary. At each of these, four tidal levels are considered, namely, high water, half tide, low water, and sublittoral. Table 6–2 shows the range of salinities that will be experienced at each level and at each station. It must be borne in mind that, as the tide drops, successive levels are left uncovered and are

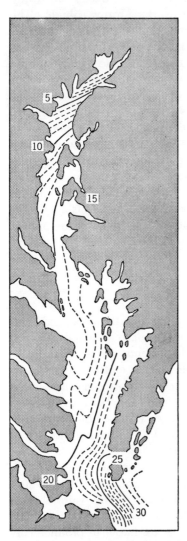

Figure 6–7. The distribution of surface salinities in Chesapeake Bay. (After Pritchard, 1950.)

thereafter unaffected by further salinity changes of neighboring water. Two important points emerge from consideration of this table. First, at any given tidal level the salinity range tends to be greater toward the middle region of the estuary and less toward the mouth and the

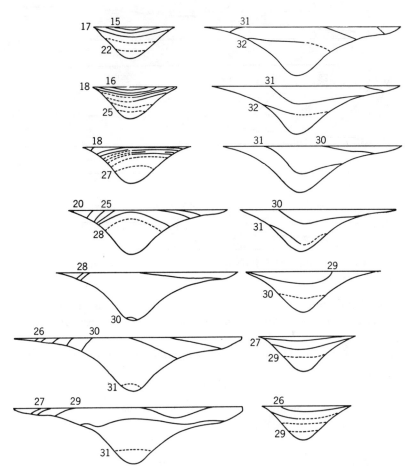

Figure 6–8. Salinity distribution at 1-hour intervals in a cross section of the Tamar estuary. *Left*, top to bottom, a rising tide; *right*, top to bottom, a falling tide. (After Milne, 1938.)

head. Second, at all points in the estuary, the salinity range is progressively greater from high water down to low water, and there is a slight tendency for a decrease in range in the sublittoral zone. That these deductions are not purely hypothetical is shown from the data given in Fig. 6–10. These are observed values for one station in the Tamar

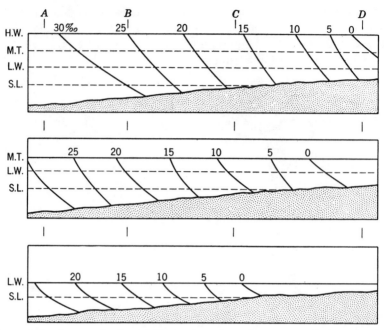

Figure 6–9. Longitudinal section of a hypothetical estuary at high water, half tide, and low water.

estuary, and they show clearly the increase in salinity range toward low water, with a decrease—in this case a marked one—in the sublittoral.

In Spooner and Moore (1940) some theoretical suggestions were

TABLE 6–2

Salinities in a Hypothetical Estuary

Tidal Level	A	B	C	D
High water	30–30	25–25	16–16	6–0
Midtide	30–29	27–20	17–10	2–0
Low water	30–23	28–16	18–1	3–0
Sublittoral	30–27	30–17	19–5	—

	Range at above positions			
	A	B	C	D
High water	0	0	0	0
Midtide	1	7	7	2
Low water	7	12	17	3
Sublittoral	3	13	14	—

offered about the effects of such salinity distribution on the variations
in optimum levels of various types of organisms in an estuary. It
seems, however, that some elaboration of these theories is called for
in view of the complexity of response of different forms to varying
salinity. An attempt to do this is made in Fig. 6–11. To begin with,
organisms may be grouped into those "unprotected" forms that are
permanently exposed to the water, and so are limited by the worst
conditions that can occur at a given place at any stage of the tidal
cycle, and those that are "protected" by a shell or burrow, and so, by

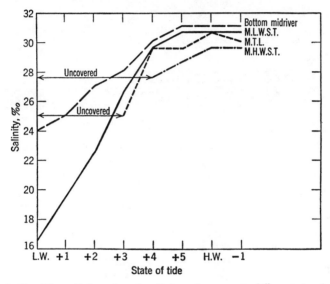

Figure 6–10. The tidal cycle of salinity changes at different levels in the
Tamar estuary. (After Milne, 1938).

exposing their bodies only when the conditions are favorable, are
limited by the occurrence of better-than-limiting conditions at some
stage of the tidal cycle. Again, and within both groups, there may
be some forms that have certain limits of salinity beyond which they
cannot tolerate, and others that can tolerate a certain range of variation within one tidal cycle but are so adapted, in different parts of the
estuary, that this range centers at different salinity values. Consideration of Fig. 6–11 will show that a wide range of distribution patterns
exists. Most of them indicate that the optimum or limiting tidal level
of a species should vary with position in the estuary, although how
this varies depends on whether the organism is protected or unprotected, whether it is typically a marine, an estuarine, or a fresh-water

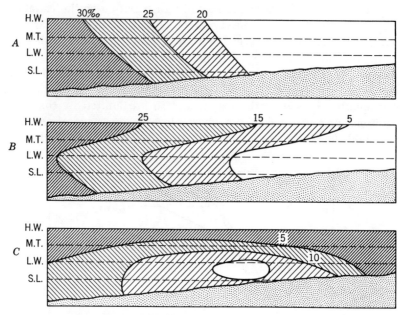

Figure 6–11. Distribution in the hypothetical estuary shown in Fig. 6–9, of organisms having various types of salinity limitations. The darkest shading represents the most favorable conditions for the organism.

A. "Protected" marine organism, limited by the availability of water above a certain salinity at some part of the tidal cycle.

B. "Unprotected" marine organism, limited by the minimum salinity encountered at any stage of the tidal cycle.

C. Marine, brackish, or fresh-water organism, limited only by the range of salinity encountered during the tidal cycle and not by the absolute value of the salinity.

species, and whether it is controlled mainly by absolute salinity or range of variation of salinity. In the latter there is still another complicating factor, for most organisms can tolerate a greater range of variation in a given factor if the change takes place slowly than if the change is rapid. On the open shore, tidal movement of the water is greatest around half tide and slowest at high and low tides. In the estuary this situation is complicated by the fact that at low water the water is restricted to a much smaller channel, and so longitudinal currents are greatly increased. Toward high water, the wide flat areas typical of the upper levels are flooded, and, although there is some lateral water movement, longitudinal movement is decreased. Since longitudinal water movement brings greater salinity change than does lateral movement, the middle and the lower levels might therefore be

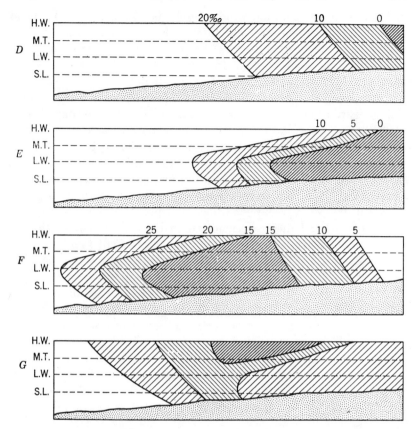

D. "Unprotected" fresh-water organism, limited by the highest salinity encountered at any stage of the tidal cycle.

E. "Protected" fresh-water organism, limited by the occurrence at some stage of the tidal cycle of water of a sufficiently low salinity.

F. "Protected" brackish-water organism, limited toward the upper part of the estuary by the occurrence, at some part of the tidal cycle, of water of sufficiently high salinity, and toward the sea by the occurrence, at some stage of the tidal cycle, of sufficiently low salinity.

G. "Unprotected" brackish-water organism, limited to water whose salinity does not vary either way beyond certain limits at any stage in the tidal cycle.

expected to be less favorable than the upper levels from the point of view of rate of change of salinity. The example analyzed here is not necessarily typical. It has been covered in detail in order to stress the complexity of estuarine conditions. It must be remembered that there are other types of estuary in which quite different conditions are found (Day, 1951). For example, some estuaries are seasonally isolated from the sea by a bar. Some have a reversed salinity gradient, with evaporation producing higher salinities in the head-waters. Again, some are non-tidal, whereas some, such as the Amazon, are so long that a series of high and low waters occur simultaneously along their length. In some, also, currents are so strong that there is little or no vertical salinity gradient.

Seasonal variations in salinity also play an important part in determining distribution. These may be very large. For example, Milne (1938) gives surface values for Saltash, in the Tamar estuary, which range from below $10°/_{00}$ in January to above $30°/_{00}$ in late summer In considering limiting conditions we may, therefore, have to consider the extremes that may be met with during the year. The protection offered by shells or burrows may carry an organism through a period of several days of extreme conditions, but probably not much longer. On the other hand there are many animals capable of migrating up or down the estuary, either with the tide, or seasonally, and there are also relatively short-lived forms able to colonize at one season parts of the estuary that they cannot inhabit at the opposite season.

So far we have discussed salinity in considerable detail, assuming that it is the salinity itself which is the important factor. Salinity, however, serves as an index of various other factors such as silt and pollution, which are associated with either the fresh or the salt water fraction only of the water entering the estuary and are subject to dilution paralleling that of the salt. The main sources of pollution are industrial wastes and human sewage. The number of substances that can thus be added to water is very great, and it would be impossible to discuss them in detail here. However, some generalization can be made about their effects. Ecologically, pollution may be considered from three aspects—solid matter added to the water, soluble chemicals added to the water and able to affect organisms directly, and substances that alter the natural characteristics such as oxygen content of the water. Both human sewage, when discharged untreated, and certain industrial wastes such as those from paper mills may add a large amount of particulate matter to the water, and when this settles it may have a marked effect on bottom fauna. Even if the waste itself is not toxic, it may have a blanketing effect on burrowing forms, or may clog the gills or other parts of forms such as oysters which live on the bottom. Since such deposition is most rapid where the water is quiet, the effect will be greatest on the upper flat levels and in backwaters and less near low water and in the main channels. Where such deposits contain much organic matter, they, or the bacteria, protozoa, etc., which feed on them, may form a rich feeding ground for deposit feeders, with beneficial results to the fauna. On the other hand the oxidation of the organic matter usually tends to produce anaerobic conditions in the deposits, thus limiting the forms that can inhabit them.

Soluble substance added to the water may have a serious toxic effect on the animals living there. For example, Galtsoff et al. (1938) showed a toxic effect on young oysters in a water-soluble constituent of oil. Phenylmercuric lactate, which occurs in the effluents from some pulp mills, has been shown to have a bactericidal effect and also to clog the gills of fish (Ellis, 1947). On the other hand, some effluent products appear to be actually beneficial. Specht (1950) has shown that phosphate waste may result in an increased oxygen content and a decreased biochemical oxygen demand in the neighboring water. Hart et al. (1933) considers that the nitrogenous matter added to the water in the neighborhood of pilchard processing works is beneficial to the flora and fauna of the neighborhood. Smith et al. (1950) give volumes of plankton, as indicated by the average catch throughout the year, for four stations close to Miami, where there is heavy sewage pollution. These were 5.1, 5.2, 4.9, and 5.3 cc. per standard tow. For seven stations in the lower part of Biscayne Bay, the last two being on the outside of the line of keys, the corresponding values were 1.7, 1.3, 1.2, 1.4, 1.5, 1.6, and 2.4 cc. The amount of fouling on test panels showed similar results, as did the growth rate of the fouling organisms. For the barnacle *Balanus amphitrite,* the maximum growth (diameter in millimeters) observed in one month was 20, 14, 12, and 20 mm. at the first four stations, and 8, 4, 10, 9, and 10 mm. at the others.

Probably the most generally serious effect of pollution is the reduction in the oxygen content of the water owing to the chemical or biological oxygen demands of the effluents. Tully (1949) considers this the major effect where paper mill waste is concerned. Most of the components of paper waste become oxidized, after dilution, in about 5 days, but the lignin fraction may take 90 to 140 days (Eriksen and Townsend, 1940). The high oxygen demand is characteristic of various other types of pollution also.

It is not proposed to discuss the physiology of pollution in detail here, but it may be pointed out that it is not essential for a particular pollutant to have a toxic effect in order to harm an organism. It has been shown that the presence of certain substances in water may cause oysters and other forms to remain closed. By so doing they fail to open and feed for the normal period, and so, even if they survive, are found to be in poor condition. It will be seen that all these effects of pollution are closely correlated with salinity, since the latter gives an index of the degree of dilution of the river water entering the estuary, and with it of the pollutants. Even if the latter are discharged into an area of the estuary where the water is brackish, the salinity still gives an indication of the further dilution.

Temperature fluctuations in the waters of an estuary are usually greater than those on the open shore. To begin with the river water is frequently considerably colder in winter, and warmer in summer, than the sea. Then the great extent of tidal flats over which the high tide floods may exaggerate the difference still further. Milne (1938)

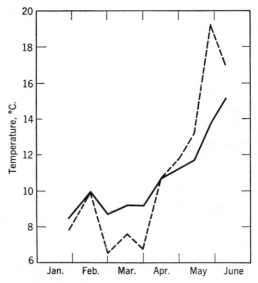

Figure 6–12. Comparison of the seasonal temperature variations in the surface waters of the Tamar estuary (broken line) and just outside the estuary, in Plymouth harbor (solid line). (After Milne, 1938.)

gives the values shown in Fig. 6–12 for the Tamar estuary compared with the open water at Plymouth Breakwater. He points out that these are average values and that much greater extremes can no doubt be recorded for brief periods. These temperature extremes may be significant in limiting the distribution of the fauna, although, since much of this is burrowing in habit, it will receive some protection from short-period fluctuations. However, it should be remembered that temperature may be an important factor in modifying tolerance to change in salinity, so that even relatively small temperature changes may be important. Fluctuations in *p*H are probably rarely of significance in estuarine waters since the sea water is sufficiently well buffered to overcome any acidity or alkalinity of the fresh water. Milne (1938) gives winter observations for the Tamar estuary which mainly drains an area of peat moor and which must therefore receive rather acid fresh water. His values are given in Table 6–3.

TABLE 6–3

*p*H and Salinity in the Tamar Estuary

(Milne, 1938)

Locality	*p*H	Salinity, $^0/_{00}$
Pentillie	7.54	9.8
Saltash	8.18	29.7
St. John's Lake	8.23	32.4
Drake's Island	8.15	33.9

The silt in suspension in most estuaries is a major factor in the ecology of estuarine organisms, affecting them through their food, substratum, illumination, etc. So far as food is concerned, it is known that estuarine muds can maintain very high populations. Again, quoting values for the Tamar estuary, Spooner and Moore (1940) record the following numbers per square meter: polychaetes—*Ampharete grubei*, 4033, *Heterocirrus zetlandicus*, 3000, *Nereis diversicolor*, 3030,

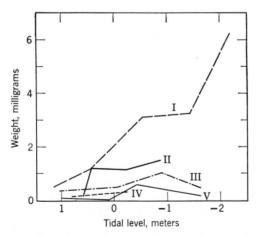

Figure 6–13. The effect of estuarine conditions on the growth of the barnacle *Balanus balanoides* at different tidal levels. Growth is indicated by the tissue weight of first-year individuals: I, fully estuarine conditions, II and III, in Plymouth harbor into which estuaries discharge considerable silt, V, at the mouth of a neighboring estuary, IV, outside conditions with clean water and high wave exposure. (After Moore, 1936.)

the gastropod *Hydrobia ulvae*, 22,660; the lamellibranch *Scrobicularia plana*, 1094. Although there is no direct evidence that good food supply is responsible for these high populations, this seems probable. Unfortunately there are few data available that allow comparison of growth rates in silty and clear waters. Such data are available, however, for the barnacle *Balanus balanoides* (Fig. 6–13). This shows that the growth attained in the first year in the most estuarine locality

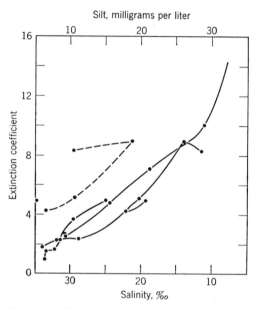

Figure 6–14. The relation between extinction coefficients and silt in the Tamar estuary. The broken line shows the trend toward higher extinction coefficients with increased silt content, and the solid lines show the increase in silt content up the estuary as the salinities fall. For simplification, notations on the state of the tide have been omitted. (Modified from Cooper and Milne, 1938.)

examined (I) was several times that at the two harbor locations (II and III), and these in turn were greater than that in clear outside water (V). That similar growth rates were maintained in older barnacles was indicated by other measurements. It is known that the growth of barnacles is favored by movement of the water, which apparently helps to bring more food within their reach. In general it has been shown that either wave action or a current provides this effect. In the series quoted, Amory Bight is very wave-exposed and so suffers considerably more water movement than the two harbor stations. Yet the growth rate is higher in the latter. It seems, then, that the increased growth rate is associated with the increased food content rather than with the water movement, although the two no doubt combine in the beneficial influence at the most estuarine station at Hen Point.

Although silt plays a direct part in providing food for the estuarine fauna, it also plays a very important role, though indirectly, in providing food for plants. Cooper and Milne (1938, 1939) have studied the penetration of daylight in the water of the Tamar estuary. Since the silt is brought in with the fresh water, they found, as might be expected, a fairly close correlation between the salinity at successive distances up the estuary and the transparency of the water (Fig. 6–14). They recorded extinction coefficients for green light (500 μ) greater than 14. The significance of this will be realized if it is remembered that clear oceanic water may have an extinction coefficient as low as 0.035 at a wavelength of 0.515 μ (Sverdrup et al. 1946). As a rule-of-thumb method, we may consider the compensation depth as being that at which noon sunlight is reduced to about 1 per cent of its surface value. In the open ocean this would be as deep as 100 meters. For comparison, Table 6–4 shows data for Number 15 buoy, well up

TABLE 6–4

Depth in Meters at Which Surface Light Is Reduced to 1 Per Cent, Assuming a 15 Per Cent Surface Loss

	Breakwater Buoy No. 1		Buoy No. 15	
Wavelength, μ	High Water (summer)	Low Water (winter)	High Water (summer)	Low Water (winter)
0.434	3.44	1.37	2.02	0.35
0.463	3.64	1.56	2.27	0.40
0.494	3.86	1.68	2.58	0.43
0.530	4.40	1.86	2.76	0.47
0.572	5.00	1.72	2.77	0.51
0.619	3.86	1.93	2.54	0.53
0.729	1.77	1.33	1.40	0.48
0.750	1.38	1.04	1.19	0.46

the Tamar estuary, and Number 1 buoy at the entrance to Plymouth Sound. Data are shown for low water at a spring tide in February and for high water at a neap tide in June. These illustrate the differences caused by season and state of tide.

When it is considered that the Tamar estuary, which has been taken as an example, is considerably less silt-laden than many others, it will be realized that growth of algae below low water must normally be greatly restricted under estuarine conditions. Actual observations on the zonation of submerged algae in an estuary will be deferred to a later section. It should be noted that the silt content is much higher, at a given part of the estuary, at low tide than at high. Thus the sublittoral algae will benefit less by increased illumination at low tide than will those on a shore with clearer water. Further, the increased silt content of the water in winter will amplify the normal winter effect of decreased illumination caused by the lower altitude of the sun.

There is less range in nature of substratum in an estuary than on the open shore. Rocky and gravelly beaches may occur, but the surfaces of the stones are usually covered with a film of silt. Although larger forms, such as adult barnacles, can protrude through this with, apparently, no ill effects, settlement of the small spat appears to be difficult. Clean sandy beaches are rarely found, since the sand tends to trap particles of silt. Mud, of varying texture, is by far the most abundant estuarine substratum. Because of this the greater part of the estuarine fauna is either burrowing in habit or, as in the case of fish, shrimps, etc., is capable of migrating over the upper flats when the tide is in and returning to the main channels at the tide drops. Algae find little ground suitable for attachment except on the few stones and solid structures such as jetties and buoys. Those forms growing on the mud itself are usually filamentous or other small forms. On the other hand there is frequently a great development in the upper tidal levels of a special marsh or swamp flora, largely composed of grasses in the cooler waters and of mangroves in tropical seas.

Estuarine currents have already been referred to. With the configuration of the bottom shown in Fig. 6–8, these often tend to be stronger near low water than at high water. For attached forms, such as barnacles, which benefit from the extra food brought to them by a current and are not likely to be carried away by it, there is a marked advantage in a low-level habitat, as will be seen from Fig. 6–13. For burrowing forms, however, and for those that crawl on the surface of the mud, the swifter currents, often combined with the steeper slope, near low water, make this a more dangerous habitat, and it is frequently found that they inhabit it only in places specially sheltered from water movement.

We have taken a fairly shallow, temperate estuary as a typical example, but there are various modifications of it that deserve special consideration. Particularly in northern areas there may be a strong development of fjords in which the water is very deep. Their length and narrowness, and the supply of fresh waters from rivers, may result in great reduction of salinity in the surface waters, whereas the deeper water is of more or less normal salinity. The deposition of silt may be much less, so that the shores are often clean rock or gravel, with only limited areas of mud. The supply of fresh water tends to be strongly seasonal in character, so that the surface water may vary from salt to partically fresh at different seasons. In many cases winter conditions include freezing of the surface waters, exterminating much of the intertidal fauna unless it is able to migrate down to a depth below that reached by the ice. Much of the fauna and flora may, as a result, be of either a seasonal or a migratory nature.

In those parts of the tropics where there is an intense rainy season and a dry season, a similar marked seasonal variation in conditions may occur. Panniker and Aiyar (1937) have described such an area which opens into the Bay of Bengal. During the rainy season from October to December there is a strong flow in the river, and it cuts a deep channel discharging into the sea. When the river flow slackens, its level drops and the marginal areas of the estuarine backwaters begin to dry out. At the same time, a fairly strong flow of sea water into the estuary occurs, and its salinity rises. With reduced river flow, a bar forms at the river mouth, and by March this becomes complete so that the estuary is isolated from the sea. By this time also the river has practically ceased to flow. In Table 6–5 monthly average data are given for a station inside the bar.

TABLE 6–5

Seasonal Changes in a Tropical Estuary

(Pannikar and Ayar, 1937)

	Nov.	Dec.	Jan.	Feb.	Mar.	Apr.	May	June	July	Aug.	Sept.
Temperature	26.6	25.4	25.0	26.2	27.7	28.2	29.6	28.8	28.5	28.5	28.2
pH	—	8.50	8.48	8.55	8.46	8.46	8.65	9.07	9.15	8.82	8.70
Excess base	—	30.15	20.73	23.20	17.59	25.16	24.90	24.52	25.35	23.50	23.30
Salinity	—	25.10	28.17	30.44	29.92	17.29	19.74	16.91	17.19	18.30	19.38
Chlorine	—	13.84	15.59	16.85	16.56	9.56	10.92	9.35	9.51	10.12	10.72

Two points are of special interest here, namely the rather extreme range of pH and the vary small range of temperatures.

In temperate estuaries the lowest salinities almost always occur in winter or spring, usually the latter when much of the fresh water comes from melting ice and snow. In such estuaries, the lowest temperatures and lowest salinities occur at the same season. It should, however, be remembered that in other localities, particularly in many tropical estuaries, the wet season, with low salinities, may be in the summer, at the time of maximum temperatures, or there may be two wet seasons in the year.

Salt marshes present another special case of estuarine conditions, although they may sometimes exist where there is no great lowering of the salinity. In general they represent areas of sheltered water where flowering plants, mainly grasses, have taken over the role of the larger algae to a great extent and form a fairly complete surface cover. This cover is, of course, broken by channels and pools. The grasses do not normally extend far below high watermark and are normally flooded by sea water only by spring tides or during stormy weather. The cover of vegetation traps fine silt, so that the substratum is typically muddy. The constriction of water movement by the vegetation results in increased flow in the channels, which tend to be scoured to a lower level than the grass areas; as a result they are usually flooded by more than just spring tides. The vegetation constantly tends to build up new land from the estuary, unless current erosion at its margins can keep pace with this process. Once it has built up to high watermark, however, the accumulation of estuarine silt practically ceases, and with it further elevation. Salt marshes thus tend to be extremely uniform in elevation. Within their channels, and particularly in isolated pools, conditions of salinity, temperature, etc., are subject to very wide and often rapid changes. When isolated during periods of neap tides, the pools undergo wide diurnal temperature changes, and their oxygen content also shows a large diurnal variation. During rainy weather their salinity drops very low. With the flooding tide, as in all pools, there is likely to be a sudden and drastic change as the water is replaced by that from the estuary.

7

Organisms

ABYSSAL ORGANISMS

Our knowledge of the biology of abyssal animals is largely a matter of inference, since few have been brought to the surface alive, and of these only some bacteria have survived for long under the unaccustomed surface conditions. Until recently we have had to rely on the contents of dredge hauls for picturing abyssal conditions, but in the last few years the development of underwater photography has allowed us to see some of the abyssal animals in their natural habitats.

The early conception of a completely barren abyssal sea bottom has given place to one with a significant, although sparse, fauna. Unless growth rates and food requirements are much less there than in shallower waters, the fauna must be sparser, since we know that the rate of supply of food is much less. We have very few grab samples taken from a known area of bottom to allow an estimation of fauna density, and comparison of dredge hauls from different depths is somewhat

207

suspect, since there is the possibility of less efficient operation of the dredge on very long cables. Even allowing for this, however, the results in Table 7–1 probably indicate a marked drop in fauna density in deeper water. Spärk (1951) records an average of 12.5 animals per square meter, with a net weight of 1.85 gm., for a series of stations at a depth of 820–2680 meters off the Congo. Off Angola, at 1000–4000 meters, the values were 35 individuals, weighing 2.5 gm. These were, presumably, mainly actinians and synaptids, with a dry weight of only about 2 per cent of the wet weight.

TABLE 7–1

Average Catch in Dredge Hauls Made at Different Depths

(Murray, 1895)

Depth, meters	Number of Stations Averaged	Average Number of Specimens per Haul
180– 900	40	150
900–1800	23	87
1800–2700	25	80
2700–3600	32	39
3600–4500	32	25.6
4500– —	25	24

It is difficult to evaluate the results of the many deep-bottom photographs already taken, for no data are published on the rather high proportion showing *no* life or burrows. We would judge, though, that these indicate a marked faunal decrease with increasing depth; probably those from the deepest water average but one or two organisms in a field of several square meters. From grab samples taken on the *Galathea* expedition, Spärk (1951) quotes a density of 10–12 gm. per square meter at depths of 6000–8000 meters, and about $\frac{1}{2}$ gm. per square meter at one station at a depth of 10,120 meters. The average for their deep hauls was about ten animals, weighing about 1 gm. per square meter. Besides the effect of decreasing with increased depth, sedimentation and food supply also decrease with increasing distance from the nearest land. Murray (1913) gives average contents of dredge hauls made in depths ranging from 1800 to 3650 meters. The series taken less than 500 km. from shore averaged 121 specimens of 39 species, and those from similar depths, but more than 500 km. from shore, averaged only 21 specimens of 10 species. If sedimentation rate is even an approximate index of food supply, then the abyssal bottom receives less than 1 per cent of that in, say, Loch Striven in Scotland, and correspondingly less again than

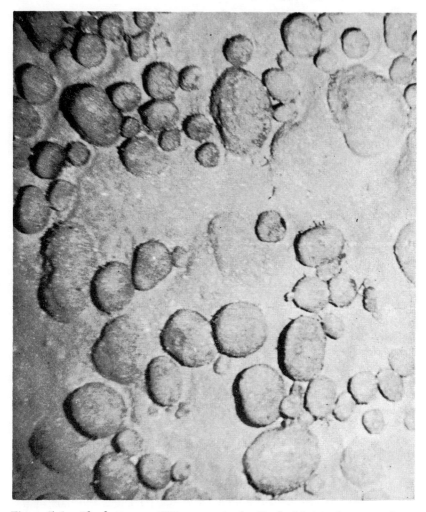

Figure 7–1. The bottom at 5500 meters in the North Atlantic showing a dense association of what may be either sponges or manganese nodules. The largest of these are about 15 cm. in diameter. (Photograph D. M. Owen, Woods Hole Oceanographic Institution.)

many areas of rapid sedimentation. It seems reasonable to suppose that the fauna differs in a similar way. Some photographs of the abyssal bottom (Fig. 7–1) show a considerable concentration of life, but it must be remembered that along with these, there were numerous photographs which showed no animals at all. Although the photographs shown here are of bottom-living forms, a few have also been taken of swimming forms such as fish and shrimps.

The organic content of abyssal sediments is no lower than in some inshore ones, and deposit feeders must be able to find a considerable food supply there unless the organic matter is present in a non-utilizable form, and there is no evidence of this. Among some deposit feeders, such as lamellibranchs, a process of selective feeding has been observed. The siphons suck up the surface layer of sediment, and its finer content is passed into the gut. The feces leaving the anus are consolidated in pellets of much larger size than the original particles, and these pellets are of quite resistant character. Pellets, along with fine sediment, are sucked in by the inhalent siphon but are sorted out

TABLE 7–2

Relative Specific Varieties in Some Groups of Bottom Animals, Expressed as the Percentage of the Total Number of Species

(Zenkevich and Birstein, 1956)

	Depth, meters				
	Over 1000	Over 2000	Over 3000	Over 4000	Over 5000
Hydroidea	?	?	0.4	0.4	0.2
Polychaeta	?	3.7	2.6	1.7	0.6
Peracarida	?	1.3	?	?	?
Pantopoda	?	9.7	4.5	1.5	?
Bryozoa	?	?	1.2	0.4	0.1
Crinoidea	21.6	7.7	2.9	1.8	0.5
Echinoidea	18.7	?	5.4	1.6	0.5
Ophiuroidea	?	?	5.2	2.2	0.4
Asteroidea	33.3	?	9.3	3.7	1.2
Holothuroidea	22.7	?	12.3	8.4	2.9

and rejected unswallowed through the exhalent siphon. There is thus a selective mechanism which, in effect, packages the part of the sediment from which digestible material has been extracted, so that it will not be eaten a second time. If, therefore, the rate of renewal of fine material is low in abyssal sediments, deposit feeders may have relatively little food material from which available nourishment has not already been extracted. There are few records of the abundance of fecal pellets in abyssal sediments, the highest known being the rather low concentration of 246 pellets per cubic centimeter at a depth of 4224 meters (Moore, 1933). This is far less than the count of 3400 per cubic centimeter in the shallower water of Loch Striven.

Deposit feeders are able to move about in search of their foods, but attached filter feeders cannot do so. They are completely dependent on what rains down on them, together with whatever may be stirred up into the bottom water by more active forms. Currents cannot be sufficient to bring much extra food within their reach. There can hardly, then, be competition for food between neighboring individuals. Growth may be very slow, with so slow a food supply, but if growth is possible at all, it is hard to see why, in the extremely uniform conditions present, relatively crowded conditions should not exist. Perhaps they do in the rather dense crinoid beds inferred from the contents of dredge hauls in certain areas or in the sponge bed shown in Fig. 7–1. It seems likely that predation is the limiting factor and that extremely slow growth reduces the repopulation of depleted areas.

TABLE 7–3

Maximum Depths, in meters, Recorded during the *Galathea* Expedition

(Braun, 1956)

Actiniaria	10,190	Neopterygii	7,130
Echiuroidea	10,190	Porifera	6,960
Holothuroidea	10,190	Cirripedia	6,960
Lamellibranchiata	10,190	Antipatharia	6,940
Polychaeta	10,150	Scaphopoda	6,940
Amphipoda	9,790	Ophiuroidea	6,660
Isopoda	9,790	Ascidia	6,660
Tanaidacea	8,210	Scyphozoa	6,620
Sipunculoidea	8,210	Nematoda	6,620
Crinoidea	8,210	Pycnogonida	6,480
Gastropoda	8,210	Alcyonaria	6,140
Hydrozoa	8,210	Zoantharia	6,140
Asteroidea	7,630	Ostracoda	5,850
Echinoidea	7,250	Bryozoa	5,850
Cumacea	7,130		

In addition to the decrease in fauna density with increasing depth, there is also a decrease in the number of species present. This is brought out in Table 7–2.

Certain groups have adapted better to abyssal conditions, as brought out in the results from the *Galathea* expedition (Table 7–3).

It has been stated by some authors that abyssal animals tend, in general, to be smaller than their equivalents in shallower water because of the shortage of food or other factors. There seems to be little evidence for this. We have less adequate means of capturing the larger and more active forms at great depths than we have for those in shallow water. Further, large abyssal animals, when they die, are less likely to float to the surface and be washed ashore where we can see them. Finally, where less active forms are concerned, there is evidence of various groups having particularly large representatives in deep water. For example, the hydroid *Monocaulus* grows to a length of 2 meters, certain pycnogonids to a length of 30 cm. or more (Fig. 7–2), and the holothurian *Pelopathides* (Fig. 7–3) to about a meter. There is no reason to think that there are not also large fish, cephalopods, and other forms present at great depths.

Sparsity of fauna poses the problem of there not being a male and

Figure 7–2. The bottom at about 2000 meters in the North Atlantic showing a large pycnogonid, spanning about 50 cm., and an ophiuroid. (Photograph D. M. Owen, Woods Hole Oceanographic Institution.)

female near one another at the time when the ova are ready for fertilization. Some deep-sea species—for example, some angler fish barnacles, and others—have complementary males to meet this problem. There are, however, no analyses to show whether the fraction of complementary males is higher in the deep-water fauna than in the shallow-water fauna.

Apart from small food supply and possible difficulties in mating, the abyssal environment does not appear to be a disadvantageous one. Its high carbon dioxide content renders the deposition of calcareous skeletons difficult, but to offset this there is no call for strong skeletal support to resist water movement and all that is lost is armored protection from predators. Furthermore, light weight is distinctly advantageous to forms that have to move over the soft bottom ooze. We find, in fact, structures, such as spider-like legs apparently specially adapted for such progress. Low temperature is not a barrier, since similar values exist in shallower parts of polar seas where there is an abundant fauna. In view of the small food supply, the low temperatures may actually be advantageous in reducing metabolic rates. Of the effects of very high pressures we know little beyond the fact that

Figure 7–3. The bottom at a depth of 3800 meters in the North Atlantic showing a very large holothurian resembling *Pelopathides gigantea.* (Photograph B. C. Heezen, J. Northrop, and J. Ewing, Columbia University.)

they must involve special tissue modifications and that animals from most, if not all, phyla have been able to produce these modifications.

Darkness is apparently no particular disadvantage, and sightless forms become increasingly abundant in deeper water. On the other hand these are found living alongside others with enlarged eyes adapted to collect the maximum amount of light of bioluminescent origin. Bioluminescence is particularly well developed in deep water, serving both as a lure for prey and, probably, as a recognition signal for individuals of a species. Admittedly, the purpose of some highly developed luminescent organs is at present unknown, for example those that shine into a body instead of toward the outside. Unlike planktonic and pelagic animals, bottom-living forms are not heavily pigmented at great depths. They become less so below about a thousand meters, and in the abyssal zone are characteristically yellow or white (Zenkevich and Birstein, 1956).

One characteristic of many deep-sea fishes is the possession of highly extensible jaws and stomachs, allowing them to swallow relatively enormous objects. This would appear to be an adaptation to the problem of food scarcity since, when such a fish meets a prospective meal that would otherwise be too big for it, it is often able to swallow it whole. Thorson (personal communication) has pointed out that when prey is sparsely distributed, and the predator cannot locate it at a distance, the slower-moving predator will encounter food more rarely than a faster moving one. A predator, therefore, must be able to swallow prey of any size encountered in proportion as the prey is sparse or the predator is slow moving. As an example, the slow-moving starfish *Asterias* can swallow a much larger object than the faster-moving *Astropecten*. It seems to be significant that there are almost no predators below about 10,000 meters (Zenkewich and Birstein, 1956). At these extreme depths, bottom deposit eaters predominate and there are no suspension feeders.

Finally, the method or reproduction of abyssal invertebrates is modified in relation to their environment. Thorson (1950) has shown that, in warm, shallow waters, larvae are predominantly planktonic, and that this type becomes progressively less abundant toward polar seas. In the latter, and also in abyssal water, planktonic development very rarely occurs. Usually a few large yolky eggs are produced, which hatch in an advanced stage of development; very often the parents are viviparous. As for the shallow-water forms, Thorson associates the absence of planktonic development with the shortness of the season during which there is a sufficient production of phytoplankton to feed them. Similarly, he attributes the type of abyssal larval production to shortage of suspended food in the water, and in this connection it should be remembered that, for their weight, larvae are much faster growing and have much higher food requirements than the adults.

MID-DEPTH PELAGIC ORGANISMS

Our knowledge of the ecology of mid-depth pelagic animals is probably even less than that of abyssal ones. Some work has been done on the diurnal migrations of those forms living in the upper part of this zone, but, since they can migrate up at night into the upper layers, they are considered in the next section. Welsh and Chase (1937, 1938) have successfully brought some deep-water decapods to the surface and kept them alive for study of their eyes, and others have observed luminescence in various forms which remained alive for a short period after being caught, but otherwise little is known of the living animals. The inadequacy of tow nets for catching fast-moving animals has probably resulted in an even more inadequate picture of the midwater fauna than that yielded by dredges and trawls for the bottom. The relative scarcity of adults of the more active forms makes it almost certain that a high proportion of them are escaping capture.

As with the abyssal forms, we can only deduce some of their ecological relations from known environmental conditions and from structures that appear to be adapted to particular needs. Here also the absence of daylight has been accompanied very often by a reduction in the size of eyes, although in some animals they are unusually large. Reduction of eyes appears to be progressive with increasing depth and to occur more often in forms that are not provided with luminous organs than in ones that are. This is well brought out in Table 7–4,

TABLE 7–4

Ratio of Diameter of Cornea to Length of Carapace in Various Species of *Sergestes*, the Presence or Absence of Photophores in the Species, and the Depths (meters) at Which They Were Recorded (Welsh and Chase, 1937)

	Eye Ratio	Photophores	0	200	400	600	800	1000	1200	1400	1600	1800	2000	2050
S. mollis	0.052	—	—	—	—	x	x	x	—	—	x	x	x	x
S. sargassi	0.085	—	—	—	—	x	—	x	—	—	x	—	—	—
S. pectinatus	0.099	—	—	—	x	x	x	x	—	—	—	—	—	—
S. arcticus	0.090	—	—	—	x	x	x	x	x	—	—	—	—	—
S. corniculum	0.072	—	—	—	—	x	—	x	—	—	—	—	—	—
S. edwardsi	0.098	—	—	—	—	—	x	—	x	—	—	—	—	—
S. cornutus	0.092	—	—	x	—	x	—	—	—	—	—	—	—	—
S. vigilax	0.097	—	—	x	—	x	—	x	x	—	—	—	—	—
S. atlanticus	0.105	—	—	x	—	x	—	x	—	—	—	—	—	—
S. tenuiremis	0.088	x	—	—	—	—	—	x	—	—	—	—	—	—
S. grandis	0.081	x	—	—	—	x	—	x	—	—	—	—	—	—
S. crassus	0.132	x	—	—	—	x	—	x	—	—	—	—	—	—
S. robustus	0.115	x	—	x	x	x	x	x	—	—	—	—	—	—

which shows data given by Welsh and Chase on the relative eye size of various species of sergestid shrimp and the depths at which they were taken.

There seems little doubt that sight is largely dispensed with, at any rate in many of these forms, as a means of locating food. The extreme development of such structures as barbels and fin rays in many species suggests their use for locating food by touch (Fig. 7–4). Possibly the complicated arrangements of luminous organs found in many forms are associated with the recognition of their own species, in which case this might be the main function of the eyes. Associated with the scarcity of food and the particular advantage of being able to eat even a very much oversized piece of food when this is found is the ability of many deep-sea fishes to swallow and to accommodate in their stomachs objects often considerably larger than themselves. Marshall (1954) gives an excellent account of the eyes and luminous organs of deep-sea fishes.

With the lack of seasonal change in the environment in these depths, and the wide geographic range of comparatively constant conditions,

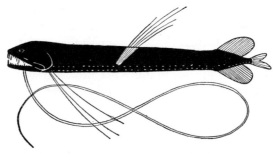

Figure 7–4. *Bathophilus metallicus,* an example of a deep-sea fish with extremely elongate fin rays. (After Beebe and Crane, 1939.)

it might be expected that the inhabitants of these depths would exhibit very much wider geographical ranges than do most shallow forms. Coe (1946) has brought together the results of deep hauls in the Bermuda area. Of 36 species of caridean decapod crustacea taken, mostly from below 1000 meters, 25 had been previously described. Of these, 15 had been recorded from the Indian Ocean, 11 from the equatorial Atlantic, 11 in the eastern North Atlantic, 6 off the Cape of Good Hope, 5 off the coast of Ireland, 9 in the western Pacific, 6 in the eastern Pacific, 4 in the southern Pacific, and 4 near the Hawaiian Islands. Of the 14 species of nemerteans taken, 8 had not previously been described, 3 were known only from the North Atlantic, and 3 from both North and South Atlantic. Two of the species had also been taken from the Indian Ocean. Coe's data bring out not only the fact of the wide distribution of many of the species but also the extreme rarity of many of them. In any collection it may be expected that there will be single representatives of certain species whose center of distribution is elsewhere. It may be that the centers of distribution of many of the bathypelagic forms have yet to be discovered, but it seems very possible that the high proportion of rare forms in the catches is rather indicative of a very sparse population of these species. For example, of 42 known species of bathypelagic nemerteans from the Atlantic, 18 are at present known from single specimens only. Of the remaining 24, 8 are known from 2 specimens, 5 from 3, and 11 from 4 or more specimens. Of 36 species of caridean crustacea taken in the Bermuda area, 7 were represented in the hauls by single specimens only. Of 98 species of amphipods from the same hauls, 28 were represented by only a single specimen. Russell (1935) has analyzed the distribution of a large number of planktonic animals in connection with the bipolar distribution of many of them. Some species are known to occur in comparatively shallow water in the Arctic and Antarctic, and much deeper in the equatorial region. Others occur in one polar region only, or in both but without a connecting equatorial population. Russell points out that, although forms that have evolved near the surface in the equatorial region may be carried either north or south and so, in time, adapt themselves to the waters of either the Arctic or Antarctic, deep-living forms are more likely to be carried southward by the deep oceanic currents. Thus, a species evolving in either the Arctic or the deep water of the equatorial region is very likely to be carried into the Antarctic, but neither the deep equatorial species nor one evolved in the Antarctic is likely to be carried into the Arctic. This will be discussed more fully in the next section. Some of the effects of increasing depth in the plankton are different from those we have seen in the bottom fauna. The number of species of bottom forms decreases steadily with increasing depth, whereas some groups of plankton increase downward, not decreasing until the abyssal zone is reached. This is shown in Tables 7–5 and 7–6.

TABLE 7–5

Numbers of Species of Calanids per Cubic Meter at Different Levels of the Kuril Trench

(Brodsky, 1952; quoted by Zenkewich and Birstein, 1956)

Horizon, meters	0–25	25–50	50–100	100–200	200–500	500–1000	1000–4000
Number of species	7	7	9	10	28	30	87

Another difference is in the depth at which loss of pigmentation occurs. Most bottom animals are colorless below a depth of about 2000 meters, whereas many pelagic animals are pigmented at depths of 6000–7000 meters; only in the ultra-abyssal zone is the plankton really without pigment (Zenkewich and Birstein, 1956).

TABLE 7–6

Numbers of Species of Pelagic Gammarids at Different Levels of the Kuril Trench

(Birstein and Vinogradov; quoted by Zenkewich and Birstein, 1956)

Zone and Subzone	Number of Species
Surface	1
Transitional	1
Upper abyssal	13
Lower abyssal	12
Ultra-abyssal	6

There are comparatively few bathypelagic species for which the environmental requirements have been defined, except their vertical distribution. The cephalopod *Vampyroteuthis infernalis* has already been referred to. This form appears, from the available data, to be limited to a particular water density, and the depth at which it occurs correlates more closely with this than with either temperature or sa-

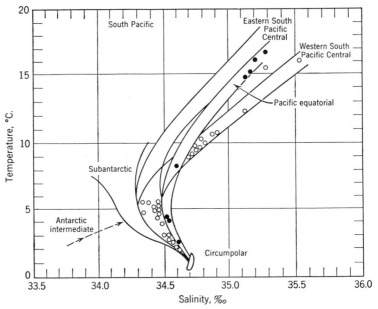

Figure 7–5. Salinity-temperature diagrams for certain Pacific water masses. On these are superimposed the occurrences of two subspecies of bathypelagic fish, *Chauliodus sloanei dannevigi* (open circles) and *C. s. secundus* (solid circles). (After Haffner, 1952.)

linity alone. Furthermore, there is a progressive change in density optimum from the eggs through the larvae to the adults.

Haffner (1952) has defined the conditions under which the bathypelagic fish of the genus *Chauliodus* are found. In general, the different species and subspecies are rather closely limited to particular

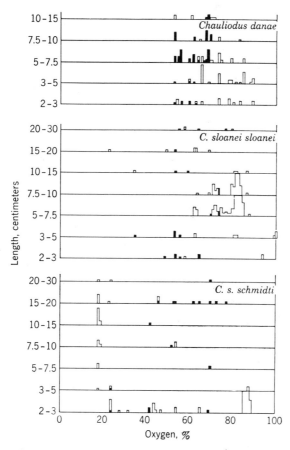

Figure 7–6. The occurrence of three bathypelagic fish with reference to the oxygen content of the water. *Chauliodus danae* has the least tolerance of reduced oxygen concentration, *C. sloanei sloanei* is intermediate, and *C. s. schmidti* has the greatest tolerance. (After Haffner, 1952.)

water masses, regardless of the temperature, salinity, or density at different levels within the mass in question. This is shown clearly for two Pacific subspecies in Fig. 7–5.

These fish carry out an extremely extensive diurnal migration which is described later. In the course of this vertical movement they may encounter a considerable variation in the oxygen content of the water. Tolerance of lowered oxygen saturation varies considerably in the different species as shown in Fig. 7–6. This apparently explains certain peculiarities of their distribution. Where the oxygen content is high, *C. danae* predominates and the other two forms cannot compete. At lower concentrations, *C. sloanei sloanei* is the most successful, whereas at still lower values, *C. s. schmidti*, which cannot compete at the higher oxygen concentrations, is the most successful.

THE UPPER OCEANIC ZONE

When this zone was considered as a habitat, it was subdivided into three levels. Near the surface there is a zone in which the daytime illumination is too high for survival of most phytoplankton and zoo-

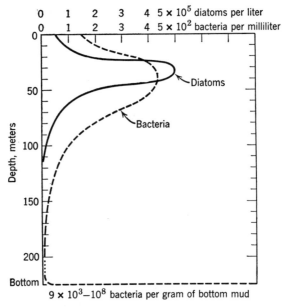

Figure 7–7. The vertical distribution of diatoms and bacteria in the sea. (After Sverdrup et al., 1946.)

plankton, only a few specialized forms being normally found there. Below this is a zone in which photosynthesis is active, or at least there is a fairly rich supply of falling food material. Below this again is a zone occupied by zooplankton which migrates up at night into the richer surface feeding grounds. Let us first consider the typical vertical distribution of organisms in these zones. Figure 7–7 shows that the main diatom concentration lies near, but definitely below, the surface. Since the rain downward of dead phytoplankton, as well as of dead animals and animal excreta, provides food for many of the bacteria, the concentration of the latter is greatest a little deeper (Table 7–7). The daytime concentration of the upper zooplankton is below

TABLE 7–7

Numbers of Bacteria per Cubic Centimeter at Three Stations

(Zobell and Anderson, 1936)

Depth, meters	Bacteria		
1	147	344	261
10	238	400	360
20	292	528	395
50	86	620	208
100	14	17	53
200	3	2	0
500	2	0	0

this again. In the Sargasso Sea, as shown in Fig. 7–8, it is at about 100–150 meters, the level varying from day to day according to the light conditions. At night most of this zooplankton ascends close to the surface.

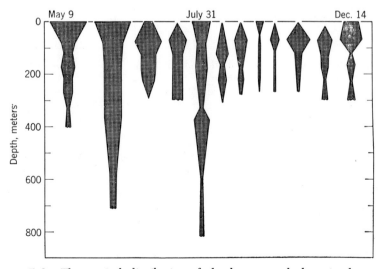

Figure 7–8. The vertical distribution of the larger zooplankton in the upper waters in the neighborhood of Bermuda. (After Moore, 1949.)

Leavitt (1938) has determined the vertical distribution of the larger zooplankton below these depths. The 100–150-meter concentration is barely indicated in his figures (Fig. 7–9). Both the total plankton and the individual groups of salps, chaetognaths, fishes, etc., showed marked concentrations at 800 meters and again at about 1600 meters. These data are from one area in the North Atlantic, and there

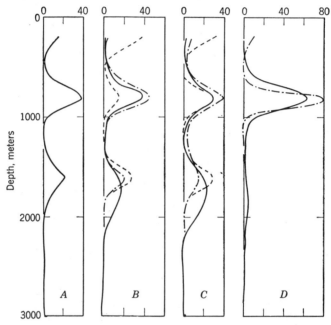

Figure 7–9. The vertical distribution of the larger zooplankton in the western North Atlantic, omitting the surface layers. *A*, total catch. *B*, fish (solid line), copepods (dot-dash line), euphausids (broken line). *C*, decapods (solid line), chaetognaths (dot-dash line), salps (broken line). *D*, coelenterates (solid line), residue (dot-dash line). (After Leavitt, 1938.)

are no comparable data to show whether this type of distribution is found in other oceans also. However, there is little doubt that the echo phenomenon known as the scattering layer is caused by some form of plankton or nekton, and this is apparently world-wide at a depth of some 400–800 meters. This, then, probably corresponds to Leavitt's 800-meter concentration. A still deeper echo, and one that has been less well explored, comes from about twice this depth and may correspond with his deepest concentration. It is also known that many of the species composing this deep layer, in the region where it has been demonstrated, are very wide distribution elsewhere. As an example of this wide distribution, Table 7–8 shows the known distribution of the various caridean decapods recorded by Chase from off Bermuda. The wide distribution of the species is indicated by the fact that these figures cover a total of only 33 species. The inadequacy of our knowledge of these mid-depth forms is also indicated, for of the 33 species, 8 were described for the first time.

TABLE 7–8

Bermuda Planktonic Caridea Recorded from Other Areas

(Chase, 1940)

Area	Number of Species
Sargasso Sea	4
North Atlantic, north and west of the Gulf Stream	6
Off the coast of Ireland	5
Eastern North Atlantic—Bay of Biscay to Cape Verde Islands	11
Mediterranean	2
Bahamas and West Indies	9
Equatorial Atlantic	11
South Atlantic	2
Off the Cape of Good Hope	6
Indian Ocean	15
Malay Archipelage and Philippine Islands to Japan	9
South Pacific	4
Hawaiian Islands	5
Eastern Pacific—California to Peru	6

Very little is known of the ecology of these forms. Probably at least some of them execute a diurnal migration, although it would appear that the deeper-living ones could not receive sufficient illumination to control a diurnal rhythm. However, Waterman et al. (1939) have demonstrated the existence of extensive diurnal migration in animals living, in the daytime, as deep as 800 meters, the diurnal range being 200 to 400 and perhaps even 600 meters. Fig. 7–10 shows the results for the decapod *Gennadas elegans*. Sonic methods have indicated diurnal migration of plankton as deep as 1000 meters in the daytime.

We have rather more information with regard to the concentration of zooplankton which comprises the peak at about 800 meters in Fig. 7–9. There is now little doubt that the echoes received by the sonic recording apparatus are reflected by zooplankton. Various authors have suggested fishes, cephalopods, or euphausids as the organisms responsible, and there is still no conclusive evidence to settle this. From the physical aspects, fishes, with their highly reflecting swim bladders, seem the most likely, although from the biological point of view much of the evidence points toward the euphausids. It is, of course, possible that the echoes come from fishes and that these are predators which follow the movements of the euphausids very closely. It may also be that echoes return from different types of organisms in different places, and this is almost certainly true of some shallow-water echoes. Whatever the source, these scattering layer records provide very valuable information concerning the details of diurnal migration.

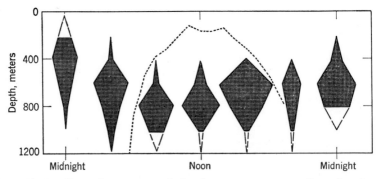

Figure 7–10. Diurnal migration of the deep-sea crustacean *Gennadas elegans.* The dotted line shows surface illuminations, and the broken lines show doubtful values. (After Waterman et al., 1939.)

Under the simplest conditions, this layer moves vertically in the daytime in such a way as to remain at a constant illumination. This must involve almost continuous movement throughout the day, since, at these depths, there is only a brief period around noon when the light is not changing rather rapidly (Fig. 5–11). Records at night are less complete, but they show that the layer has moved close to the surface, and, in one instance it was shown to adjust its level there in correlation with moonlight. Such simple conditions are found only where there is very little thermal stratification, however, as in the Mediterranean. In the Atlantic, where a change of several degrees centigrade is involved during the migration, cold water apparently acts as a barrier to continued descent during the morning, and the layer remains at a constant level throughout the middle of the day, beginning to rise again as the illumination decreases in the afternoon. This is shown in the examples in Fig. 5–13. When the diurnal cycle is presented in the form shown in Fig. 7–11, with temperature and illumination as the coordinates, it appears that there may be a sharp break between illumination and temperature as the factors controlling vertical movement. Furthermore, a lower level of illumination is more often followed during the evening ascent than during the morning descent. Finally, it is apparent that the animals comprising the layer are able to move vertically more than fast enough to be able to keep pace with the changing illumination. The fact that the depth at which arrest of descent occurs follows roughly the isotherms, being shallower where cold water comes closer to the surface (Fig. 5–14) provides further evidence that temperature forms the barrier to continued descent.

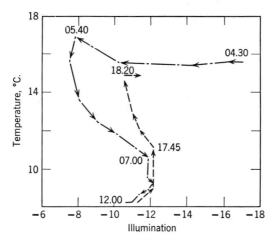

Figure 7–11. The diurnal migration of the scattering layer, plotted in terms of temperature and illumination. The illumination decreases from left to right. (After Moore, 1950.)

In connection with the geographic and vertical distribution of euphausids, the possible source of this scattering layer, Moore (1952) suggests that a combination of temperature and illumination is sufficient to define the observed distributions of the species that have been studied. At the day level, too high a temperature might necessitate an impossible extensive migration before an allowable temperature was reached. On the other hand, too low a temperature arrests descent into still colder water and necessitates tolerance of increased illumination. As a factor expressing the joint action of temperature and illumination at these depths, the value of T_{I-12} is used, this being the temperature at the depth at which 10^{-12} illumination occurs at noon in summer. The illumination scale is based on a value of 100 arbitrary units at the surface with overhead sunlight. In the same way, temperature at the night levels is considered to be limiting, too low a value possibly restricting feeding rate and too high a value either reducing the period during which the organisms can remain in the food-rich upper layers or else restricting them to deeper and cooler, but less rich, levels. Maximum summer surface temperatures are used as a measure of this factor. When the values of these two factors are calculated for different parts of the ocean, and the abundance of different species is plotted using T_{I-12} and T_s as ordinates, it is found that each has a characteristic pattern, as seen in Fig. 7–12. Generalized curves were produced relating the "survival index" of an organism to departure from optimal temperature conditions. A second series of curves then showed the combined effect of the departure from optimum temperature of the type occurring in an alternating climate, such as that encountered by the zooplankton in the course of its diurnal migration. In this case, it was assumed that the over-all survival index in a given locality was the product of the indices for the day and the night conditions. The "survival index" is a deliberately vague term comparable with the "prosperité" of Fischer-Piette (1948) and intended to parallel the degree of dominance of the species in a particular population. The North Atlantic distribution of one species of euphausid was calculated, basing the local values of its survival index on these generalized curves and on known local physical conditions of illumination and temperature; the calculated distribution was found to agree reasonably well with that observed from actual net hauls. It seems probable, then, that the two factors considered, namely T_{I-12} and T_s, are those mainly responsible for the distribution and relative abundance of many euphausids. One interesting point emerging from this consideration of the role of temperature is that, to meet the observed facts, most species must have two optimum temperatures, and the ideal conditions are those in which one is encountered at the day level and the other at the night level. The beneficial effects of an alternation of temperature have already been demonstrated in some other animals and Allee et al. (1949) go so far as to say that "in the laboratory organisms exposed to variable temperatures frequently, perhaps usually show accelerated development as compared with those held at a constant temperature of the same value, if other conditions remain equal." Such an advantage from alternating temperature may well lie behind the diurnal migration of so many animals, a process which has not previously been very convincingly explained.

In more northerly waters, Einarsson (1945) has shown that the distribution of euphausids may be accounted for in terms of temperature

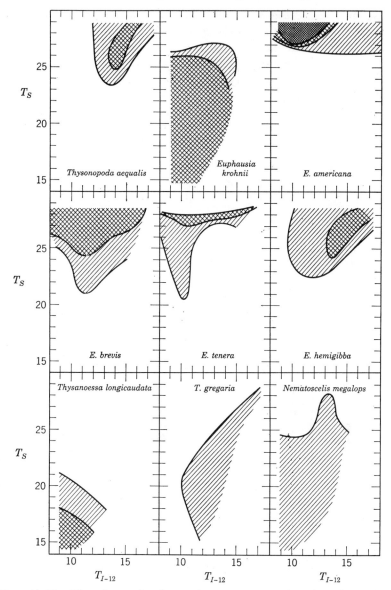

Figure 7–12. The relative abundance of various species of euphausids in relation to the local surface temperature and deep temperature. The latter is expressed as the temperature at the depth reached by a specified level of illumination at noon. Each species is absent in localities where the conditions correspond to those indicated in the unshaded areas and is most abundant in the most heavily shaded areas. (After Moore, 1950.)

and salinity, and in the Antarctic, John (1936) has similarly shown the restriction of the southern species to particular water masses (Fig. 7–13). Euphausids may comprise a large part of the diet of the whalebone whales, and the concentration of the best whaling grounds in areas rich in euphausids has already been referred to. Euphausids are long-lived among plankton animals, northern species living for 3 or more years. During this time they may be carried long distances

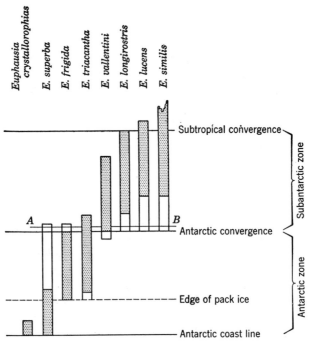

Figure 7–13. The distribution of antarctic euphausids in relation to water masses. The shaded areas represent normal ranges, and the unshaded areas possible ranges. (After John, 1936.)

by the current systems. In the Antarctic it appears that there is a regular cycle in which the immatures and adults are, in general, carried into lower latitudes by the shallower water movements, and the eggs are returned to high latitudes by deeper, southward-flowing water movements.

In discussing the effects of temperature, it was pointed out that there are likely to be marginal zones around the area inhabited by a particular species in which temperatures are suitable for survival but not for breeding. Such areas depend for repopulation on a supply of immigrant larvae or adults. An animal with a short life span may not have time to be carried far from its breeding area before it dies and may, therefore, not attain a region where temperature would limit survival. Euphausids, with their relatively long life span, however, have the opportunity of being carried long distances by the currents, and Einarsson (1945) has shown that they may have extensive fringes of non-breeding population.

Euphausids have received particular emphasis here because more is known about them than about the other inhabitants of this zooplankton concentration. It must be realized, however, that other

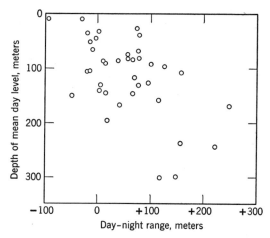

Figure 7–14. The relation, for a number of zooplankton species, between the depth occupied in the daytime and the extent and direction of diurnal migration. (After Moore, 1949.)

forms, many of them with equally extensive diurnal migration, play their part. These include other crustacea such as mysids, amphipods, and copepods as well as chaetognaths, cephalopods, fishes, and other forms. Diurnal migration is a widespread phenomenon in the upper waters, although the extent of the migration is more limited. Figure 5–16 shows the diurnal movement of this upper plankton as a whole, and Fig. 7–14 shows how, considering all species together, those that live deepest during the day have the greatest range of diurnal migration. It also brings out the interesting point that some of the shallowest of them show no diurnal migration at all, and a few even exhibit a reversed type of migration, in which they ascend in the daytime and descend slightly at night. Mackintosh (1934) illustrates such an apparent reversed diurnal migration pattern in the amphipod *Primno macropa* in the Antarctic. Figure 7-15 shows the variation through-out the day in the catches of this species in a shallow net. Some species show a variation in day level with the cloudiness of the sky, descending deeper on a sunny day. This reaction appears at present

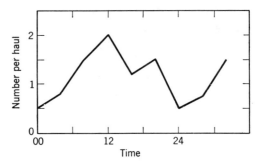

Figure 7-15. "Reverse"—type diurnal migration as shown by the antarctic amphipod *primino macropa.* (After Mackintosh, 1934.)

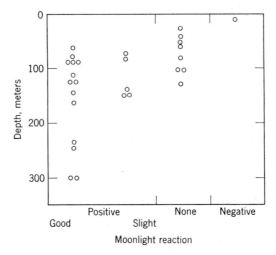

Figure 7-16. The relation, for various species of zooplankton, between the nature and extent of their reaction to moonlight (by vertical movement) and the level occupied by them in the daytime. A positive moonlight reaction indicates swarming to the surface at night at full moon, a negative reaction swarming to the surface at new moon. (After Moore, 1949.)

to be specific and not correlated with the depth at which the species lives. Many species also show a greater abundance at the surface at night at full moon than at new moon; and in this case there is a definite correlation with both the depth at which they live in the daytime and the extent of their diurnal migration (Figs. 7–16, 7–17). The deepest-living species, and those with the greatest diurnal migration, show the greatest tendency to appear at the surface on a moonlit night. Finally, if vertical spread or diffuseness is measured by the difference in depth between that above which 25 per cent of the population of a given species occurs and that at which 75 per cent occurs, then the deeper-living forms are found to have a greater spread than the shallower ones (Fig. 7–18).

Diurnal migration is just as prominent a feature in the behavior of

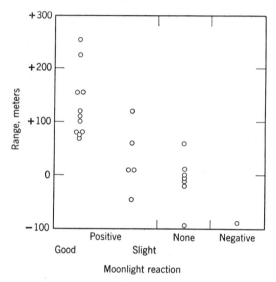

Figure 7–17. The relation, for various zooplankton species, between the extent of diurnal migration and the reaction to moonlight. The latter is expressed as in Fig. 7–16. (After Moore, 1949.)

many of the nektonic fishes and cephalopods as it is in that of the plankton. In fact, the extent of the diurnal migration may, apparently, be much greater. This is well illustrated by the bathypelagic fish *C. sloanei* in the Pacific (Fig. 7–19). Ranging down 2500 to 3000 meters in the daytime, this species was not taken below 500 meters at night (Haffner, 1952). In the Atlantic, this same species ranged from 1000 to 1500 meters in the daytime and from the surface to 600 meters at night.

The importance of diurnal migration in the life of zooplankton appears to be felt in many aspects. It allows them, to some extent, to avoid conditions of illumination that appear to be harmful to them. It allows them to feed in the food-rich upper layers, when, according

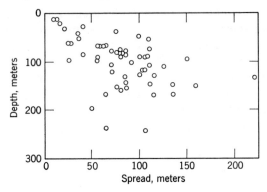

Figure 7–18. The relation, for various zooplankton species, between the degree of vertical diffuseness (spread) and the level occupied in the daytime. (After Moore, 1949.)

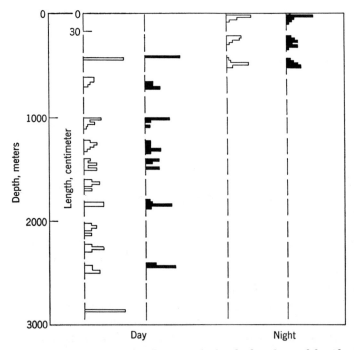

Figure 7–19. The vertical distribution of the bathypelagic fish *Chauliodus sloanei* in the daytime and at night in the Pacific and in the Sulu Sea. The small groups of histograms indicate the size distribution at the different levels. Besides showing very extensive diurnal migration, these indicate that both day and night the smaller fish are concentrated closer to the surface than the larger ones. (After Haffner, 1952.)

to some authors, the darkness gives them some degree of immunity from their predators, and retreat to poorer but safer layers during the daytime. On the other hand it carries them through a diurnal cycle of very widely varying temperatures and other conditions, the full significance of which is not yet known. One suggested mechanism linked with diurnal migration is that of avoiding areas unsuitable to phytoplankton production.

It is generally found that where phytoplankton is rich, the zooplankton tends to be poor in quantity, and vice versa. The classic explanation, that is in all probability very often true, is that abundant

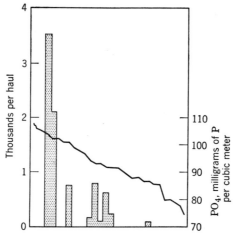

Figure 7–20. Antarctic shallow stations, arranged in order of phosphate content, to show the correlation between number of euphausids (blocks) and phosphate (solid line). (After Hardy and Gunther, 1935.)

zooplankton, by its food requirements, prevents the development of a rich phytoplankton population in its neighborhood. Where, for some reason, zooplankton is sparse, the phytoplankton may have an opportunity to flourish. In the Loch Striven area, already referred to, there is a delay of several weeks between the spring outburst of phytoplankton and that of copepods, which are the main herbivorous zooplankton feeding on it. This is to be expected, since the diatoms can reproduce very much more rapidly than the copepods. Such a situation is improbable, however, in the case of long-lived and slower-reproducing animals such as euphausids. Hardy and Gunther (1935) have shown that such a relationship exists between phytoplankton and euphausids in the Antarctic. This is shown in Fig. 7–20, in which the decrease in the phosphate content of the water is used as an index of the extent of phytoplankton production. They showed that it is a good index, decreasing in proportion as the phytoplankton increases. Among the Antarctic copepods, they found that three major groups could be distinguished. In the first and largest group, there was marked absence from areas of rich phytoplankton and all the species showed considerable diurnal migration. In the second group there was very uniform distribution and no correlation with abundance of phytoplankton; the species in this group showed little or no diurnal migration. The third group contained two species, one of which was found in

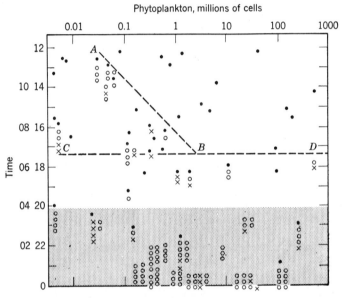

Phytoplankton, millions of cells

Figure 7–21. The extent of diurnal migration of antarctic zooplankton, taken in shallow hauls, in relation to phytoplankton concentration. For explanation, see text. (After Hardy and Gunther, 1935.)

maximum numbers in high, but not extremely high, phytoplankton concentrations, and the other in the highest concentrations. These two species both underwent diurnal migration but remained near the surface at night for a very much longer period than did those in the first group. They also showed that, for the species exhibiting this "exclusions," where there is a rich phytoplankton the animals are present in deeper levels below the phytoplankton, although absent from the phytoplankton layer. In fact, they were taken closer to the surface in the daytime and were taken in greater numbers near the surface at night in inverse proportion to the amount of phytoplankton present. Figure 7–21 shows the catches of these animals plotted against time of day and amount of phytoplankton for the upper layers. Figure 7–22 shows a similar plot for a level below that of the phytoplankton. In both, a dot indicates a haul of less than 50 animals, an "x" a catch of over 50 animals, and a circle one of over 100. The trend of the line *AB* indicates their appearance in the upper waters nearer midday where the phytoplankton is poor and their late ascent where it is rich.

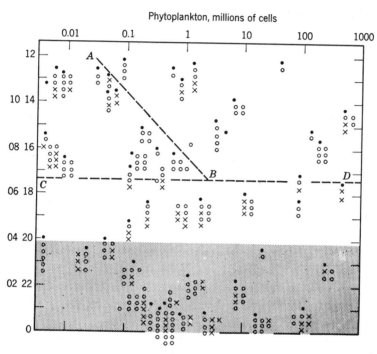

Figure 7–22. Diurnal migration of antarctic zooplankton, taken in deep hauls, represented as in Fig. 7–21. (After Hardy and Gunther, 1935.)

They point out that there is usually some difference in currents between the upper layers, where the phytoplankton is, and the deeper layers inhabited by the zooplankton in question in the daytime. This difference may be in either direction or velocity or both. In either case, an animal that executed a diurnal migration would spend part of its time in one current and part in the other, and as a result would not ascend on a succeeding night into the same mass of overlying water as on the previous night. Figure 7–23 illustrated this with currents of different directions. Here the light solid lines indicate surface current, the light broken ones deep current, and the heavy lines the course of a plankton in successive days in such a situation. Where the currents were similar in direction but differed in velocity, the direction of drift would be the same, but there would still be a differential movement between the organism and the surface water. Since the phytoplankton is in the upper water, any diurnally migrating animal will tend to move horizontally relative to the phytoplankton. Furthermore, if there is an area of concentrated phytoplankton, an animal which varies its normal diurnal pattern by either not rising to as shallow a level at night where the phytoplankton patch is, or else

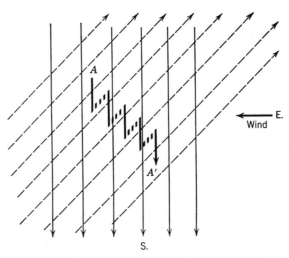

Figure 7–23. Diagram showing how diurnally migrating plankton, by taking advantage of differential water movements, may travel in a direction different from that of the water. For further explanation see text. (After Hardy and Gunther, 1935.)

rising to the normal level but not remaining as long as usual, will tend to concentrate away from the area. Similarly, one that ascended to a shallower level or tended to remain near the surface longer where the phytoplankton was rich would tend to concentrate there. Finally, one that did not undergo diurnal migration would show no correlation with phytoplankton abundance. The mechanism thus fits well with the observed facts.

In an earlier section we have discussed the presence in sea water of substances that have a harmful or deterrent action on animals (Lucas, 1947). It is not unreasonable that such a substance might be present where there is excessive phytoplankton, and it is, in fact, known that some phytoplankton, such as that which causes "red tide," may be fatal to animals in the neighborhood. The relative merits of the "grazing" and "exclusion" theories have been much discussed, and the answer will probably be found to lie in local conditions, the one being operative in some areas and the other in others.

The plankton of the upper oceanic zones may be subject to considerable seasonal variation in both quantity and quality. The changing conditions that give rise to this have been more fully explored in inshore waters and will therefore be discussed in a later section. In general, however, it may be said that seasonal changes are less pronounced in oceanic waters than in inshore waters, and less in tropical seas than in cold seas. Figure 7–24 shows the seasonal change in the total quantity of larger zooplankton in one area of the Antarctic, one of the few open-sea areas that has been fully examined throughout the

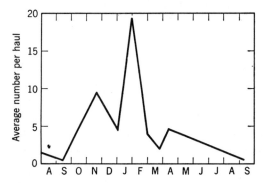

Figure 7–24. The seasonal cycle of zooplankton in the neighborhood of South Georgia. (After Mackintosh, 1934.)

year. By contrast, almost no seasonal change in total zooplankton was found in Bermuda waters. The average volumes per haul in three cruises made respectively in December, May, and July were 13.2, 14.6, and 13.9 cc. (Moore, 1949).

Since illumination varies seasonably with the changing altitude of the sun, the day level of zooplankton would be expected to vary seasonally in those species and in those areas where illumination is the chief factor controlling their depth. In some species, as we have shown, temperature may be the controlling factor and, except close to the surface, this would normally show little seasonal variation. Nikitine (1929) (Figs. 5–28, 5–29) has demonstrated such a seasonal shift in both the upper and the lower limits of vertical distribution of a number of species. Bogorov (1946) has shown that in the Arctic there is normal diurnal migration in the autumn when there is an alternation of day and night, but during the summer period of permanent daylight such migration ceases and the zooplankton remains at a constant level. He does not present any data on the behavior during the winter period of permanent darkness.

There is a further complication in the fact that individuals of a given species frequently differ in their vertical distribution according to their state of maturity, sex, and brood. In many zooplankton there is a tendency for the younger stages to live closer to the surface than the adults. Since the food requirements of the young are relatively greater than those of the adults, this might be advantageous in keeping them closer to their food supply in the upper waters. In some of those that pass through several generations during the year, the successive generations vary in level, the summer brood appearing to be less sensitive to light and occuring nearer the surface than those produced at other seasons. Russell (1933) has given an excellent example in his summary of the behavior of *Sagitta elegans*. *Sagitta* is an animal which passes through several generations in the year, possibly five or six according to the species. During November to January there is no breeding. The adults of the different broods grow to different sizes, the adults appearing in April and May being the largest on the average. During the spring months the *Sagitta* are living in the upper water layers in the daytime, appearing to dwell around a depth at which a light intensity of a little below 20 k.m.c. will be found. At the same time the larger individuals tềnd to seek lower intensities and thus go deeper in the water which is consonant with the increased sensitively with advancing age. At this period of the year (April and May), on dull days the *Sagitta* will be nearer the surface than on fine days. The brood succeeding in June appears to show a similar habit and on very bright days may retire almost to the bottom itself. But the new broods appearing in July and August show a marked difference, not avoiding on bright days those depths in the upper water layers where intensities of 20 k.m.c and over may be found. At this time of year if the day is dull they appear to be indifferent to the light and may be found in almost equal numbers at any depth. The offspring of the last spawning brood in September in *S. elegans* and October in *S. setosa* perhaps (if the bottom net results be rightly construed) leave the upper layers and keep near the bottom until the following February, when they are mature and ready to spawn, at which time they appear to rise in the water again, as indicated by the sudden increase in numbers of *S. elegans* in the oblique hauls in February. Throughout the year, at any rate in the summer months, the vertical distribution of *Sagitta* changes daily when night comes on, the animals either migrating right to the surface at dusk or exhibiting other types of distribution ending in an even distribution at night according to their position in the water on the previous day." Russell also quotes similar changes in behavior in the summer in the copepod *Calanus finmarchicus,* the polychaete *Tomopteris helgolandica* and the postlarval young of teleostean fish.

Some aspects of the ecology of the plankton of the upper zones can best be discussed in connection with the inshore plankton. This is particularly applicable to the question of productivity. On the other hand, certain characteristics such as diurnal migration are better seen

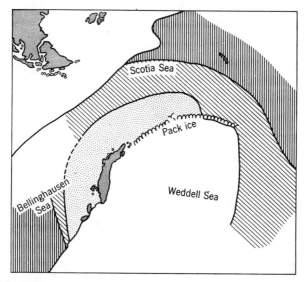

Figure 7–25. The quantitative distribution of the larger zooplankton in the Antarctic. Density of shading indicates abundance of plankton. White areas were not sampled. (After Mackintosh, 1934.)

in the extended vertical range available beyond the continental shelf. The zooplankton of oceanic waters is, on the whole, less abundant than that inshore. Clarke (1940) found that, in the western North Atlantic, the average standing crop for the area was about four times as great, by volume, in slope water as in oceanic water, and about four times as abundant in coastal as in slope water. On the other hand, as will be seen later in Riley's work, the standing crop is not the best index of productivity, and the relative productivities of these waters is much closer than the standing crop figures suggest. This must be remembered in considering the significance of the following figures. The standing crop varies widely in different parts of the ocean. Figure 7–25 shows distribution, in terms of numbers of organisms, in

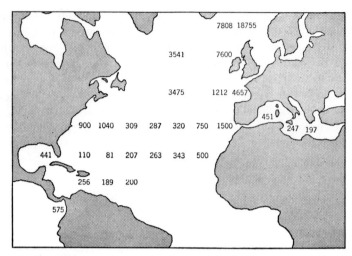

Figure 7–26. The quantitative distribution of the larger zooplankton in the North Atlantic surface waters as represented by the volume (cubic centimeters) of standard hauls. (After Jespersen, 1923.)

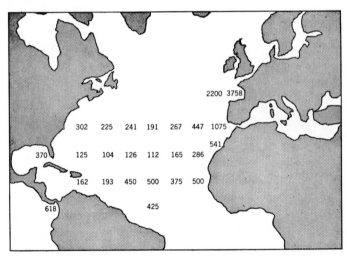

Figure 7–27. The quantitative distribution of the larger zooplankton in the North Atlantic deeper waters as represented by the volume (cubic centimeters) of standard hauls. (After Jespersen, 1923.)

part of the Antarctic, and Figs. 7–26 and 7–27 show quantity, by volume, at two depths in the North Atlantic. In general, the colder waters have a much larger standing crop than do tropical waters. This difference is only partly offset by the facts that most of the polar values were estimated during the summer season of high productivity

and that, in the clearer tropical waters, plankton production extends
to a greater depth. The connection between the richness of the
plankton and hydrographic conditions will be discussed in connection
with the phytoplankton.

TABLE 7–9

**Oceanic Distribution of Holoplanktonic Animals and
Meroplanktonic Coelenterates**

Number of Species in Oceanic Areas

Organisms	Arctic	Arctic-boreal and Boreal	Ant-arctic	Subant-arctic	Bipolar Epiplank-tonic	Cosmo-politan	Warm	Deep Sea	Total
Coelenterata									
Antho-, Lepto- and Scyphomedusae	20	100	10	15	—	—	370	20	535
Trachy- and Narco-medusae	4	10	3	6	—	—	90	21	134
Siphonophora									
Calycophorae	—	—	2	—	1	—	64	5	72
Physophorae	—	1	2		—	—	29	2	34
Ctenophora	1	2	2	1	—	2	69?	3	80?
Nemertea	—	—	—	—	—	—	—	34	34
Polychaeta									
Tomopteridae	—	1?	4?		1	—	38	?	44
Chaetognatha	—	2	2		2	—	18	6	30
Crustacea									
Cladocera	—	1	—	—	(3)	—	3	—	7
Copepoda	7	10	32	5	1(5)	10	489	195	754
Amphipoda									
Hyperiidea	2	—	10	—	—	2	250	28	292
Gammaridea	7	—	—	—	—	—	20	17	44
Euphausiacea	—	6	2	7	(1)	—	46	23	85
Mollusca									
Pteropoda			2	1(1)?		—	44		
Thecosomata	—	—						3	51
Gymnosomata	—	1	2	(1)?		—	37	?	41
Heteropoda	—	—	—	—	—		90	—	90
Tunicata									
Appendicularia	2	1	6	—	1	1	48	3	61
Thaliacea									
Doliolidae	—	—	1?	—	—		11	—	12
Salpidae	—	—	1	—	—	—	24	—	25
Pyrosomidae	—	—	—	—	—	—	8	—	8
Total	178		115	17	15		1753	360	2433
Total excluding mero-planktonic medusae	58		90	17	15		1378	340	1898

The nature of ocean currents varies greatly with depth, and so the
depth normally inhabited by a species is likely to have considerable
bearing on its geographical distribution. Russel (1935) has compiled the data on the oceanic distribution of certain zooplankton
(Table 7–9).

This table brings out several points. First, there is a much greater number of species in warmer oceanic waters than in colder ones. Second, if we except the meroplanktonic medusae and the essentially bottom-living gammarid amphipods, all groups show a preponderance of southern over northern cold-water forms. Bipolarity in its original sense refers to the discontinuous distribution of a species which occurs in both the Arctic and Antarctic but not in between. Russell's term "bipolar-epiplanktonic" refers to species that occur near the surface in polar waters and in the deeper, colder water of the connecting equatorial regions. From a consideration of the shallow and deep circulation of the oceans (Figs. 7–28), he shows that a species which evolved in the tropics into a deep-water, and hence a cold-water, form, would tend to be carried by the currents into the antarctic regions where it

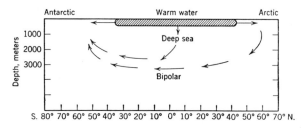

Figure 7–28. Diagram of the north-south circulation in the Atlantic to show how arctic species may spread to the Antarctic and so become bipolar in distribution, although species evolving in the Antarctic are more likely to remain confined to that region. (After Russell, 1935.)

would find comparable temperature conditions nearer the surface. There would be considerably less current to carry it northward to the arctic regions. A species that evolved in the arctic waters, if it were able to live at a considerable depth, would also tend to be carried across the equator into the Antarctic. An antarctic form would not, however, tend to be carried into the Arctic. On the basis of this reasoning, it would be expected that more of the species that are restricted to one pole would be found in the Antarctic than in the Arctic, since more of the northern species would have become bipolar in the course of time. Since such transit from the Arctic to the Antarctic requires the ability to live in deep water in the tropic area, it is interesting to note that two of the groups which have no bipolar species, the Tunicata and Ctenophora, are groups of essentially shallow-living species. Deep-sea species are, as we have said, more likely to be carried south than north, whereas shallow-living species, if they can withstand the more drastic temperature changes involved, may be carried either way from the tropics. Bipolarity, on the other hand, is more likely to be found in shallow-living species, provided they are capable of living deeper for the requisite time to make the pole-to-pole passage. In support of this, Russell presents an analysis of the known data on copepods. He considers as deep-sea genera those in which more than 50 per cent of the species are deep sea, and as surface genera those in which more than 50 per cent of the species are shallow-living. The results are given in Table 7–10.

TABLE 7–10

Distribution of Surface and Deep-Sea Genera

	Number	Total Number of Species	Number of Arctic and Boreal Species	Number of Antarctic and Subarctic Species	Number of Bipolar Species
Surface genera	76	525	13	19	5
Deep-sea genera	36	228	3	18	1

Although the numbers are small, it is clear that there are relatively more bipolar species among surface genera, and that the inequality between numbers of species in the Antarctic and Arctic is greatest in the deep-sea genera. Thorson has commented on the fact that, despite the absence of planktonic larvae there are also more species of bottom-living invertebrates in the Antarctic than in the Arctic.

Much less is known of the ecology of oceanic phytoplankton than of that of the zooplankton. However, since oceanic phytoplankton is restricted to the upper layers, its ecology is more comparable with that of coastal-water phytoplankton, and much of the data to be given in that section would probably be applicable here also. In particular, discussion of the work on phytoplankton productivity will be deferred and included later in this chapter. Probably our most comprehensive knowledge of oceanic phytoplankton is for the antarctic area, as described in various papers in the Discovery Reports.

It will be realized that working conditions in the Antarctic were such as to make year-round observations difficult. In addition, it was not possible to visit the same area at as frequent intervals as could be done in the temperate plankton surveys. However, in the neighborhood of South Georgia it was possible to show that there was a marked seasonal variation in the phytoplankton, with a maximum in the southern summer and some evidence of a spring and autumn outburst. For the various areas of the Antarctic, although the details were obscured, the great difference between summer and winter was clearly shown (Fig. 7–29). The zooplankton also showed a summer increase following the spring diatom outburst, followed by lower numbers in winter. This is illustrated for the commoner copepods by the data shown in Table 5–5, taken from Hardy and Gunther (1935). With the peculiar light conditions in polar regions, diurnal migration is frequently less pronounced than in warmer seas, and Bogorov (1946) found that it ceased altogether in the Arctic during the period of continuous daylight.

The antarctic phytoplankton differs from that of warmer waters both in its enormous richness and in the great predominance of dia-

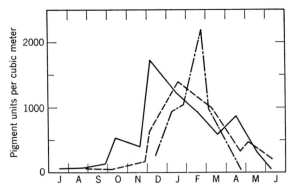

Figure 7–29. The seasonal phytoplankton cycle in three antarctic regions. The solid line represents the northern region, the broken line the intermediate region, and the dot-dash line the southern region. (After Hart, 1942:)

toms over dinoflagellates or other forms. This is brought out in the data for a series of stations shown in Table 7–11 (Hart, 1934).

The importance of the very small nannoplankton in the phytoplankton has probably been greatly underestimated in the past. The forms involved are so small that they pass through fine silk plankton nets and can be collected only by filtration or contrifuging. Most of them, having no protective skeleton, break up very easily and so are difficult to handle. Atkins (1945) compared the annual productivity in the English Channel, as estimated from phosphate turnover, with that estimated from silicate turnover. The results of this preliminary survey showed that only a comparatively small fraction of the photosynthetic organisms could be ones possessing siliceous skeletons. The remainder were, presumably, nannoplankton. Knight-Jones and Walne (1951) made estimates of the abundance of a very small member of the nannoplankton, *Chromulina pusilla,* only 1.5 μ in diameter, in the English Channel. This was found in all water samples examined, including ones from creeks, estuaries, and the open sea. Concentrations determined by a dilution method, and believed to be underestimated, ranged from 50 to 3500 per milliliter with an average value of 1000. In examples quoted by the authors, plant pigment determinations have shown that 90 per cent of the phytoplankton may pass through a fine silk net with a 40×50 μ mesh, and as

TABLE 7–11

Geographic Distribution of Phytoplankton Groups

(Hart, 1934)

Latitude	Diatomales		Dinoflagellata		Schizophyceae	
	Total	Per Cent	Total	Per Cent	Total	Per Cent
57°36′S	11,046,400	99.88	12,800	0.12	—	—
53°34½′S	6,249,200	100.00	—	—	—	—
49°58¾′S	354,600	98.42	5,700	1.58	—	—
44°52′S	14,700	89.09	1,800	10.91	—	—
43°08′S	52,200	76.99	15,600	23.01	—	—
38°10½′S	1,200	26.67	2,400	53.33	900	20.00
34°08′S	—	—	1,800	100.00	—	—
31°16¼′S	4,200	35.00	7,800	65.00	—	—
26°06½′S	22,500	81.53	5,100	18.47	—	—
21°13′S	2,000	20.83	7,600	79.17	—	—
15°37′S	400	8.69	3,600	78.26	600	13.05
09°47′S	2,600	26.00	7,400	74.00	—	—
03°17¾′S	800	2.98	6,000	22.39	20,000	74.63
02°59′N	5,400	7.11	4,600	6.05	66,000	86.84
14°27¼′N	1,600	12.31	9,000	69.23	2,400	18.46

much as 40 per cent through a Whatman number 2 filter paper. Preliminary experiments in the Florida Current area have shown that the phytoplankton retained by a filter may be as much as a thousand times, by weight, that retained by a silk net. It is apparent then, that our ideas on phytoplankton abundance and production, which are based largely on diatoms obtained from silk nets, may have to be drastically revised in the light of future knowledge. It should be remembered, also, that these nannoplanktonic organisms have for a few species such as oyster larvae and *Calanus* been proved to be an ideal food, and possibly the principal natural food supply.

Among the diatoms, at least, there is a general difference in form between those of cold waters and those of warm waters. Hendey

(1937) expresses this as follows: "Broadly speaking, it may be said that a warm-water diatom flora is one whose individuals, under a given set of chemical and physical conditions, seek to obtain maximum cubical capacity with a minimum of surface area, whereas a cold-water diatom flora, existing under an entirely different set of conditions, seeks to obtain maximum surface area for a minimum cubical capacity for its individuals." The question of the relation of form in plankton to temperature is an involved one, since there are other forms in which increased surface area appears to be associated with a warm, rather than a cold, habitat. For non-motile forms, increase in spination increases the relative surface area and so retards sinking or flotation when the organism has a different specific gravity from the medium. If it is heavier than the surrounding water, mere slowing of the sinking rate is not sufficient to maintain the organism within the photic zone, but turbulence may be expected to bring some individuals back toward the surface and so provide a breeding stock to replace those that have sunk. Since an increase in temperature from 0 to 25°C. is sufficient to halve the viscosity of sea water, it would appear that phytoplankton might be in danger of sinking faster in tropical waters than in the Arctic and so need some adaptive mechanism to compensate for this. However, this applies only when the phytoplankton and the surrounding water differ in specific gravity. If a diatom can adjust its specific gravity to correspond with the seasonal and other changes it encounters in the water, the difficulty is met. One way of adjusting specific gravity is the inclusion within the test of droplets of liquid lighter than sea water—either water in which there is an accumulation of light ions or oil droplets. If this is done, increased relative internal capacity such as is described in warm-water diatoms would be an advantage. Since the siliceous test of diatoms is heavier than water, some control could be attained by modifying its thickness; it is a fact that tropical diatoms tend to be relatively thinner-shelled than antarctic forms (Hendey, 1937).

Gross and Zeuthen (1948) have discussed the possibility of diatoms' regulating their specific gravity in accordance with varying external conditions. They found that actively growing diatoms have the same specific gravity as sea water, and resting spores are heavier. If this is true, it is possible that under certain conditions, such as during the auxospore stage, diatoms may be lighter than sea water. Hardy and Gunther (1935) produced data (Fig. 7–30) which they interpret as indicating an actual diurnal migration of the diatom *Coscinodiscus bouvet,* in which the diatoms move upward in the daytime and downward at night. If they are correct in their interpretation of the data,

then the process would apparently have to be due to a diurnal modification of specific gravity. Their migration, however, is of the order
of 100 meters, and it is hard to see how this could occur. Gross and
Zeuthen (1948) give a settling rate of about 7 meters in 24 hours for
resting spores of the diatom *Ditylium Brightwelli*. It is true that

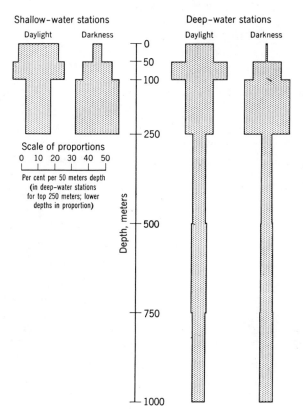

Figure 7–30. Apparent diurnal migration in the antarctic diatom *Coscinodiscus
bouvet*. Day and night vertical distribution at shallow and deep stations. (After
Hardy and Gunther, 1935.)

Coscinodiscus might settle faster by reason of its greater size, and
possibly also its better streamlining, but a 100 meters in less than 12
hours still seems unaccountably large. An alternative possibility
would be that there was no actual change in level of the individual
diatoms, beyond some relatively slow settling, but that the population of the upper layers was heavily reduced each night by the invasion of diurnally migrating herbivores. During the daytime these
would be absent from the upper layers, feeding in the deeper levels,

TABLE 7–12

April	3°C.	*Thalassiosira nordenskioeldi*
		Porosira glacialis
		Chaetoceros diadema
May	6°C.	*C. debilis*
June	9°C.	*C. compressus*
August	12°C.	*C. constrictus*
		C. cinctus
		Skeletonema costatum

and meanwhile the daylight would be favoring the repopulation of the upper layers by reproducing diatoms.

Mainly on the basis of geographical distribution, it is known that certain phytoplankton groups and certain species within these groups are cold-water forms and others are characteristic of warm water.

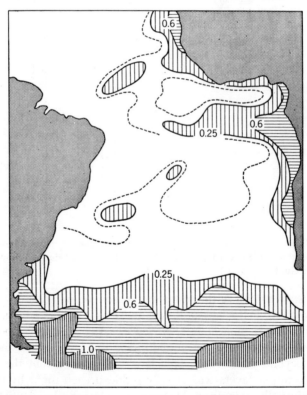

Figure 7–31. The distribution of phosphate in the South Atlantic, milligrams of P_2O_5 per cubic meter. (After Sverdrup et al., 1946.)

Some also are known to be eurythermic and others stenothermic. The increase in proportion of dinoflagellates to diatoms in warm water is an example of group differences. Evidence from relative time of maximum abundance within a given area may also indicate different optimum temperatures. Thus Gran and Braarud (1935) give the values in Table 7–12 for the Gulf of Maine.

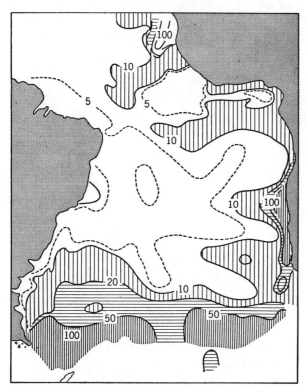

Figure 7–32. The distribution of total plankton in the South Atlantic, thousands of individuals per cubic meter. (After Sverdrup et al., 1946.)

Although there is an apparent correlation with temperature in such instances, it may be dangerous to assume that temperature is the principal determining factor in deciding which species shall dominate at a particular time. Other specific differences such as varying light requirements, varying response to high or low concentration of nutrient salts, and so on, may well be the cause in the seasonal succession of species.

The relation between phytoplankton production and nutrient salts will be discussed in more detail later, but we may note here the existence of an over-all correlation between oceanic plankton and the availability of nutrient salts.

Regions of upwelling, where extra amounts of nutrients are brought into the surface waters, are known to be areas also of great phytoplankton production. Sverdrup et al. (1946) give two charts (Figs. 7–31, 7–32) in which the parallel distribution of areas of high phosphate content and areas of high plankton content is obvious. In the same way, the nutrient-rich region of the Humboldt Current off the west coast of South America is known to be associated with upwelling

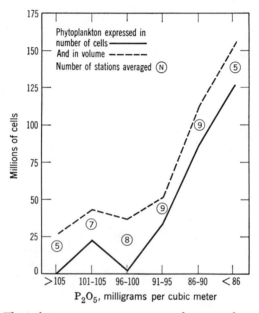

Figure 7–33. The relation, in antarctic waters, between the concentration of phytoplankton and that of phosphate. (After Hardy and Gunther, 1935.)

and particularly rich plankton growth. There is liable to be confusion here, however, because the amount of depletion of phosphate may also be used as an index of phytoplankton production. This can only be done, of course, if the normal phosphate content of the water is known, or if it is a case of comparing samples taken at different times in the same water mass. Figure 7–33, an example taken for a single area in the Antarctic, shows a fairly close correlation between increase in phytoplankton and decrease in phosphate.

In the warmer waters of the North Atlantic, the *Sargassum* community is peculiar in its ability to tolerate intense insolation. The alga itself includes several species of *Sargassum* (Winge, 1923; Hentschel, 1921; Timmermann, 1932) which reproduce almost entirely vegetatively. The weed floats at or close to the surface. If it is carried deeper, the floats implode and it then sinks rapidly. There is a considerable attached fauna including barnacles, bryozoa, and hydroids. Some of the latter are stated to be more or less restricted to one species of *Sargassum*. There is also a fauna crawling or sheltering within the weed, including nudibranchs, shrimps, the crab *Planes minutus,* and such fishes as *Syngnathus* and *Pterophryne.*

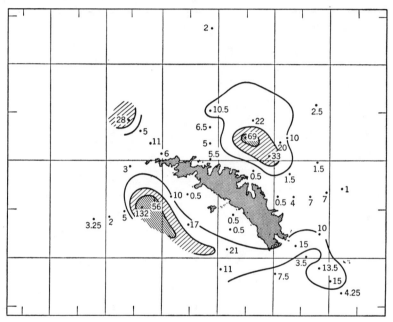

Figure 7–34. Chart of the South Georgia area of the Antarctic showing regions of rich phytoplankton. (After Hardy and Gunther, 1935.)

The weed provides some shelter from the sun, but, probably more important, a surface for attachment and place to hide. It circulates continuously in a rather limited region, mainly between about 20 and 40° north and from about 30° west to the American coast, and so remains under conditions that do not vary to any great extent.

Hardy (Hardy and Gunther, 1935) postulates that where there is mixing of different water masses, phytoplankton growth is stimulated, provided there are sufficient nutrients present. The suggestion is that the mixing results in changed conditions of temperature, etc., and possibly of specific limiting metabolites, thus stimulating the blooming of forms until then inhibited. He supports this by the correlation between the occurrence of rich phytoplankton areas off South Georgia and the areas in which water mass mixing is known to take place (Figs. 7–34, 7–35).

Brotskaja and Zenkevich (1939) have endeavored to show that, in northern seas, certain areas, such as the seas around Iceland, where different water masses meet, are particularly productive of phytoplankton, which in turn supports a particularly rich bottom fauna.

In the daytime, the extreme surface waters have only a very limited

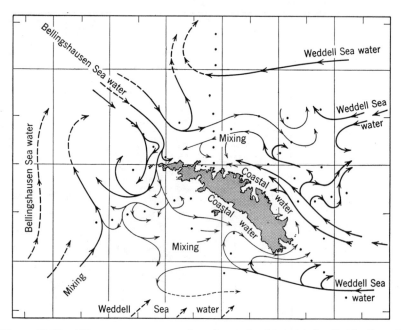

Figure 7–35. Water movements and regions of mixing in the South Georgia area. (After Hardy and Gunther, 1935.)

fauna and flora. At night diurnal migration may bring them a large temporary animal population. Of some seventy species of plankton from the upper waters of the Bermuda area, only two had their maximum concentration in the daytime in the top 25 meters. These were the chaetognath *Sagitta planktonis* and the siphonophore *Diphyes dispar.* Seven others had maximum concentration between 25 and 50 meters. These very shallow species tended to show either no diurnal migration or even a reversed one, with descent at night. Unlike the deeper species, their abundance at the surface at night tended to show no correlation with the phase of the moon, or else, in one case, to show a reversed relation. It appears, then, that their reactions to illumination are definitely different from those of animals living at lower illuminations (Moore, 1949). Phytoplankton growth also is very limited in these extreme surface levels, although, in parts of the North Atlantic, a floating flora of sargasso weed (*Sargassum* spp.) inhabits the water-air interface. This provides not only food but also shelter and attachment to a specialized fauna.

The oceanic nekton is composed mainly of fishes, cephalopods, and mammals. Of the ecology of the fishes, except for one or two such as the tuna, very little is known but the researches of the Discovery Expedition have yielded a considerable body of knowledge on the ecology of the southern whales. The various species of whales carry out very extensive migrations, the humpback even crossing the equator

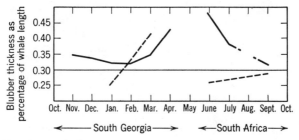

Figure 7–36. Seasonal changes in the blubber thickness of female fin whales in relation to their migrations between South Georgia and South Africa. The solid line represents individuals more than 20 meters long, and the broken lines those less than 18 meters. (After Mackintosh and Wheeler, 1929.)

during the southern winter and moving into high southern latitudes during the southern summer (Matthews, 1937). The blue and fin whales also migrate to a considerable extent, at least between the Antarctic and the South African coast. Sperm whales, which are characteristically warm-water forms, also may move into polar waters. The correlation between the concentration of blue and fin whales in South Georgia waters and the great masses of euphausids there has already been referred to. It appears that the whales fatten considerably in that area but find only a small supply of food in South African waters. This is reflected in the seasonal changes in the thickness of their blubber (Fig. 7–36) (Mackintosh and Wheeler, 1929). Perhaps the most surprising thing about these whales is their growth rate. Blue whales (Laurie, 1937) have a gestation period of 10 to 11 months and are born with a length of 23 feet. The lactation period is 6 to 7 months, and at 2 years they are sexually mature and have reached a length of about 78 feet. The oldest whale taken was about 30 years old. Ruud et al. (1950) give 3 to 7 years as the age of males at maturity, and 2 to 6 years for females. In any case, this high growth rate implies a very adequate supply of food.

One particular modification required in diving mammals, and for that matter in diving birds also, is connected with respiration. Their oxygen supply is intermittent and must be sufficient to last for the duration of a dive, and there might be a risk of "caisson sickness." Although the normal duration of a dive in whales is about 10 minutes, much longer periods have been recorded. Usually the whale expires and inspires only once after a dive. The lung content is not much higher than in land mammals, but exhalation is more complete (Laurie,

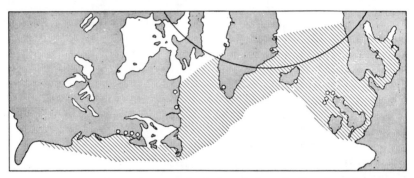

Figure 7–37. Breeding colonies (○) of the plankton-feeding Leach's petrel in the North Atlantic, and the regions of rich plankton (hatched area). (After Atkinson, 1948.)

1933; Scholander, 1940). The oxygen content of the blood is not particularly high, but that of the muscle may be seven times that of beef. In some diving mammals it is known that submergence is accompanied by a reduction in rate of heart beat from 80 to 10 per minute, together with a vasomotor reflex which cuts off the circulation to the main muscle mass. The available oxygen is thus conserved, during the dive, for essential processes. The muscles, during this period, can tolerate extreme reduction of oxygen and heavy concentration of lactic acid.

The problem of resistance to caisson sickness seems to be at least partly countered by the fact that only the lung contents are taken down at the beginning of the dive, and respiration does not continue underwater. Thus, no very great amount of nitrogen is available to produce oversaturation when the animal rises again. In addition to this, the blubber of whales is able to take up considerable amounts of nitrogen, and there are organisms, referred to as "X" bodies, in the blood stream which appear to remove dissolved nitrogen.

Certain families of birds are specially adapted to oceanic life and play an important part as predators on both plankton and nekton. Some of these, shearwaters and petrels, for example, may spend their entire life at sea except for the breeding period. Like the whales, their concentration is in areas of rich feeding, and therefore of high plankton production. Jespersen (1930) has shown the correlation, in the North Atlantic, between the oceanic bird population and the standing crop of larger zooplankton, and Atkinson (1948) has shown how the breeding sites of Leach's petrel all lie along the northern band of rich zooplankton in the same area (Fig. 7–37). Since especially rich feeding is available to them in the summer in polar waters, many of them make extensive seasonal migrations.

INSHORE PLANKTON

The interrelation of organisms and environment has probably received more adequate study in the case of the inshore plankton than in any other major marine community. This is not to say that the ecology is at all completely understood as yet, but the basic principles are beginning to emerge, and it has been possible to apply numerical values to various processes and obtain a fairly successful prediction of the total animal and plant production.

The general seasonal succession of phytoplankton, as exemplified by conditions in a Scottish sea loch, has already been outlined. Quantitatively, there is a period of small standing crop during the winter, a great outburst of phytoplankton during the spring, a decreased crop during the summer, and, usually, a smaller outburst during the fall. A similar sequence has been traced in various other temperate and cold areas, but the seasonal differences are usually much less pronounced in tropical waters. Qualitatively, there is a seasonal succession of different species comprising the phytoplankton. For example, in the English Channel (Harvey et al., 1935), the spring diatoms *Bacillaria, Biddulphia,* and *Coscinodiscus* largely disappear during the summer but appear again in the fall. Their place is taken during the summer by species such as *Guinardia flaccida, Rhizosolenia alata, R. Shrubsolei, R. Stolterfothii,* and *Navicula membranacea,* which are present throughout the year but occur in maximum numbers in summer. The factors involved in determining the dominance of particular species are not understood. In the English Channel the temperatures during the dominance of *Biddulphia,* etc., do not correspond for the spring and fall periods. On the other hand the length of day is more or less the same. Other constituents of the phytoplankton such as dinoflagellates appear to be even more sporadic in their appearance (Marshall and Orr, 1927).

The plankton community is mainly composed of forms with a rapid reproductive rate. Diatoms, for instance, may reproduce about once a day. Copepods may pass through a generation in a few weeks and chaetognaths in a month or two. A typical bottom community, on the other hand, is generally much slower growing, and individuals one or more years old are typical, at least among the larger forms. The plankton community, as a result, is in a constant state of flux and is much more rapidly responsive to changing environmental conditions. This is particularly so for the rapidly reproducing phytoplankton.

Riley and his co-workers have developed a treatment of the relation between the production of plankton and various chemical and physical factors in the environment; the treatment promises wide applicability. Various assumptions have had to be made on account of the inadequacy of present available data, but despite this, the predictions agree so well with observed values that there is no doubt that the general principles are sound. For phytoplankton production, the following basic formula was produced (Riley, 1946)

$$\frac{dP}{dt} = P(P_h - R_p - G) \tag{1}$$

in which the rate of change of the phytoplankton population P is dependent on the photosynthetic coefficient P_h, the respiratory coefficient R_p, and the grazing coefficient G. It is assumed that the phytoplankton population, as represented by its carbon content, increases by the amount of carbon photosynthesized and decreases by the amount respired and by the amount eaten by herbivores. Other possible sources of loss, such as removal by natural death, by water movements, etc., are considered later. The value of P_h is arrived at as follows. It is known that the rate of photosynthesis of various diatoms is a linear function of the illumination within wide limits. At very high illumination, photosynthesis is reduced, but this occurs only in the surface layers of the sea. If the surface illumination I_0 is known, then the illumination at a depth L is obtained from the formula:

$$I_L = I_0 e^{-kL}$$

where K is the extinction coefficient of the water. Below a limiting illumination where there is no depletion of nutrient slats,

$$P_h = KI$$

where K is a photosynthetic constant, combining the two equations, the photosynthetic rate at a depth L is given by

$$P_{hL} = KI_0 e^{-kL} \tag{2}$$

and the total photosynthesis in a column of water from the surface to a depth L is given by:

$$\overline{P_h}_{0 \to L} = \frac{KI_0}{kL} (1 - e^{-kL}) \tag{3}$$

The photosynthetic rate is reduced when there is nutrient salt deficiency, and here it is deficiency of phosphate that is considered. The effect is apparent when the concentration of phosphate in the water drops below a value of 0.55 mg.-atoms of phosphorus per cubic meter. Then the values on the right of equation (3) must be multiplied by a factor v_p in which

$$v_p = 1 - \left(\frac{0.55 - \text{microgram-atoms P per cubic meter}}{0.55} \right) \tag{4}$$

A further source of reduction of the photosynthetic rate may be the removal of phytoplankton from the euphotic zone by vertical turbulence. As an approximation, the value A'' for this is given by the formula

$$A'' = \frac{z_1}{z_2} \qquad \text{where} \qquad z_1 \leq z_2 \tag{5}$$

and where z_1 is the depth of the euphotic zone and z_2 the depth of the mixed layer. The former is defined as the depth at which the light intensity is 0.0015 gm. calories per square centimeter per minute and the latter as the maximum depth at which the density is no more than 0.02 of a σ_t unit less than at the surface. At this stage, no allowance is made for the effect of temperature in modifying the photosynthetic rate.

In the absence of adequate data on the relation of respiratory rate to temperature, the following formula is assumed to hold:

$$R_T = R_0 e^{sT} \tag{6}$$

where R_T is the respiratory rate at a temperature T, R_0 the rate at 0°C., and s the rate of increase of the respiratory rate with temperature.

Finally, the effect of grazing is given by the expression WH, where W is a constant and H is the population of herbivores. Taking these various expansions, the original equation (1) becomes

$$\frac{dP}{dt} = P \left[\frac{KI_0}{kL} (1 - e^{-kL}) A'' v_p - R' e^{sT} - WH \right] \tag{7}$$

As a test of the value of this equation, Riley calculated phytoplankton population for Georges Bank for a year and compared this, as shown in Fig. 7–38, with the observed values for six cruises. As can be seen, the fit is good, the average error being 27 per cent. No correction was applied in the equation above for the effect of temperature

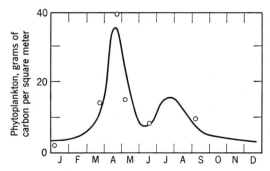

Figure 7–38. Curves showing calculated values for the phytoplankton population on Georges Bank. The circles show observed values. (After Riley, 1946.)

on rate of photosynthesis. In a later paper (Riley et al., 1949) it is suggested that it would be better to modify the equation

$$P_h = KI$$

to read

$$\log \frac{P_h}{K'I_0 - p_h} = 22.884 - \log I_0 - \frac{6573.8}{T'} \tag{8}$$

where T' is the absolute temperature.

In a similar way, equations were developed to describe the herbivore fraction of the zooplankton (Riley, 1947; Riley et al., 1949). The herbivore population H increases by assimilation of food (A_H) and decreases by respiration (R_H), predation by carnivores (C), and natural death (D); thus

$$\frac{dH}{dt} = H(A_H - R_H - C - D)$$

Some of the components of this equation are difficult to evaluate at present because of inadequate data. With regard to the rate of assimilation, it is assumed that filtration of the water by the herbivores proceeds at a uniform rate, regardless of the concentration of phytoplankton present. How this rate may be modified by temperature is not well known. Although the amount of phytoplankton removed by filtration appears to be a more or less linear function of the concentration of the phytoplankton, the amount assimilated by the herbivores is similarly linear only when the phytoplankton concentration is not very rich. Various workers have shown that, at the time of the spring diatom increase, copepods and other forms may take in more food than they can digest, and a considerable amount of partially digested food material may be passed out with the feces. The effect of temperature on respiration is based on experimental evidence, and, since the data do not fit any simple mathematical expression, a characteristic graph is used for obtaining the values under given conditions. The loss by natural death is made to include removal from the area by currents, etc., and is assumed to be constant. The *Sagitta* present were assumed to be the main carnivores, and their effect was considered as

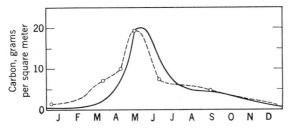

Figure 7–39. The seasonal cycle of zooplankton on Georges Bank. The solid line represents calculated values, and the broken line connects observed values (circles). (After Riley, 1947.)

the product of their concentration and a constant representing their rate of feeding. In a test series (Fig. 7–39) the predicted seasonal changes in the herbivore population at least followed the same trend as the observed values.

In this work on productivity, only a general picture has been drawn in which variations between species have been ignored. Various simplifications have also had to be assumed in the descriptions of the operative environmental factors. Some of the data used were drawn from natural mixed populations of plankton in which no consideration was given to the species present. As such, they were representative of conditions prevalent at the time. Other data, such as those on copepod respiration, filtration rates, and the effects of varying illumination on photosynthesis, were drawn from experiments with particular species. The extent to which it is permissible to accept such data as typical of the plankton as a whole were, of course, discussed. Recent work (Nielsen, 1952, etc.) suggests that Riley's productivity figures may be too high, at least for regions of low standing crop. This should not, however, affect the general scheme of interrelation of factors. At this stage, an impossible degree of complexity would be introduced if allowance were made for specific differences, differences between seasonal broods, etc. When such information is available, it will no doubt be possible to construct more accurate equations. In the meantime, and in view of the general paucity of information on the various characteristics of the zoo- and phytoplankton, it appears valuable to indicate at least some of the source material on the subject. No full coverage will be given, but rather a reference to certain particularly relevant work from whose bibliographies further information may be obtained.

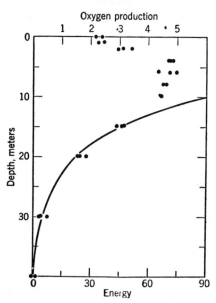

Figure 7–40. Photosynthesis of the diatom *Coscinodiscus excentricus* at different depths in the English Channel. The curve shows the total average energy at these depths. (After Jenkin, 1937.)

Both qualitative and quantitative surveys of the seasonal changes in the phyto- and zooplankton have been made for inshore waters in many parts of the world. Among many, we might mention those of Marshall and Orr (1927, 1930, etc.) in Scotland, of Harvey et al. (1935) in the English Channel, and of Bigelow and Sears (1939) and Bigelow et al. (1940) in the western North Atlantic. There is much work such as that of Allen (1928) and others for the Pacific coast of North America. For the tropics, there is the work of various members of the Great Barrier Reef Expedition, of Dakin (1934, etc.), and others.

There has also been a particular concentration of work on the quantitatively important copepod *C. finmarchicus* and the diatom *Nitzschia closterium*. The availability of the latter in cultures has led to its use in many experimental studies, despite its doubtful systematic status. In the sections on ecological factors we have indicated some of the data available on photosynthesis, respiration, feeding, etc. Jenkin (1937) showed the relation between the oxygen production of the diatom *Coscinodiscus excentricus* and illumination. Figure 7–40 shows the results of one of her series of experiments, with oxygen production paralleling available solar energy except in the upper layers where the illumination was too bright and photosynthesis decreased. Ketchum (1939) demonstrated the increase in growth rate of a diatom culture on the addition of phosphate up to 50 mg. PO_4 per cubic meter and the absence of further increase above this amount. Riley (1938) showed the increase in both growth and photosynthesis with the addition of nitrate, but in his experiment addition of phosphate had little effect. Harvey (1933) showed the increased photosynthesis of diatoms with addition of phosphate, nitrate, and ammonium. Various workers have demonstrated the necessity of various trace elements in such cultures, and Harvey (1933) showed that the addition to a culture of water obtained from melted ice, and so presumeably enriched in trihydrol, increased growth in the culture. Riley et al. (1949) have discussed the combined effects of nutrient concentration, temperature, and illumination on diatom photosynthesis (Fig. 2–10). At high temperatures, the effect of phosphate deficiency in decreasing the photosynthetic rate is slight except where phosphate deficiency is great. At low temperatures, on the other hand, there is a fairly steady decrease in photosynthetic rate with decreasing phosphate concentration. When phosphate is very deficient, increased temperature has a marked effect in increasing photosynthetic rate, whatever the illumination, whereas at higher phosphate concentrations this temperature effect is marked when the illumination is high and is much reduced at low illuminations.

A seasonal succession of species in the phytoplankton is well known, but there is at present little information on their specific requirements and tolerances that might explain the succession. Indications that such differences exist, however, are found in such work as that of Braarud (1944), on the rates of reproduction of various species of diatoms under similar conditions, and are implied also in the varying geographical distribution of the various species.

The life histories of many of the most important zooplankton species are known, at any rate, in temperate waters. Rates of growth, seasonal succession of broods, vertical distribution, and diurnal migration are known for a few, particularly the copepod *C. finmarchicus* and the chaetognaths *S. elegans* and *S. setosa*. Figure 7–41 (Russell, 1935) summarized the seasonal histories of a few inshore forms. Height above the base line indicates size, and the darkened areas represent sexual maturity. Knowledge of *C. finmarchicus* has been brought together in a book by Marshall and Orr (1955).

Although *C. finmarchicus* has received more detailed study than any other species of copepod, a number of more recent studies have been

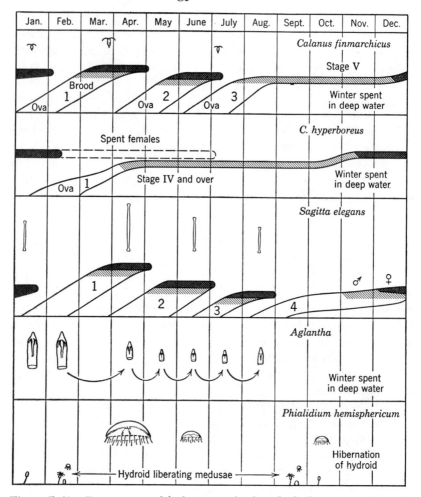

Jan.	Feb.	Mar.	Apr.	May	June	July	Aug.	Sept.	Oct.	Nov.	Dec.

Figure 7–41. Diagrammatic life histories of selected planktonic animals. The height of each diagram, as well as the size of the drawing of the animals, is proportional to the adult size of that brood. The periods of full maturity are indicated in dark tone, and the period immediately preceding this by hatching. The number of broods per year will, at least in some cases, vary in different localities. (After Russell, 1935.)

made on the smaller, and less numerous, species in the northern plankton. Some of these may form a successive series during the year, as shown in Fig. 7–42. Along with them, there is, of course, a succession of other forms, some of which are indicated in Fig. 7–43. Except for *Sagitta* spp., few of these have been studied intensively.

Marshall et al. (1935) studied the respiration of *C. finmarchicus* and

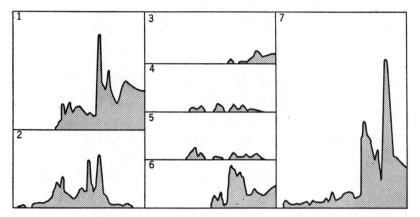

Figure 7–42. Seasonal abundance of seven species of copepods in the Clyde Sea area. The diagrams include only immature individuals. *1, Pseudocalanus; 2, Microcalanus; 3, Paracalanus; 4, Centropages; 5, Temora; 6, Acartia; 7, Oithona.* (After Marshall, 1949.)

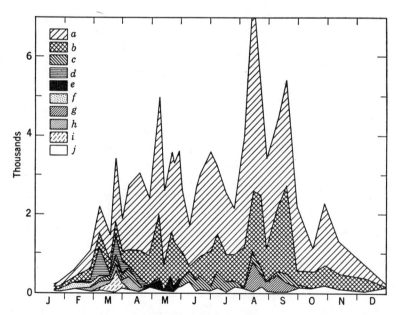

Figure 7–43. The seasonal cycle of abundance of various planktonic animals in the English Channel. *a,* copepod nauplii; *b,* copepods and copepodites; *c,* appendicularia; *d,* cirripede nauplii; *e,* cladocera; *f,* polychaete larvae; *g, Limacina; h, Noctiluca; i,* rotifera; *j,* others. (After Harvey et al., 1935.)

its relation to temperature. They showed, as had Zeuthen (1947) for another copepod *Centropages hamatus,* that there is a decrease in respiratory rate for a time after capture. The reason for this is not clear, although it may be connected with feeding. They also showed that there is a marked increase in respiratory rate when *Calanus* is exposed to light, although there is no apparent increase in activity. Both these phenomena complicate the application of experimental data to consideration of the behavior of copepods living under natural conditions. Further, although under experimental conditions these copepods showed a marked increase in respiratory rate with increase of temperature, it is not clear to what extent the differences between

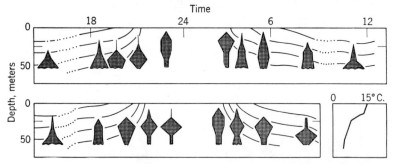

Figure 7–44. Diurnal migration of the copepod *Metridia lucens,* showing the arrest of evening ascent at a thermocline. The vertical distribution of temperature is shown at the right. (After Clarke, 1933.)

summer and winter temperature affect them. In various marine animals it has been shown that slow adaptation to seasonal changes in temperature may take place so that normal respiratory rates show little or no regular seasonal variation. The same may be true of members of the same species living in areas of different temperature. Yet, on the other hand, other species show little ability to undergo such adaptation and show markedly different summer and winter respiratory rates. It remains to be shown whether such adaptation is characteristic of some planktonic species and not of others, and how successive seasonal broods vary in their physiology.

Diurnal rhythms, including diurnal migration, are as important in coastal plankton as in oceanic. Diurnal migration, which occurs in a wide range of animals, is of a type similar to that already described, although necessarily over a more limited range. Illumination is apparently the principal controlling factor. Oceanic plankton moving up from a considerable daytime depth may find the night illumination

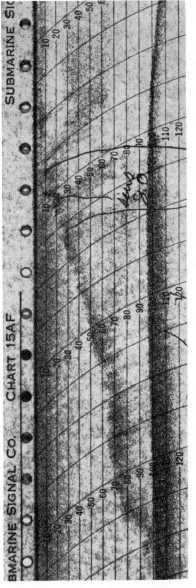

Figure 7–45. Sonic record of the evening ascent of an unidentified, diurnally migrating organism. These left the bottom (100 fathoms) about 40 minutes before sunset (shown as "suns"), reached the surface just after sunset, and then sank again, becoming more diffuse vertically at the same time. (After Moore, 1950.)

too bright at the surface. The inshore plankton and also the shallower oceanic plankton may find the night surface illumination considerably less than their day optimum. As a result, they may concentrate close to the surface at about sunset but then diffuse again through the water column as the illumination becomes insufficient to stimulate upward movement. This migration pattern is shown diagrammatically in Fig. 7–44, and Fig. 7–45 shows the details of such an upward migration and subsequent diffusion as revealed by sonic methods. Somewhat before

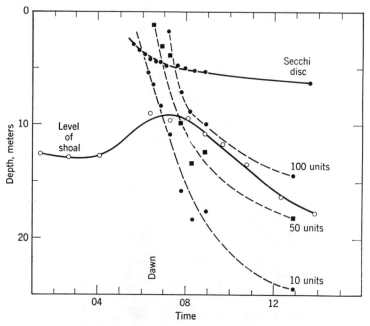

Figure 7–46. Movements of the upper limit of a shoal of herring at dawn in relation to the changing illumination. (After Richardson, 1952.)

sunrise the organisms again concentrate close to the surface before beginning their morning descent. Such a midnight downward diffusion has also been observed occasionally in oceanic plankton (Moore, 1949).

Diurnal migration is not limited to the plankton but is frequently equally conspicuous in the nekton. Thus Fig. 7–46 shows the movement during the morning hours of the upper limit of a school of herring. The downward movement in response to increasing illumination is clearly shown; in fact the downward path corresponds closely to the isolumes. The record also shows the slight rise, just before sunrise, that is frequently found in plankton populations. In this study (Richardson, 1952) it was shown that the fish could be made to retreat to greater depths if the illumination was increased by directing a searchlight vertically downward from the ship. It was also shown that the day level occupied by the herring shoals showed a correlation with the clarity of the water, the shoal lying deeper when the water was clearer (Fig. 7–47).

Diurnally migrating plankton may encounter barriers it cannot pass

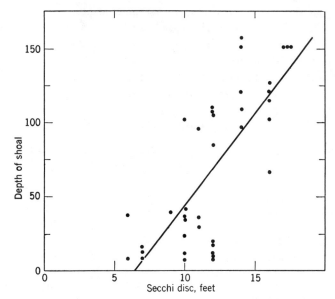

Figure 7–47. The relation between the day level of herring shoals and the transparency of the water. (After Richardson, 1952.)

in its upward or downward movement. Figure 7–44 shows the movements of the copepod *Metridia lucens,* which are arrested at the thermocline during the evening ascent. Hansen (1951) describes a particular instance in which there was a very sharp discontinuity layer with a change of 10–20°C. and $15^0/_{00}$ in a vertical distance of a few meters. Various copepods, euphausids, siphonophores, chaetognaths, etc., were unable to pass this barrier and were restricted to the water either above or below it. On the other hand, a few forms were able to pass freely through the barrier. The factors involved in depth control, including temperature, illumination, pressure, etc., have been considered already. Much of the information on the subject has been reviewed by Kikuchi (1930). Reactions to these factors under experimental conditions have been demonstrated in a number of plankton animals. However, the experimental results have often proved conflicting, even for the same species. It is apparent that the method of control of level varies in different species, and probably also in different stages and broods of the same species. Furthermore, the modification in reaction induced by such conditions and feeding is little understood at present.

Although the evidence of any diurnal migration in diatoms is still rather doubtful, it definitely occurs in some dinoflagellates. Hasle (1950) has demonstrated this in the somewhat atypical hydrographic conditions in Oslo Fjord. Here the water is rather heavily sewage-polluted, is turbid, with reduction of light to 1 per cent of the surface value at about 10 meters, and is most transparent to red light. Under these conditions certain dinoflagellate species concentrate very close to the surface, as shown in Table 7–13.

TABLE 7–13

Vertical Distribution of Certain Dinoflagellates in Oslo Fjord

(Hasle, 1950)

	Number of Cells per Liter		
Depth in Meters	*Ceratium fusus*	*Ceratium tripos*	*Prorocentrum micans*
0.00	13,250	1,100	1,100
0.25	15,400	15,750	221,000
0.50	11,550	21,850	500,500
1.00	25,450	14,800	478,000
2.00	75,400	10,300	158,000

Dinoflagellates may be able to migrate comparatively rapidly in response to light. *Ceratium fusus* can move 1 mm. in 4–16 seconds, and *C. tripos* can move the same distance in about half the time. These two species showed a typical pattern of diurnal migration, moving to a deeper level in the daytime. On the other hand, two other species, *Goniaulax polyhedra* and *Prorocentrum micans* showed a reversed type of migration, the first occurring at the surface in maximum numbers a little before sunset and the second about noon (Fig. 7–48). Diurnal rhythms other than migration play an important part in the plankton but have been less well explored. Wimpenny (1938) has brought together much of the literature on the subject. From the evidence of gut contents it appears that most zooplankton feed more at

night than during the daytime. The extent of this diurnal difference
in feeding rate is, apparently, modified by the concentration of food
available. He also suggests that there is a tendency for spawning to
take place principally in the daytime, although more recent work by
Marshall and Orr (1951) shows that the copepod *C. finmarchicus*
spawns mainly at night (Fig. 7–49). It has since been shown (Harding et al., 1952) that, although this is true of the stock of overwintering
females, the spring brood behave differently, spawning throughout the

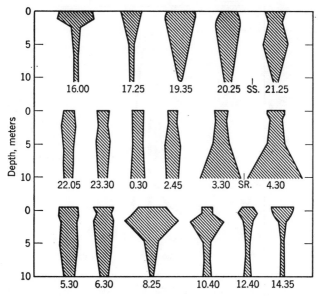

Figure 7–48. Diurnal migrations of the dinoflagellate *Prorocentrum micans.*
(After Hasle, 1950.)

24 hours. Finally, egg production by these copepods is closely dependent on the supply of food available (Fig. 7–50).

A few observations have been made on the feeding rates of herbivores. When feeding on small particles, filtration of the water appears to proceed at a uniform rate, regardless of the concentration of
food in it. This has been shown for a mysid, *Neomysis,* and for a
copepod, *Eurytemora* (Lucas, 1936), and for the copepod *C. finmarchicus* (Harvey, 1937; Fuller and Clarke, 1936). Filtration of
large species of diatoms appears to be more efficient than that of
small ones. Harvey (1937) used cultures of three species of diatoms,
the larger *D. brightwellii,* the smaller *Lauderia borealis,* and the very
small *N. closterium* var. *minutissima.* From the decrease in the dia-

tom populations during the experiments, he calculated the amount of water swept free by one *C. finmarchicus* in 1 hour. This was 8.5, 3.0, and 0.19 cc., respectively. He also showed that there was some measure of selection of the species on which the copepods had previously been feeding. *Calanus,* which had previously been fed for 8 days on *Ditylium* only, when placed for 7 hours in a mixed culture, ate 23.4 ± 3.5 per cent of the *Lauderia* and 70.5 ± 6.3 per cent of the *Ditylium–Lauderia*-fed individuals, under the same conditions, ate 38.4 ± 3.4

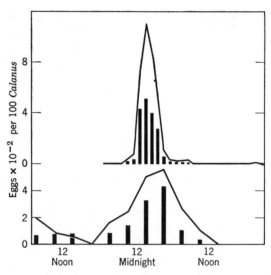

Figure 7–49. Diurnal rhythm in the egg-laying of the copepod, *Calanus finmarchicus.* The upper figure represents 1-hour periods and the lower 3-hour periods. The lines show the numbers of eggs produced, and the blocks the percentage of females that were laying. (After Harding et al., 1951.)

per cent of the *Lauderia* and 64 ± 5.9 per cent of the *Ditylium.* Fuller (1937) showed that the feeding rate of *C. finmarchicus* on *N. closterium* was greatest at an optimum temperature, and less above or below this. The values at 3, 8, and 13°C. were 0.35, 2.83, and 1.09 cc. per copepod per day. Some forms, such as crab zoeas, which are presumably filter feeders under normal conditions, will eat larger dead organisms when these are available, but the extent to which they normally do this, and the food requirements of carnivores, is not known.

One problem raised by the observed filtration rates of copepods is that they would appear to be quite inadequate to provide under natural conditions, the calculated food requirements of a copepod. Pütter considered this to be an argument in favor of their obtaining a considerable fraction of their nourishment from dissolved organic matter. Gauld (1951) has made some recent observations on the rates at which various copepods filter suspensions of nannoplankton. For various reasons this may be better experimental material than suspensions of diatoms. His conclusion is that, with the considerably higher rates observed, these are of the correct order to provide adequate food supply. He refers to Lowndes' (1935) argument that copepod feeding may not be non-selective but may be largely a selective catching of larger organisms such as other copepods. In Gauld's experiments, the number of nannoplankton organisms captured per second makes it highly improbable that there would be time for any active selection

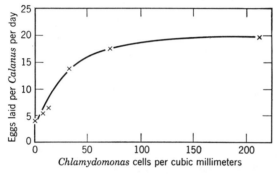

Figure 7–50. The effect of food concentration on the egg laying of the copepod *Calanus finmarchicus*. (After Marshall and Orr, 1952.)

and capture of the particles under such conditions. Two interesting points are brought out in this work. The rate of filtration was roughly proportional to the square of the length of the copepod. There is some evidence that feeding is not continuous throughout the 24 hours but that it is restricted to the period of darkness.

Recent work has emphasized the importance of the nannoplankton, showing that it may bulk far larger than the diatoms in the total phytoplankton. Most previous surveys of phytoplankton abundance have been based on net hauls. When Gauld's results are considered in the light of these facts, it seems quite probable that the nannoplankton may prove to be the major diet of filter feeders such as copepods.

Larvae play a much more important role in inshore waters than they do in oceanic areas. In the latter, the larvae present are mainly those of adults which are themselves planktonic, although there is some addition from nektonic forms such as fishes and cephalopods. In coastal

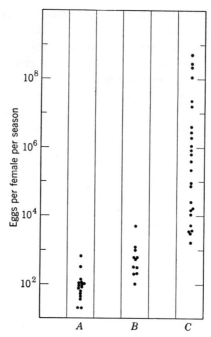

Figure 7–51. The relation, for a representative series of Danish bottom inverte-brates, between the type of larvae and the number of eggs laid per individual. The left-hand column (*A*) includes species with a high degree of brood protec-tion and no pelagic larval phase. The central column (*B*) shows ones with large eggs or primitive brood protection and no pelagic larval phase. Those in the right-hand column (*C*) have small eggs and a long pelagic larval phase. (After Thorson, 1950.)

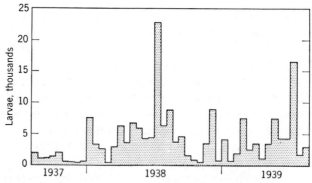

Figure 7–52. The seasonal cycle of abundance of invertebrate larvae in Danish waters. The numbers shown are those in a column of water reaching from sur-face to bottom and under a surface area of 0.5 square meters. (After Thorson, 1946.)

waters there is an enormous additional contribution of the larvae of bottom-living animals. Thorson (1950) gives data on the number of eggs produced per female per breeding season for a number of bottom invertebrates (Fig. 7–51); 26 of the 53 produced planktonic larvae, and of the 26, nearly half produced over a million eggs per year. Moore (1935) calculated that the intertidal barnacle *B. balanoides*, which produces only a few thousand larvae per individual, contributes

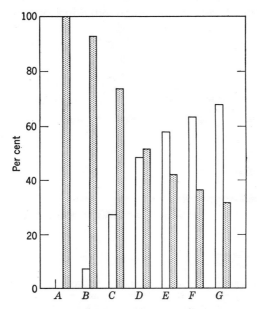

Figure 7–53. Diagram showing the percentages of prosobranch molluscs with pelagic larvae (white) and nonpelagic larvae (stippled) and the change in proportions of the two from cold waters toward the equator: *A*, East Greenland; *B*, North and East Iceland; *C*, West and South Iceland; *D*, Faroes, Shetland, and Orkneys; *E*, South Norway, West Sweden, and Denmark; *F*, South England and Channel Islands; *G*, Canary Isles. (After Thorson, 1950.)

between 20,000,000 and 1,000,000,000,000 larvae to the plankton each year from 1 km. of shore. Although the settlement of spat in an area may represent many more individuals than the area could support as adults, nevertheless it is clear that only a relatively small proportion of the larvae released into the plankton can ever settle. The bulk of the mortality occurs during their planktonic existence, and Thorson (1950) considers that death is caused mainly by predation and not by lack of food or other adverse factors. These larvae provide an important food source for carnivores of various sizes, as Lebour (1933, 1934, etc.) and others have shown from the examination of the food contents of the stomachs of young fish. However, most species are seasonal in their occurrence because of limited breeding seasons. The total production of larvae also tends to be seasonal, breeding in cold waters being so timed as to liberate the larvae into the plankton when there is the maximum supply of phytoplankton for food (Fig. 7-52). In tropical waters, where there is much less seasonal variation in the quantity of phytoplankton, breeding shows more tendency to be continuous throughout the year, although individual species may still have

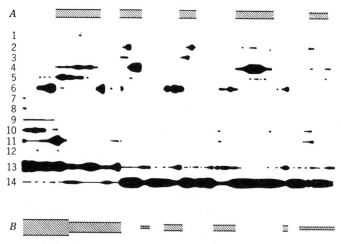

Figure 7–54. Diagram showing the relation between the occurrence of various plankton species in the waters off Plymouth and the water masses present. A, Southwestern water; B, Western water; 1, *Euchaeta;* 2, *Doliolum;* 3, *Salpa;* 4, *Muggiaea;* 5, *Liriope;* 6, *Cosmetira;* 7, *Thysanoessa;* 8, *Meganyctiphanes;* 9, *Clione;* 10, *Stephanomia;* 11, *Aglantha;* 12, *Sagitta serratodentata;* 13, *S. elegans;* 14, *S. setosa.* (After Russell, 1935.)

restricted breeding seasons. The restriction of the season in which an adequate food supply is available for planktonic larvae in cold waters puts a premium on those species that produce yolky eggs and protect them in egg capsules or by other means. In so doing, they lose the advantage of dispersal of the planktonic forms. Thorson (1950) has brought out clearly the steady transition from non-pelagic development in arctic waters to largely planktonic development in the tropics (Fig. 7-53). Fewer data are available for the Antarctic, but apparently the situation is the same there.

An important aspect of inshore plankton that has emerged from the study of the species present is the study of indicator species. In vari-

TABLE 7–14

Plankton Animal Indicators

(Russell, 1935)

ARCTIC WATER

1. Species for which a high temperature is fatal and they soon perish.

Ctenophore	*Mertensia ovum*	Gulf of Maine
Medusae	*Ptychogena lactea*	Gulf of Maine
	Sarsia princeps	Labrador Current
Pteropod	*Limacina helecina*	Barents Sea and North of Ireland
		Gulf of Maine
Tunicate	*Oikopleura vanhöffeni*	Gulf of Maine
		Newfoundland

2. Species able to survive for a considerable period and even reproduce to some extent.

Copepods	*Calanus hyperboreus*	East Iceland Polar Current
		Gulf of Maine
	Metridia longa	East Iceland Polar Current
		Gulf of Maine
Pteropod	*Clione limacina*	Gulf of Maine

MIXED ARCTIC AND ATLANTIC WATER

Species unable to breed in high (or low) temperatures.

1. Surface layers.

Chaetognath	*Sagitta serratodentata*	Gulf of Maine
Euphausian	*Nematoscelis megalops*	Gulf of Maine

2. Intermediate layers (say below 50 meters).

Chaetognath	*Eukrohnia hamata*	Gulf of Maine
Siphonophore	*Diphyes arctica*	Gulf of Maine

3. Deepest layers (150 meters or deeper).

Chaetognath	*Sagitta maxima*	Gulf of Maine

4. Entering northwestern North Sea.

Euphausian	*Thysanoessa longicaudata*	North Sea

Note: In Newfoundland a relation has been shown between the abundance of *Sagitta serratodentata* and that of the squid *Illex illecebrosus* during the years studied, 1931, 1932, and 1933.

ATLANTIC WATER

1. Species that occur in water entering northwestern North Sea round north coast of Scotland.

Euphausians	*Meganyctyphanes norvegica*	North Sea
	Thysanoessa inermis	
	(in winter only)	North Sea

TABLE 7–14 (Continued)

2. Species that occur in regions away from influence of Arctic water.

Medusae	*Aglantha digitalis* var. *rosea*	S. W. Dogger swirl Channel
	Cosmetira megalota	S. W. Dogger swirl
	C. pilosella (in spring and summer only)	Channel
Siphonophores	*Agalma elegans*	S. W. Dogger swirl
	Stephanomia bijuga	Channel
Chaetognath	*Sagitta elegans* (should probably also prove of value in southern North Sea)	Channel
Euphausians	*Meganyctiphanes norvegica*	Channel
	Thysanoessa inermis	Channel
	Nyctiphanes couchi	S. W. Dogger swirl
Pteropod	*Clione limacina*	S. W. Dogger swirl Channel
Echinoderm	*Luidia sarsi* young	Channel S. W. Dogger swirl
Tunicate	*Oikopleura labradoriensis*	S. W. Dogger swirl Newfoundland (typical of mixed temperate waters)

WARM ATLANTIC WATER

Tunicates	*Salpa fusiformis*	North Sea, Channel, Gulf of Maine
	S. democratica	North Sea, Channel, Gulf of Maine
	Cyclosalpa bakeri	North Sea
	Doliolum nationalis	North Sea, Channel
	D. gegenbauri	North Sea, Channel

Note: There are no boreal or arctic salps or doliolids; the presence of any species in these groups may therefore be regarded as an indication of water from warmer latitudes.

Medusa	*Liriope exigua*	Channel
Siphonophores	*Muggiaea atlantica*	Channel
	M. kochi	Channel
	Physophora borealis	North Sea and Norwegian coast
	Cupulita sarsi	North Sea and Norwegian coast
Actinia	Arachnactis larvae	North Sea and Norwegian coast
Cirripedia	*Lepas fascicularis*	North Sea and Norwegian coast
Copepod	*Anomalocera patersoni*	Norwegian Sea

TABLE 7–14 (Continued)

COASTAL WATER

Medusae	*Cyanea capillata*	Norwegian Ocean
	C. lamarcki	North Sea
	Sarsia princeps	Spitzbergen
	S. flammea	Spitzbergen
	Catablema eurystoma	Spitzbergen
	Bougainvillea superciliaris	Spitzbergen

Note: Any meroplanktonic species with a fixed bottom stage in its life history is indicative of coastal water, and its distance offshore is dependent on its length of life in the planktonic stage.

Chaetogneth	*Sagitta setosa*	Channel (probably also North Sea)

Note: The coastal water of the Channel and southern North Sea is also distinguishable from Atlantic water by its poverty of animal plankton.

Certain species are given by Kramp as likely to be carried into the southern North Sea via the Channel.

Medusae	*Turritopsis nutricula, Amphinema dinema, Slabberia halterata, Gossea corynectes, Octorchis gegenbauri, Cosmetira pilosella.*
Euphausian	*Nyctiphanes couchi*

Of these, *Cosmetira* and perhaps *Nyctiphanes* will have been carried in Atlantic water.

EASTERN AND SOUTHERN KATTEGAT

Kramp gives as visitors introduced from the north:

Medusae	*Bougainvillea britannica, Laodicea undulata, Staurophora mertensii, Melicertum octocostatum, Mitrocoma polydiademata, Cosmetira pilosella.*

ous places, particular species have been found that are characteristic of certain water masses to which they are restricted; these species can be used as an indication of the presence in the area of water of a certain origin. Although various precautions are necessary in interpreting the results, the method has proved valuable. Russell (1935) gives a list of species that have proved valuable as indicators in various parts of the world (Table 7–14).

Figure 7–54 (Russell, 1935a) shows the changes during a 5-year period in the indicator species present in the English Channel at Plymouth. It shows clearly the temporary incursions of fauna typical of western and of southwestern water. Figure 7–55 (Redfield, 1939) shows the progress of an intrusive mass of water containing the pteropod *Limacina retroversa* in the Gulf of Maine. The progress of this population was followed, and incidentally provided useful information on the rate of growth of the species (Fig. 7–56).

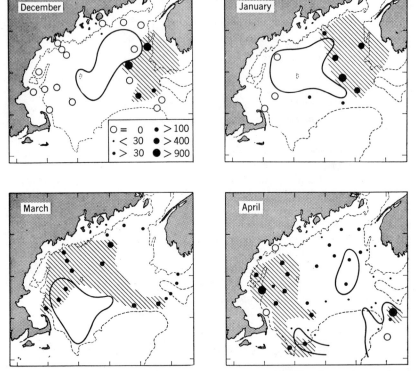

Figure 7–55. The history of an intrusive mass of high-salinity water (contoured) and its population of the pteropod *Limacina retroversa* (hatched) in the Gulf of Maine. (After Redfield, 1939.)

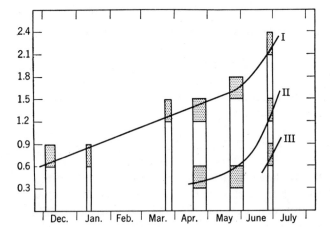

Figure 7–56. Diagram showing the growth of modal classes (stippled) of the pteropod *Limacina retroversa* referred to in Fig. 7–55. (After Redfield, 1939.)

8

Organisms

(Continued)

INSHORE PELAGIC

Two commercial inshore fisheries, both pelagic and bottom, have received such long-continued and intensive study that they call for a chapter to themselves. Although it is highly artificial to consider them all under a single habitat, this does allow widely spread information to be brought together in a single section and avoids unnecessary duplication in the section on bottom organisms. Economically important invertebrates such as the oyster, clam, lobster, and crab have similarly warranted particular attention, and much study of the bottom fauna and the plankton has been inspired by the recognition of their importance in the food chains of the various fishes. Despite, or perhaps because of, the mass of work already done on fishery biology, we still have extremely uncertain knowledge of the various interacting processes involved. To quote Merriman and Warfel (1948), "The truth of the matter is that most of the major issues in fisheries biology are still highly controversial. For example there is no unanimity of opinion as to demonstrable instances of over-fishing. We know only a modicum about the causes of fluctuations in abundance. The subject of inter-and intraspecific competition in populations of marine fishes is little understood. And a nice question is posed by the fact that the dominant year-classes (the exceptionally high survival of the young born in any one year resulting in ultimate benefit to the fishery) sometimes occur when the adult stock is at a comparatively low level. All this may be taken as a sad commentary on our lack of progress in the half century dating from Hoffbauer's discovery of the possibility of determining ages and growth rates by means of scale analyses."

Before considering the status of our knowledge, it is necessary to refer to some of the advantages and disadvantages peculiar to fishery studies. In the first place the majority of the fish with which we are concerned are migratory to a greater or less extent. It is difficult, therefore, to keep track of a particular population and follow its progress without fear of periodic admixture with other populations whose characteristics may be very different. In fact it is often not possible to keep track of the particular population at all for more than a limited period. Adequate sampling of the population is the next serious problem. A large fraction of the necessary data has to be obtained from commercial catches. In these there is always selective catching of certain sizes, so that such catches do not give a true picture of the population as a whole. In addition commerical fishing tends to concentrate where the best yield is obtained and is unrepresentative for this reason also. Then again the methods used in the commercial fishery are constantly changing, and interpretation of results from commercial catches has to be correspondingly modified. To offset these disadvantages, the enormous amount of commercial fishing allows far more extensive sampling than could otherwise be possible. Finally, many fishes have the great advantage over invertebrates other than lamellibranchs that the age of individuals may be determined from an examination of annual rings in the scales, otoliths, or other structures. Not only this but as estimate of growth rate in previous years may often be made from the spacing of these rings, although the method is open to certain errors

In the work by Riley and others on the dynamics of plankton populations, the problems were greatly simplified by treating the whole phytoplankton community as a single unit, with no consideration for the fluctuating species comprising it. The zooplankton was considered to be composed of two categories of animals, the herbivores and the carnivores, but no further breakdown was attempted. Since, from the economic aspect, we are usually concerned with a fishery for a particular species of fish, a far more detailed breakdown is called for. Also most fishes change their habitat and their environmental relations at different stages in their life history. Thus the eggs may be layed on the bottom, where they are subject to predation by bottom-living forms as well as pelagic. They may also be subject to such factors as deficiency of oxygen if they are layed in thick layers. The newly hatched larvae may be planktonic and subject to predation by quite other forms. Their food supply may at first be a self-contained yolk sack and later forms in the plankton. After this may come a period in which the fish take to a habitat similar to that of the adults,

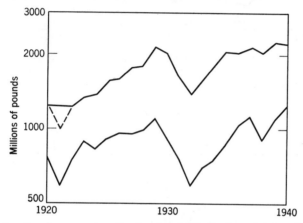

Figure 8–1. Graph comparing the trends of fish food production (upper) and general industrial production (lower) in the United States. (After Taylor, 1951.)

with perhaps similar food, but in which they are subject only to natural mortality, not being taken in commercial catches. After this again follows the period when they are subject to commercial fishing, and this period may require subdivision according to whether or not the fish are sexually mature. This is important not only from the point of view of the production of future broods but also because the food utilized for the production of gonads is, unless the fish are taken before spawning, a loss to the fishery, in so far as production of marketable flesh is concerned.

Lying behind the study of fish populations is the desire to operate fisheries in such a way that they will produce, and will continue to produce, the most valuable yield possible. Such aspects as the exploration of possible new fishing grounds do not concern us here. Since no generally acceptable comprehensive theory of the dynamics of fish populations has yet been produced, the best we can do is

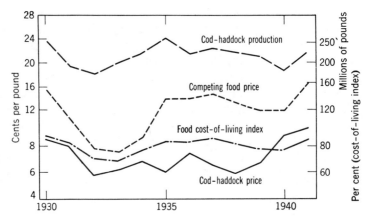

Figure 8–2. Graphs comparing the trends in the United States, of amount of fish landed, price of competing foods, general cost of living index, and price of fish. (After Taylor, 1951.)

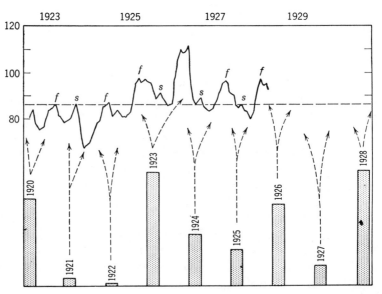

Figure 8–3. The upper curve shows fluctuations in the catch of haddock in the North Sea, with spawning concentrations indicated by "*s*" and feeding concentrations by "*f*." The block diagram below shows the relative success of different year broods, as indicated by their relative representation in catches. Displacement of the time scale allows comparison of the success of the broods with success of the catches 2 or 3 years later, when the fish have reached marketable size. (After H. Thompson, 1930.)

to survey some of the views advanced on particular aspects of the problem.

To begin with, there is no doubt that the catches of many fish fluctuate widely from time to time. Although economic trends and changes in methods undoubtedly influence the landings, it is apparent that there are also fluctuations in the available stock of fish. Taylor (1951), for example, has shown that there is a rather close correlation between general economic conditions and the amount of fish landed (Fig. 8–1). He also quotes data to show that both the amount and the total value of fish landed are positively correlated with the cost of competing food (Fig. 8–2). On the other hand, over short periods, the price obtained for the fish is negatively correlated with the amount marketed. It is clear, then, that at least a significant part of the observed fluctuations in fish landings is due to economic factors rather than to changes in the availability of the fish in the sea. On the other hand, there are year-to-year fluctuations, such as those shown for the North Sea haddock (Fig. 8–3) which are undoubtedly attributable to variations in success of the broods from which the recruitment of the stock took place (H. Thompson, 1930). The way in which particularly successful year broods may dominate the population for many years thereafter is well illustrated in the case of the Norwegian herring (Fig. 8–4; Lea, 1930).

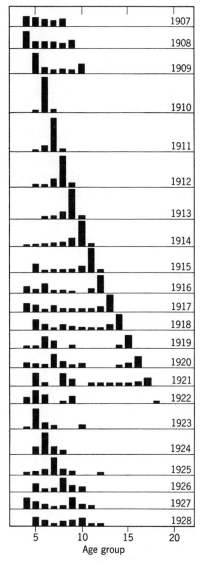

Figure 8–4. The age composition of Norwegian herring in successive years, showing how a successful brood may dominate the population for a number of years thereafter. (After Lea, 1930.)

It is the study of such fluctuations that should guide us to the understanding of the significant factors affecting fish populations. As a first simplification we may break down the study of a particular species of fish so as to treat it as a series of populations, all interrelated, just as the plankton community was broken down into the food chain: phytoplankton → herbivores → carnivores. In this way we would get, in a typical case:

$$\text{Eggs and sperm} \rightarrow \text{larvae} \rightarrow \text{immatures} \rightarrow \text{matures}$$

Since we are much concerned with the effects of fishing, it would be better to subdivide the third group according to whether or not they were taken in the commercial catches. We would then arrive at the following subdivisions:

$$\text{Eggs and sperm} \rightarrow \text{larvae} \rightarrow \text{not fished} \rightarrow \text{fished} \begin{cases} \text{immature} \\ \text{mature} \end{cases}$$

Each of these is directly dependent on the previous group for recruitment, but there may also be interrelations between contiguous groups by reason of competition for food, predation, and other causes.

For any one group we may say that

$$P_t = P_o - M + R$$

where P_o is the initial population (by number), P_t the population at the end of a period "t," M the mortality by all causes (including fishing), and R the recruitment during the period from preceding groups. This assumes that there is no interchange with neighboring populations.

Considered in terms of weight, rather than numbers, we get:

$$W_t = W_o - M + G - L + R$$

where W_o is the original weight of the population, W_t the weight after an interval "t," M the mortality, L the loss by change into the next higher group (i.e., larvae to not fished), R the recruitment, and G the growth of all the surviving individuals. It is not profitable to develop the formula further at this stage. Instead we will consider the information available in so far as it may be applied in the various groups.

Earlier fishery workers were much concerned with the need for maintaining a sufficient supply of spawning adults in the population, fearing that overfishing would reduce their numbers to a point where insufficient spawn would be produced to restock the population.

Statistics have not supported this, and, in fact, Hjort (1914) showed the 1903 and 1904 broods of cod, which, when they had grown to catchable size, resulted in outstanding catches in the Lofoten fishery, were the product of exceptionally poor spawning years. It has been suggested that heavy spawning may be detrimental in the case of the herring. If the eggs are layed in thick masses on the bottom, the lower layers may die from shortage of oxygen, and only those eggs near the surface develop. It appears probable, then, that there is almost always an ample supply of eggs. Before they hatch, these eggs are subject to predation and to possible failure to develop on account of unfavorable environmental conditions. Further, delayed development, owing, for example, to low temperatures (Fig. 2–6) leaves them liable to predation for a longer period, and unless the feeding rate of the predators is correspondingly reduced, they will suffer a higher mortality. Enough evidence on the subject is not available, and we do not know whether such effects could seriously reduce the recruitments into the larval population. Since the larvae of most of the commercial fishes are planktonic, it is unlikely that a serious fraction of the eggs will be swept by currents into habitats that are unsuitable for the succeeding larvae.

It is becoming increasingly apparent that the larval stage is the critical one in determining fluctuations in a marine fish population. Thorson (1940, etc.) has shown clearly that, in invertebrates, those forms with pelagic larvae are far more subject to year-to-year fluctuations in adult population than those in which the eggs are protected in some way and there is no planktonic phase. The mortality rate is very high during this stage, and larvae are subject to great fluctuations in available food supply, predation, environmental conditions, etc., as well as the risk of being carried by currents into areas in which postlarval life is impossible. If this is an inherent characteristic of pelagic larvae, then it will be as true of fish larvae as it is of invertebrates. That wide variation in the population of fish larvae does occur has been shown for the English Channel by Russell (1940). From Fig. 8–5 it will be seen that not only is there about an eightfold range in average catches in different years, but this follows a rather regular curve suggestive of a long-period cycle. Correlations between the occurrence of certain plankton indicator species and chemical and physical characteristics of the water suggest that the cause lies in the varying location of certain water masses. The effects of these progressive changes in the stock of young fish are reflected in the landings of herrings at Plymouth during the period. These have fluctuated considerably, with good and bad years, but there is a clear over-all drop, accompanied by a steady decrease in the proportion of young fish in the catches, as shown in Table 8–1. There is a growing feeling that success in the larval phase, combined with change over from the planktonic to the adult habitat, is a major cause of short-period, and perhaps also of long-period, fluctuations of adult fish.

The change from the planktonic larval stage to the stage of unfished young is a drastic one, probably even more so when the adults are bottom-living than when they are pelagic. Of course some species are segregated from the older fish at this stage, either by living in separate shoals or by occupying a different type of habitat, but for the sake of simplicity we are assuming here that both habitat and food are much

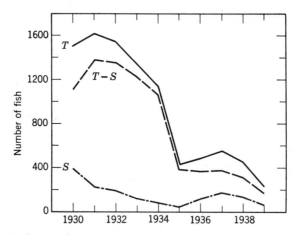

Figure 8–5. The trend over a period of years in the numbers of young fish taken off Plymouth: *T*, total young fish, excluding clupeoids; *T* − *S*, total excluding summer spawners; *S*, summer spawners. (After Russell, 1940.)

the same. For bottom-living forms it is necessary that the change to this second group should occur over the right type of bottom and where suitable food will be available. Presumably, if suitable conditions are not present, the change can be delayed for a certain period, but not indefinitely. The coincidence of water with suitable conditions for the larvae and bottom with suitable conditions for the later stages is therefore required, and the currents must be such as to produce this coincidence during a more or less limited period. The work of Walford (1938) on the haddock of Georges Bank illustrates this. This is a self-contained community in which the adults spawn on the banks, the larvae inhabit the water over the bank, and recruitment of the adult stock is dependent on these same larvae. For the 2 years studied, the current systems were such that in one the bulk of the larvae remained

over the banks and were able to settle there when old enough, and in
the other year a high proportion of them were swept off over deep
water which would be unsuitable for them as they grew up. That
otherwise suitable grounds may never receive supplies of larvae sufficient to produce the stock of adults which they are capable of support-
ing is indicated by the success of transplanted plaice and other species
in Scandinavian waters and other areas. Poulson (1930) has demonstrated as much as a fiftyfold variation in the numbers of cod larvae in

TABLE 8–1

Herring Landings at Plymouth

(Kemp, 1938)

Season, Dec.–Jan.	Weight Landed, cwt.	Average Weight of Landing, cwt.	Percentage Six Years and Under
1924–25	83,600	40	91
1925–26	82,800	23	82
1926–27	45,900	17	66
1927–28	82,800	46	83
1928–29	42,200	27.5	81
1929–30	34,300	39	71
1930–31	44,100	33	72
1931–32	21,000	18	52
1932–33	47,800	34	35
1933–34	29,780	30	35
1934–35	46,600	28	25
1935–36	33,800	16	<20
1936–37	11,700	6	<20
1937–38	28.5	9.5	

the Belt Sea in different years, and the close correlation between their
abundance and the salinity of the water points to mutual dependence
on varying water movements (Fig. 8–6). Any direct control of the
success of the larvae by the salinity is improbable in this case. This
effect of current changes may well carry larvae away from one ground
and favoring another. Within the same area it may also show different effects on species spawning at slightly different times. It is not
surprising, therefore, to find little agreement between either species or
widely separated localities for good and bad years. As for annual
fluctuations in the numbers of larvae, there is a parallel here with the
observed differences from year to year in the quantity of spat fall of
many invertebrates whose larvae are planktonic.

Having settled into the adult habitat, this unfished group is likely to be controlled largely by two factors, food supply and predation. It has been claimed that trawling on the grounds occupied by bottom fish may destroy their source of food. This is debatable, and it is probable that a far greater source of variation lies in natural fluctuations in the quantity and nature of food on the ground and in the rate of predation. We know, at present, very little about either of these

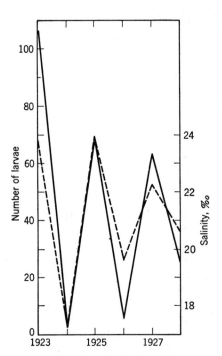

points. The existence of a predator-prey relation can be assumed, and it must be a more slowly adjusting relationship than that found in the more rapidly reproducing planktonic community. Most predators are able to change their staple diet when a food item becomes scarce, so in a season when a fish is scarce by reason of poor recruitment, its predators would not have to prey that much more heavily on the survivors but could turn to other food. Herringtom (1948) has postulated a simple case in which the predation rate decreases as the population of prey increases. Lacking evidence either way, we might equally well argue that the rate would increase with increase in the prey. Even in forms as low as copepods it has been shown that there is a degree of "learning," for an animal that has re-

Figure 8–6. Graph showing the correlation between the number of cod larvae caught in the Belt Sea in successive years (solid line) and the salinity of the water (broken line). (After Poulson, 1930.)

ceived a diet rich in a particular food species tends to take that species selectively thereafter from a mixture of available food. Further, a rich supply of food frequently results in a concentration of predators around it, whereas a poor supply stimulates them to move to other feeding grounds. Diving birds undoubtedly congregate where fish are abundant, although there is no evidence that the resulting mortality rate is higher than where both they and their prey are fewer. The nature of the predator-prey relation must, then, await further study before it will be safe to make generalizations.

It is unlikely that inadequacy of food supply often results in actual starvation. It seems more likely that the stock is thereby rendered less efficient in avoiding predators, in resisting parasitism, or in other ways. Further, since a correlation between growth rate and food supply has been proved, a well-fed, and therefore more rapidly growing, young fish will pass through this phase rapidly and therefore be subject to predation for a shorter period. The individual food supply may possibly vary by virtue of its suitability to the species in question. It may also vary because either the fish population or the food concentration may vary. As an example of the first, a heavy spat fall of a bivalve such as *Venus mercenaria* might at first provide a valuable food supply for young and old plaice. But as the *Venus* grows larger, only the larger plaice can crush their shells, and still later perhaps only rays will be capable of doing so. If alternative food is not available locally, this will constitute a changing food supply, so far as the plaice are concerned, although the quantity of food material present on that area of bottom might not have changed.

There is little information on fluctuations in the total food supply available on the fish feeding grounds. Davis (1923, 1925) showed extensive variation from year to year in the beds of small lamellibranchs which are an important constituent of the food of plaice, haddock, and other fish on the Dogger Bank. One bed was reported to contain about 4.5×10^{12} of a single species, and almost all of a single year group. In the haddock fishery on Georges Bank, a correlation has been found pointing to competition for food between adults and young. Poorer catches have followed those years when adults and young have shared the same area than when they have been on separate grounds.

When we come to the final group of fishable size, the main concern of fishery research has been to produce and maintain the most valuable possible yield from the population. Since no more can be taken out of a stock than is put into it, without depleting the stock, there is clearly a limit to the amount of sustained fishing that is possible. However, this is to a considerable extent self-regulatory (W. F. Thompson, 1937; Thompson and Bell, 1934). Other things being equal, a sudden increase in the amount of fishing gear in use on a given population will result in a corresponding quick rise in catches. If the rate of recruitment remains unchanged, the increased catching rate will at once begin to reduce the size of the population, and as the density drops, the catch per unit effort will also drop (Fig. 8–7). Finally equilibrium will become established with the same annual catch being removed from the ground but more effort being required

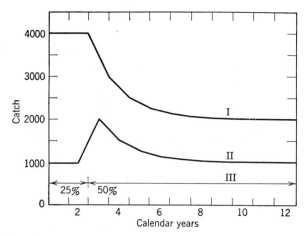

Figure 8–7. Changes in a stock of fish (I) and of the catch (II) as a result of a change, (III), at the end of the second year, from 25 to 50 per cent removal per year. (After W. F. Thompson, 1937.)

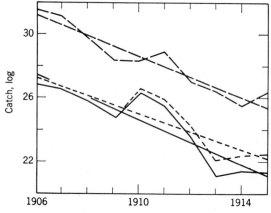

Figure 8–8. Graph showing the decreasing catch of Pacific halibut during a period when the fishing intensity was increasing. Solid line, catch per unit of gear; upper broken lines, catch per hour of fishing; lower broken lines, corrected catch per unit of gear. (After Thompson et al., 1931.)

in the process. Although this is a considerable oversimplification, it is in agreement with various observations. For example Fig. 8–8 shows the drop in yield per unit gear and per hour of fishing in the Pacific halibut fishery as the latter increased (Thompson et al., 1931), and Fig. 8–9 shows the observed values for this same fishery for a limited period of years compared with theoretical changes based on assumed natural and fishing mortality rates of 10 per cent and 47 per cent per

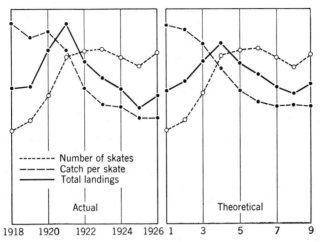

Figure 8–9. The left-hand figure shows the actual catches of Pacific halibut over a number of years, and the right-hand figure the calculated values, assuming a mortality rate of 10 per cent, and a fishing rate of 47 per cent per year. A skate is a unit of fishing gear. (After Thompson and Bell, 1934.)

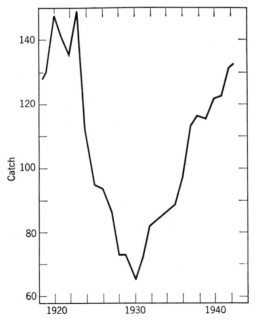

Figure 8–10. The catch of halibut on the Pacific grounds during a period of decline and recovery. (After Burkenroad, 1948.)

annum respectively. This fishery is, in many ways, an ideal test case for theories of fish population dynamics, since it is based on a self-contained population, little complicated with migration on and off the grounds, and with good records of catches, fishing effort, etc., for a series of years. Although statistics for the earlier years of this fishery are not as adequate as could be desired, there is little doubt that, coincident with the growth of the fishery, there was a decrease in the amount of fish caught per unit effort as well as in the average size of fish caught. About 1930, measures were taken to limit the amount of fishing on the ground. Figure 8-10 (Burkenroad, 1948) shows how the catch per unit effort, which had dropped rapidly prior to 1930, rose steadily thereafter. Table 8–2 (Allen et al., 1949) shows how the average size of the fish taken increased during the latter part of the same cycle.

TABLE 8–2

Change in Proportions of Three Commercial Categories of Pacific Halibut in Landing from Two Grounds

Year	Per Cent Chickens, 5–10 lb.		Per Cent Mediums, 10–60 lb.		Per Cent Large, over 60 lb.	
	Kodiak	Trinity	Kodiak	Trinity	Kodiak	Trinity
1931	18.5	23.4	68.1	71.6	13.4	5.0
1936	15.6	14.6	61.6	71.4	22.8	24.0
1942	8.4	6.4	66.2	71.9	25.4	21.7
1947	7.6	8.4	57.9	57.9	34.5	32.4

Burkenroad (1948) has examined the changes in the stock on the ground in relation to the extent of commercial fishing. According to him, the quantity of fish removed commercially is quite inadequate to account for the observed change. "Thus, a stock of estimated average magnitude of only 375 million pounds in 1932–1944, subject to a fishing mortality averaging 7 per cent per year, nearly doubled during the period. In contrast, a stock averaging 488 million pounds in 1915–1926, and then subject to a fishing mortality averaging only 4 per cent per year, declined to one third during the period." Since the Pacific halibut fishery has heretofore been considered as the most clear-cut example of the effect of fishing on a population, and since the deductions that have been drawn are, at least, controversial, it seems best to consider the reaction of a fishery to the fishing as still doubtful. On the other hand it is unlikely that the marked effects on the North Sea fisheries of the reduction in fishing intensities during World Wars I and II were coincidence. As examples, Baerends (1947) shows the rather steady decline in total landings of haddock from 1903 to 1918 and the marked rise in the first few years following the end of the war in 1918 (Fig. 8–11). Catch per unit time spent in fishing is some-times a better index of availability of fish. For the North Sea, this value as much as doubled for some species of fish after the reduction in fishing effort during World War I. Thereafter there was a steady decline again similar to that before the war. A similar effect was

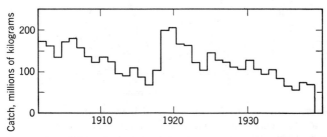

Figure 8–11. The total catch of bottom fish in the North Sea, showing the steady downward trend during peace time and the recovery after the 1914–1919 war when the amount of fishing was reduced. When fishing was resumed, the catches were markedly greater for several years. (After Baerends, 1947, in Hahn, 1950.)

shown for World War II (Margetts and Holt, 1948). Comparing the postwar year 1946 with the prewar year 1938, the ratio of catch per 100 fishing hours in the two showed a large increase for most fishes (Table 8–3).

TABLE 8–3

Catch per 100 Hours Fishing Expressed as the Ratio of the Values for 1946 to Those for 1938*

Cod	3.8
Haddock	2.8
Sole	4.7
Turbot	3.7
Whiting	1.2
Dab	1.0

* Data from English steam trawlers from the central and southern North Sea.

This increase was, at least in some fishes, accompanied by an in-crease in the average size of the fish, as shown for the cod in Fig. 8–12, and by a marked increase in growth rate of the younger fish and a decrease for the older fish, as shown for the plaice in Fig. 8–13.

It is difficult to reconcile the results for the Pacific halibut fishery with those for the various North Sea fisheries of bottom fish, in both of which it has been claimed there was serious overfishing, but perhaps the answer may lie, at least partly, in the different fishing rates. For

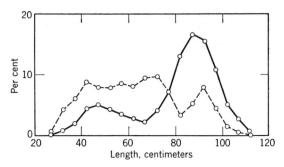

Figure 8–12. Size distribution of cod from between the Dogger Bank and the Firth of Forth. The broken line shows the condition in 1938 and the solid line those in 1946. The average size had risen during the war years when there was little fishing. (After Margetts and Holt, 1948.)

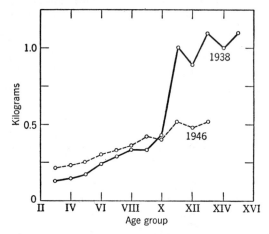

Figure 8–13. The average weight of the different year groups of plaice in the North Sea, showing the effects of reduced fishing during the war years. In 1946, after the war, the younger fish showed a much increased growth, and the larger fish a reduced growth. (After Margetts and Holt, 1948.)

the halibut Thompson and Harrington (1930) indicate a fishing mortality rate of 10 per cent per annum, and for the North Sea plaice Hickling (1938) gives a value of 40–55 per cent.

In view of these doubts, we will concern ourselves only with certain special cases where the evidence appears to be relevant and refer readers to original papers for discussion of proposed formulations of the dynamics of populations of fish (e.g., Baranov, 1918, 1925; E. S. Russell, 1931, 1939, 1942; Graham, 1935, 1938, 1939; W. F. Thompson,

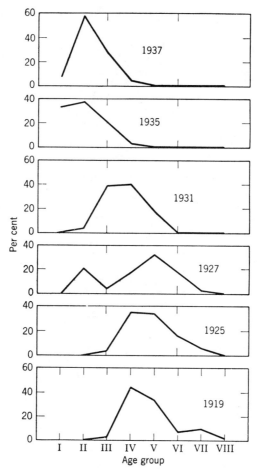

Figure 8–14. Age distribution of Baltic dab, showing the reduction in the proportion of old fish from 1919 (bottom), when there was little or no dab fishery, to 1937 (top), when the fishery was well established. (After Molander, 1938.)

1937; Ricker, 1940). Fishing almost always acts selectively on the larger specimens, and if a population shows any reaction to fishing, then it should show a relative increase in the proportion of young fish and a decrease of the older ones. The dab and flounder fishery in the Baltic appears to show this clearly (Molander, 1938). Thus (Fig.

8–14) in 1919, when little fishing was done, there was a preponderance of fourth- and fifth-year dabs; whereas, in 1937, when the fishery
was well developed, second-year fish predominated. However, despite the drop in average age, the average size of the fish increased

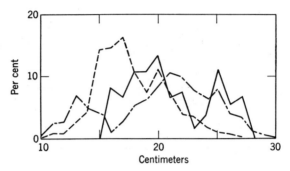

Figure 8–15. Size distribution of Baltic dab during the period covered in Fig.
8–14, showing the increase in size, despite the decrease in age, since the estab-
lishment of the fishery. The broken line represents Sept. 1921, the dash-dot
line Oct. 1927, and the solid line Sept. 1937. (After Molander, 1938.)

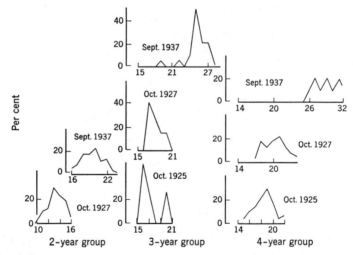

Figure 8–16. Average size of the 2-, 3-, and 4-year groups of Baltic dab, showing the increase in growth rate during the period covered in Fig. 8–14. (After
Molander, 1938.)

(Fig. 8–15), and comparison of the average size of particular year
groups at the beginning and end of this period (Fig. 8–16) shows
that the explanation lies in the great increase in growth rate. It is
assumed that the food supply was a linking factor and that the re-

moval of the older fish decreased the competition for food, allowing the younger fish to grow faster.

In the absence of such compensation of growth rate, a compensatory numerical increase in the population might be looked for, so that the total weight of fish on the ground may remain unchanged, although the average weight has decreased. Although this may have no harmful effect and may possibly have even a beneficial effect on the fish population, the market value of the landings may be affected considerably. Merriman (1941) gives a theoretical case for the striped bass in which the market price increases with greater size, whereas mortality rate, as indicated from tagging experiments, drops. Considering a single year group with an initial population of 1000 fish at the time when they reach fishable size, he obtains the values given in Table 8–4.

TABLE 8–4

	Age, years	Aver- age Length, cm.	Aver- age Weight, lb.	Total Weight, lb.	Aver- age Price, cents per lb.	Mar- ket Value
Assuming 1000 bass were available in 1936, of which 400 would be caught in 1936 (fishing mortality 40%); 200 would die in 1936 (natural mortality 33% of those not caught), leaving—	2	31	0.75	300.0	6.5	$19.50
400 bass available in 1937, of which 100 would be caught in 1937 (f.m., 25%); 100 would die in 1937 (n.m., 33% of those not caught), leaving—	3	41	2.0	200.0	9.5	19.00
200 bass available in 1938, of which 30 would be caught in 1938 (f.m., 15%); 57 would die in 1938 (n.m., 33% of those not caught), leaving—	4	50	3.5	105.0	10.0	10.50
113 bass available in 1939, of which 11 would be caught in 1939 (f.m., 10%); 34 would die in 1939 (n.m., 33% of those not caught), leaving—	5	58	5.5	60.5	10.0	6.05
68 bass available in 1940, of which 3 would be caught in 1940 (f.m., 5%).	6	66	8.0	24.0	10.0	2.40
Total number of bass caught during 1936–1940, 544.	Total			689.5		$57.45

If now this same population is allowed to live for another year before fishing begins, i.e., at 3 years old instead of 2, and a similar tabulation is made, the number of fish caught for the whole period drops from 544 to 242, but the total weight drops only slightly, from 689.5 to 661.5 lb., and the value actually rises slightly, from $57.45 to $64.48. On the other hand, if fishing does not begin for another year, there is a large drop in market value to $43.60. This indicates, then, that, from the point of view of market value, there is an optimum age at which fishing should begin, and either catching the fish too young or allowing them to grow too old before fishing begins may result in decreased cash yield.

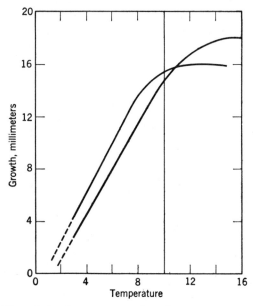

Figure 8–17. The relation between growth and sea temperature in two populations of plaice. (After Jansen, 1938.)

Burkenroad (1948) advances the possibility that fish populations may tend to undergo long-period natural fluctuations and that the observed changes in the halibut and other fisheries may be accounted for in terms of cycles in food supply or other factors little affected by fishing. Much of what has been said about the effects of such factors on the abundance, survival, and growth of the younger groups applies also to the fishable groups. Thus, from seasonal data, Jansen (1938) has shown an almost linear relation between the growth of plaice and temperature, except for the hottest months of the year when a more or less constant level is attained (Fig. 8–17). With regard to food, Dawes (1930, 1931) has shown that, in the plaice (*Pleuronectes pla-*

tessa), there is a basal requirement of about 1–2 per cent of the body weight per day. This is for fish more than about 20 gm. in weight. For a well-fed fish, about 25 per cent of the total food taken during the year is used for this maintenance, and of the remainder, about 5 gm. of food result in an increase in weight of 1 gm. in the fish. The growth increments vary seasonally, and the maintenance ratio decreases with increasing size. Beyond these figures we know little about the actual food requirements of the commercially valuable fish. Work on the growth of fish under conditions of artificially enriched

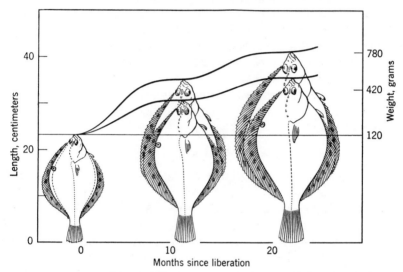

Figure 8–18. Growth of native plaice in the Belt Sea (lower curve) compared with that of plaice transferred to that area from the North Sea (upper curve). (After Blegvad, 1933.)

plankton production, as well as various experiments with transplantation of fish to areas of richer feeding, have shown the dependence of growth on food supply under natural conditions. With transplantations, however, there may be a complication because of an apparent inherent difference in growth in different races, as shown in Fig. 8–18.

Finally, and completing the cycle to the egg stage, we have the possibility that changes in the adult population will affect the supply of eggs, and so the success of resulting broods. As we have already observed there seems little likelihood of a population's being reduced to the stage where this could take place, since there are probably always ample eggs produced. If a fishery were to remove all, or a large enough fraction of the adults before they had had the opportunity to spawn once, then the condition would be serious, but this seems very unlikely. If the average size of fish in the population is reduced, then the output of spawn will be reduced, since this increases with increasing size of fish. Wynne-Edwards (1929) gives the following values for the herring,

Males   G.W. = 0.261 gm.   B.W. = 11.5 gm.
Females   G.W. = 0.266 gm.   B.W. = 16.2 gm.

where B.W. = body weight and G.W. = gonad weight. His data do not offer any evidence of senility, in which gonad production decreased in older fish, and there is little evidence to support this possibility, so that removal of the oldest fish from a population could hardly be beneficial in this connection. The significance of the conserving of sufficient spawners receives less emphasis today than it did in the earlier days of fishery work.

Returning now to our earlier attempt to formulate the changes in a group of the population over a period of time, we expressed them in the following way

$$W_t = W_o - M + G - L + R$$

where W_o and W_t are the original and final weights of the population and M is the mortality rate by all causes, G the growth, L the loss by change into higher groups, and R the recruitment from lower groups.

Since the effects of the various environmental factors vary greatly in their relative significance at different stages in the life history of the fish, accurate formulation calls for subdivision into a series of groups as we have done. For various species, reasonably good estimates have been made of the magnitude, both numerically and by weight, of the total stock of the fishable group. In all groups, growth has been shown to be dependent on such factors as food supply and temperature, and the former is a function of the total food present in the area, the total population competing for it, and possibly the suitability of the food. On none of these points is there adequate information, so growth must at present remain an average value that is known to vary rather widely and unpredictably. Very little is known of natural mortality rate or how it varies, but it appears to be, in many cases, considerably smaller than the mortality rate due to fishing, and on this there is relatively good information. However, this fact applies only to the fishable group, and to a small extent, to the next younger in so far as some of its members are killed during trawling or other fishing operations. Mortality rates in the egg and larval stages are unknown. On the values of loss from one group and recruitment into the next, our information is almost entirely confined to the recruitment into the fishable group and the production of eggs by that group. It is clear, then that only on the fishable group do we begin to have adequate data, and even here much more is needed, despite the great amount of work that has already been done. A picture of the whole cycle is needed, with all its subdivisions. Although the actual fishery is concerned with only one of these, its success appears to depend on all of them, and there are indications that the larval group, and the recruitment from this to the next older, are the two most critical stages in the life cycle in producing fluctuations in the stock.

9

Organisms

(Continued)

SUBLITTORAL BOTTOM COMMUNITIES

As in most ecological studies, the first phase of the investigation of the bottom fauna and flora of the shallower seas lies in the enumeration of the species present and in determining their relative abundance. The second phase lies in the study of the more important forms and their relation to environmental factors, and the third phase lies in the formulation of rules that will allow us to predict the nature of the community which will be produced under certain environmental conditions. As we have seen, a start has been made on this third phase for plankton.

Petersen (1914, 1915, 1918, etc.) has been a leader in the study of the soft-bottom fauna below low watermark and in the definition of the types of community found there. His work has already been referred to, and some of his typical communities are figured (Figs. 9–1, 9–2, 9–3). Certain indicator species were chosen by him to define

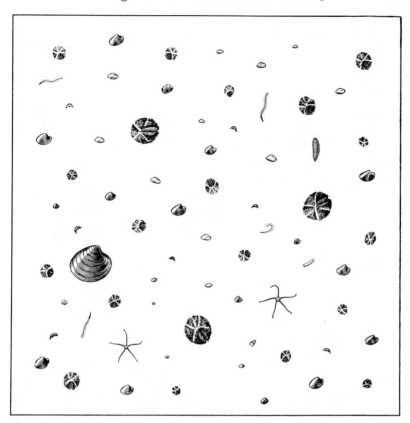

Figure 9–1. The fauna of ¼ square meter of sandy bottom with a typical *"Venus"* community. This includes:

Venus gallina	18	Echinocardium cordatum	3
Tellina fabula	10	E. cordatum, juv.	18
Montacuta ferruginosa	4	Ophioglypha albida	1
Solen pellucidus	1	O. affinis	1
Philine aperta	1	Gammaridae	7
Travisia forbesi	1	Actiniidae	1
Nephthys sp.	3		
Aricia armiger	1		

(After Petersen, 1918.)

the various communities. These were usually echinoderms or molluscs, of species that were present in sufficient numbers in relatively small grab samples and did not mix to too great an extent into other communities. They were, of course, often mixed with large numbers of individuals of species that were less suitable for definition of the community. His work was mainly confined to the shallow waters of

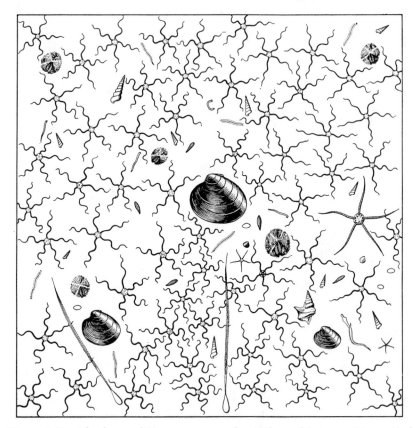

Figure 9–2. The fauna of ¼ square meter of a sandy-mud bottom with a typical *"Echinocardium-filiformis"* community. This includes:

Abra nitida	4	*Glycera* sp.	1
Corbula gibba	1	*Nephthys* sp.	6
Cyprina islandica		*Brada* sp.	5
>3 cm.	2	*Terebellides stromi*	3
<3 cm.	1	Nemertini—fragments	
Axinus flexuosus	1	*Amphiura filiformis*	60
Nucula tenuis	1	*Ophioglypha albida juv.*	2
Aporrhais pes-pelecani	1	*O. texturata*	1
Turritella terebra	10	*Echinocardium cordatum*	5
Chaetoderma nitidulum	1	Gammaridae	2
Virgularia mirabilis	2		

(After Petersen, 1918.)

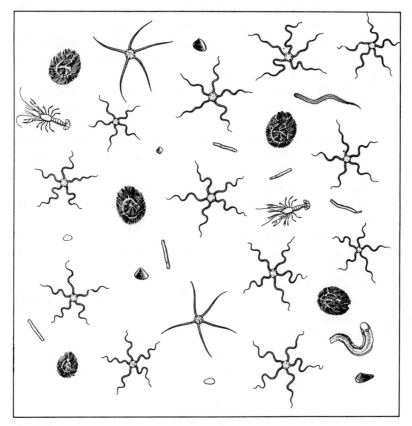

Figure 9–3. The fauna of ¼ square meter of muddy bottom with a typical "*Brissopsis-chiajei*" community. This includes:

Abra nitida	2	*Balanoglossus kuppferi*	1
Axinus flexuosus	1	*Amphiura chiajei*	12
Leda pernula	1	*Ophioglypha albida*	2
Nucula sulcata	2	*Brissopsis lyrifera*	5
Nephthys sp.	1	*Calocaris macandreae*	2
Maldanidae—present			

(After Petersen, 1918.)

the Danish coasts, and in these he distinguished the following nine communities:

I. The *Macoma* community, characterized by *Macoma baltica,* and found on the southern coasts and in the Baltic.

II. The *Syndosmya (Abra)* community, characterized by *Syndosmya alba,* and frequently containing also *Echinocardium cordatum,*

Macoma calcarea, Astarte banksii, A. borealis, and *A. elliptica.* This is found especially in the Belt Sea and fjords.

III. The *Venus* community, characterized by *Venus gallina,* frequently with *E. cordatum* and *Tellina fabula,* found on the open coasts of the Kattegat and in the North Sea.

IV. The *Echinocardium-Amphiura filiformis* community, characterized by *E. cordatum* and *Amphiura filiformis,* found at intermediate depths in the Kattegat.

V. The *Brissopsis-Amphiura chiajei* community, characterized by *Brissopsis lyrifera* and *A. chiajei* found in the deepest part of the Kattegat.

VI. The *Brissopsis-Ophiura sarsi* community, characterized by *B. Lyrifera* and *Ophiura sarsi,* found in the deeper parts of the Skagerak.

VII. The *Amphilepis-Pecten* community, characterized by the *Amphilepis norvegica* and *Pecten vitreus* found in the deepest parts of the Skagerak.

VIII. The *Haploops* community, *Haploops tubicola,* usually with *Pecten septemradiatus* and *Lima loscombii,* and found, with a rather restricted distribution, in the southeastern Kattegat.

IX. The deep *Venus* community, characterized by *V. gallina,* with *Psammobia faroensis, Abra prismatica,* and *Mactra elliptica,* and with the *E. cordatum* of the shallow *Venus* community replaced by *E. flavescens* and *Spatangus purpureus.* This is sporadic only in the Kattegat, but widespread in the North Sea.

In addition to characterizing the communities of the area, data are also given on the numbers and rough weights of the fauna per square meter. Rough weights are made wet with the shell, if any, present. Some data are provided on the relation of the dry weight of the tissues to the rough weight in the various species, so that calculations can be made of the standing crop of animal tissue per unit area. Table 9-1 (modified from Petersen, 1918, p. 27) shows rough weights per square meter of bottom for two typical areas. Tentative estimates of dry tissue weight have been added. Dry weights for other areas are also given and these range from 35.1 gm. per square meter in the North Sea to 2.0–4.9 in the Kattegat and 0.8–1.5 in the Baltic. These figures represent the standing crop in the area. Detailed information on its turnover rate is lacking, but it is Petersen's opinion that the annual production equals or exceeds the standing crop. According to Thorson, this is true for communities composed mainly of annual species, but in many the major components are slow-growing forms

TABLE 9–1

Quantities of the Commoner Forms in Grams per Square Meter
tissue weights

Organism	Thirsted Bredning Rough Wt.*	Thirsted Bredning Dry Wt.†	Nissum Bredning Rough Wt.*	Nissum Bredning Dry Wt.†
Large bivalves				
Mytilus	38.35	1.07	1.56	0.04
Modiola	0.02	<0.01	<0.01	<0.01
Cyprina	32.61	1.01	0.83	0.03
Ostrea	3.46	c. 0.01	2.28	c. 0.07
Mya truncata, large	229.91	15.15	0.00	0.00
Mya sp., small	8.68	0.57	0.03	<0.01
	313.03	17.81	4.70	0.14
Small bivalves				
Solen	9.22	0.77	0.70	0.06
Corbula	1.78	0.04	27.98	0.67
Nucula	4.21	0.22	29.67	1.54
Abra alba	7.20	0.50	3.42	0.24
A. nitida	0.00	0.00	1.45	0.10
Macoma baltica	0.00	0.00	2.48	0.14
Cardium	0.32	0.02	0.00	0.00
	22.73	1.55	65.70	2.75
Large gastropods				
Buccinum	4.18	0.47	4.06	0.45
Nassa reticulata				
N. pygmaea	2.08	0.20	2.70	0.26
	6.26	0.67	6.76	0.71
Small gastropods				
Acera bullata	0.19	0.03	0.03	<0.01
Philine aperta	0.68	0.10	0.83	0.12
	0.87	0.13	0.86	0.12
Polychaetes	10.62	1.88	9.77	1.73
Asteroids				
Asterias rubens	4.68	0.34	5.47	0.39
Ophiuroids				
Ophioglypha	11.59	0.44	12.20	0.46
Spatangoids				
Echinocardium cordatum, adult	0.00	0.00	88.80	0.09
E. cordatum, juv.	0.01	<0.01	46.44	0.47
	16.28	0.78	152.91	1.41
Tunicates				
Ascidiella	0.00	0.00	30.53	3.16
Total for all forms	360.79	22.82	271.23	10.02

* Rough weight taken wet, with shells.
† Dry tissue weight.

such as *Macoma, Astarte,* and *Turritella.* In these the annual productivity may be considerably less than the standing crop.

In the sandy and muddy areas so far considered, there is comparatively little algal growth, and what there is is mostly confined to stones and dead shells. Near shore, however, there is a belt of *Zostera marina,* and estimates were made of the amounts of both this and its fauna. The grass and algae from this zone, when detached, contribute largely to the supply of vegetable food in the deeper zones. The replacement of leaves on *Zostera* during the year is about equal to the leaves present at any one time. The many epiphytic algae growing on the leaves will be lost at the same time and so add to the contribution of vegetable detritus to the sea bottom. For the whole area of Danish coast line, the annual production of *Zostera* is roughly estimated as 24,000,000 tons wet weight. A large fraction of this is deposited in the bottom sediments which have a very high organic content. Carbon contents ranging from 0.34 to 10.2 per cent were recorded, with a carbon:nitrogen ratio of 8.1 to 12.6. Small gastropods are extremely abundant on the *Zostera,* totaling as much as 100,000 per square meter at some seasons. They are annual, however, and may drop to almost none at other times. Petersen placed great emphasis on *Zostera* as a primary producer of food. However, despite the very great reduction in the *Zostera* beds in recent years, there has been no reduction in animal production in the Kattegat.

Petersen is of the opinion that, although the nature of the sediment is undoubtedly of importance in determining the nature of the community in some species, other controlling factors are more generally important, and of these he considers animal control to be the principal one. He shows, for example, that a pure sand typically supports a *Macoma* community in Danish waters and in the Baltic, whereas in the Kattegat it characteristically supports a *Venus* community. A pure clay in the Kattegat has typically a *Brissopsis–A. chiajei* community, but in the Skagerak a *Brissopsis–O. sarsii* or *Amphilepsis-Pecten* community. The same species may also be found on quite different sediments, *Macoma,* for example, ranging from pure sand to pure mud. Petersen points out the heavy mortality in young lamellibranchs in those sediments in which ophiuroids are present to feed on them. This no doubt has a considerable controlling influence. However, Ford (1923) recorded a community in the Plymouth area which contained 1800 *Syndosmya alba* and 220 *Amphiura filiformis* at the same time. Thorson has pointed out that, about two months before spawning, the ophiuroids cease to feed, and it is just at this time that much of the mollusc spat is settling. By the time feeding is resumed, a large proportion of the bivalves have grown too large to be taken by the ophiuroids. Competition between different species of mollusc is also no doubt important.

Allen (1899), Ford (1923), J. E. Smith (1932), and others have made similar surveys of the fauna on the British coasts and for many species found a rather marked specific limitation to particular types of sediment. For attached forms, it was clear that the lack of stability of gravel where there was current or wave action was an important limiting factor.

Wilson and others have shown that certain larvae which are ready to metamorphose will not do so unless a suitable substratum is available and will even delay their metamorphosis for a considerable time if no suitable environment is found. If this is a characteristic reaction of the larvae of bottom invertebrates, then it is clear that there must be a marked selective colonization of particular types of substratum by the young. Further evidence in support of this is given by the fact that clam beds in North America (*Venus mercenaria*), which have declined in value through lack of settlement of spat, may often be recolonized when soil is spread over the surface, or even if the surface is ploughed. That many of the communities are very constant in their nature is shown by Smith's 1932 resurvey of the area covered by Allen about 1899 and by Holme's (1950) resurvey of the area covered by Ford (1923). Petersen had made a rough estimate of the bottom production in the Kattegat (Fig. 9–4). The production of *Zostera* per year is put at a wet weight of at least 24,000,000 tons. It is probably greater than this, and there is algal production also, but some will be lost by drifting out of the area. He classifies as useless animals those that are not utilized directly either by humans or by fish of commercial value. The 5,000,000 tons which these represent are composed largely of the big thick-shelled *Cyprina islandica* and the urchins *Echinocardium* and *Brissopsis*. The useful animals, totaling 1,000,000 tons, are mainly polychaetes and small bivalves. These are fed on directly by plaice and other flatfish of which the production is estimated from the annual landings as 5000 tons. They are also fed on directly by cod and other gadoids, of which the annual landings are 6000 tons, and by various carnivorous crustacea, polychaetes, and gastropods which are in turn fed on by the cod. Various small fishes, not of commercial value, feed on them and themselves serve as food for the cod. In both cases the extra step in the food chain implies less efficient utilization in the production of cod. Finally, a large fraction of the polychaetes and small bivalves are fed on by carnivores such as starfish, which are themselves of little or no value as food for the commercial fishes.

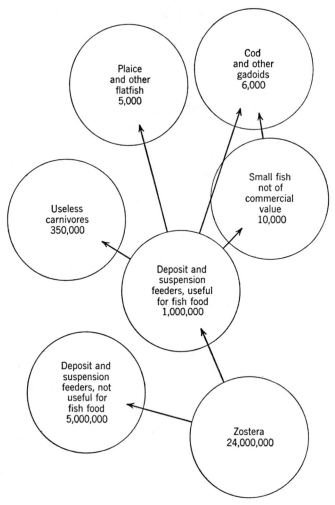

Figure 9–4. Schematic diagram of the major steps in the food chain involved in the production of marketable fish in the Kattegat. The figures are estimates of the annual production of the area in tons. (After Petersen, 1915.)

These estimates are admittedly tentative, but they serve to give some idea of the scale of production of the various forms.

Thorson (1946, 1950) has brought together a very considerable body of information on the reproduction of bottom-living invertebrates from Danish waters. In this area about 80 per cent of the bottom invertebrates have planktonic larvae, and over 60 per cent produce larvae which remain at least several weeks in the plankton. Only a small percentage of them are viviparous or produce young which hatch at a crawling stage from egg capsules or have other form of protection. The total number of larvae in the plankton is very large. The data shown in Fig. 7–52 indicate numbers usually over a thousand, and sometimes over 20,000, in a column of water from the surface to a depth of 18 meters, and under a 0.5-square-meter area. Seasonally, the numbers show a peak sometime during the summer and a minimum in winter. The relative proportions of larvae from different species is determined not only by the relative abundance of the adults but also by the numbers of eggs they produce and the duration of the planktonic existence of each species. Figure 7–51 shows the order of variation in the egg production in different species. From the known population of the sea bottom in Danish waters, and the proportions of the different groups that have pelagic larvae, Thorson has made an approximate calculation of how the groups would be expected to be represented in the plankton. As will be seen from Table 9–2, in general, the figures agree well with the observed values from net hauls.

TABLE 9–2

Comparison of Observed with Expected Larvae Output

(Thorson, 1946)

Group	Observed Per Cent in Planktonic Larvae	Expected Per Cent in Planktonic Larvae
Lamellibranchs	40	57.3
Prosobranchs	10	12.5
Tectibranchs	0.5	1.7
Polychaetes	20–25	10.9
Echinoderms	20–25	1.9
Bryozoa	3.5	12.9
Others	—	2.8

No allowance was made in these expected values for variation between different species in the numbers of eggs produced. The very low observed values for echinoderms have not been satisfactorily explained. In general there is a tendency for spawning to occur either with rising water temperature or when it is at its maximum, and since these occur later in the year in deep water than in shallow water, there is an over-all tendency for the shallow species to spawn earlier than the deeper ones (Fig. 9–5).

There is also considerable agreement between the occurrence of large numbers of larvae and the presence of rich phytoplankton.

However, as Thorson points out, most of the larval forms are incapable
of swallowing anything as large as the commoner diatoms, and their
diet comprises mainly the very small nannoplankton. The difficulties in identifying and counting the small nannoplankton forms has
so far left us with but little information on their seasonal variations in
abundance. There is little doubt that temperature is the prime factor

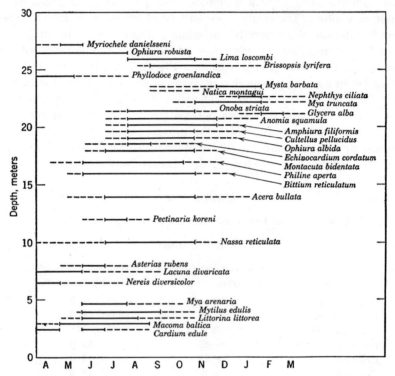

Figure 9–5. The seasons of reproduction of a series of Danish bottom invertebrates, showing the tendency to later breeding in those from deeper water.
(After Thorson, 1946.)

in controlling both the ripening of the genital products and their
spawning. The critical lower limit of temperature for spawning is
higher than that for the ripening of the genital products, and this in
turn is higher than that for survival of the adults. We would expect,
therefore, an animal which attains wide distribution by means of its
pelagic larvae to have three limiting zones. In the warmest of these,
spawning would take place in the normal way. In the next colder,
ripenings of the genital products would occur, but temperatures would
not rise sufficiently high to permit their liberation. In the third, and

still colder zone, adults survive, having settled there as spat which had been spawned in a warmer area, but neither maturation nor spawning could occur. Beyond this zone would, of course, be another in which the adults also were unable to tolerate the low temperatures. This situation is, however, complicated, as has been discussed in an earlier section, by the fact that the critical temperatures for spawning and maturation, and those for survival, occur at different seasons. For maturation and spawning, a sufficiently high temperature, of the necessary duration, at any time of year, is required, and hence it is the summer maximum temperature that is critical. For survival of the adults, it is the minimum temperature to be encountered that matters, and hence the winter minimum is critical. This could give rise to a situation in which summer spawning was possible but winter survival of the adults impossible, and therefore only those forms with a life cycle of a few months could settle and spawn in the area. Further, the area would have to be restocked from the outside each spring.

Although temperature appears to be the factor controlling the onset of spawning in many, if not most species, it is not always so. Thorson refers to *Mya truncata* and *Saxicava arctica* in Greenland waters which begin to spawn at a time when temperature conditions are remarkably stable for a considerable period. In this case there appears to be a more definite connection between the onset of spawning and the period of heavy increase in the phytoplankton. In these Greenland waters there are very few species which produce pelagic larvae, and Thorson considers that this is correlated with the shortness of the seasons during which they would be able to find sufficient food in the plankton. If this is true it is reasonable that those few species which do produce pelagic larvae should be able to control their spawning period so as to coincide with the time when there is the maximum quantity of food for their use. Incidentally, Thorson also points out that, although so few species do produce pelagic larvae in these northern waters, the few which do are among the most successful of the bottom invertebrates from the point of view of abundance. That the presence of certain food substances in the water may be the required stimulus for spawning in certain other forms is suggested by the observations of Miyazaki (1938) that spawning of male *Ostrea gigas* could be stimulated when an extract of the green algae *Ulva pertusa* and *Enteromorpha* sp. were added to the water.

In many invertebrates either true or pseudocopulation occurs, insuring fertilization of all the eggs and thus avoiding waste. Among those in which the eggs and sperm are shed freely in the water, it has been found that the male almost always begins to spawn before the female.

Further, in many of them spawning of the males is necessary before that of the females can begin, and even if temperature and other conditions are suitable, the females will retain their eggs unless sperm are present in the water.

Although the duration of occurrence of a given species of larva in the plankton will largely reflect the duration of the spawning season of the species, it may also be influenced by the duration of pelagic existence, particularly where this is long relative to the spawning period. The latter varies from a period of only a few days as in the

TABLE 9–3

Comparison of the Duration of Pelagic Existence in Northern and Tropical Echinoderms*

(Modified from Thorson, 1946)

Duration, in days	Northern, %	Tropical, %
0– 00	0	7
10– 20	0	33
20– 30	33	26
30– 40	17	17
40– 50	17	13
50– 60	17	2
60– 70	8	0
70– 80	8	0
80– 90	0	0
90–100	0	2
Number of species	12	46

* The values represent the percentage of echinoderms, for which data are available, falling within the durations shown, 25 per cent of the northern, and 39 per cent of the tropical values are minimal and should perhaps be increased.

polychaete *Arenicola marina* in Danish waters, and in the ophiuroid *Amphiura filiformis,* to forms which can be found breeding throughout the year. The duration of the pelagic state is also widely variable. In some species it is a matter of a few days or even hours. In others it is long, $2\frac{1}{2}$ months for the echinoid *Strongylocentrotus droebachiensis,* and possibly as many as 6 months in the warm-water lobster *Panulirus argus.* Within a single species the period varies considerably with both temperature and availability of food. Thus the length of pelagic life of the larvae of the oyster *Ostrea edulis* is given as 6 days at 22–23°C., 9 to 10 days at 18–21°C., and 13 to 14 days at 16–17°C. (Korringa, 1941). In cultures, at least, it has been shown that the rate of development of various echinoderms is closely dependent on the available supply of food. The average duration of the pelagic stage in northern bottom invertebrates appears to be about three weeks. Apparently this figure does not differ greatly between tropical and northern conditions. There are not many data available for the tropics, but we may compare the figures shown in Table 9–3 compiled by Thorsen, for the echinoderms, in which the differences are relatively small.

If we compare northern and tropical species of the same genus, we get the results shown in Table 9–4.

TABLE 9–4

Northern	Days	Tropical	Days
Ophiothrix fragilis	26	*Ophiothrix triloba*	40
Ophiocomina nigra	35–40	*O. savignyi*	21
		Ophiocomina erinaceus	28
		O. scolopendrina	42 (at least)
		O. lineolata	28

The fate of these pelagic larvae is of prime importance in the restocking of the beds of adults. Only its efficiency in this direction justifies the heavy drain on the parents. Thus, *Littorina littorea* may lose 25–37 per cent of its tissue weight at spawning, and *Balanus balanoides* 30–50 per cent (Moore, 1935, 1937). *Echinus esculentus* (Moore, 1934b) may lose 75 per cent of its gonad volume, and this represents a large fraction of the soft tissues. In the same way, Stott (1931) gives the decrease in glycogen content at the time of spawning as about 44 per cent in *Ostrea*, and 90 per cent in *Mytilus* and *Echinus*. Most of the larvae produced die by predation, only an almost insignificant proportion surviving to repopulate any available bottom. From the point of view of the community as a whole, it might seem more logical to consider the importance of the production of larvae to lie much less in the perpetuation of the species than in the feeding of various members of the community. Incidentally, the food material contained in the larvae which disappear by predation is not wholly lost to the parent species, since many of the parents have been recorded as feeding to a considerable extent on their own young when these are ready to settle. The larvae would thus serve as a kind of extended feeding mechanism by which the adults are able to take advantage of the food supply in a much greater area of water than they could by themselves filter. It is hardly likely, though, that the process is actually profitable to the parent.

Although mortality is heavy, larvae with a pelagic phase insure wide distribution of the species and the possibility of colonizing any space available for them. Thorson has surveyed the possible sources of wastage of larvae and believes the main source to be predation. Earlier workers considered that there was a relatively small chance of a larva's finding a suitable substratum on which to metamorphose, and that a large proportion of the larvae that had reached the stage when they were ready to metamorphose would perish for this reason. It is true that many larvae are very specific in their requirements in this connection, but on the other hand many of them have been shown to be able to postpone metamorphosis for several days or even much longer. During this period their earlier positive reaction to light becomes negative, and they tend to be drifting over the bottom under the influence of whatever currents there are. They are likely to be carried, during this time, over a wide area of bottom, with a very good chance of eventually finding and metamorphosing on the required type of bottom. Wilson (1952), reviewing work on the settlement of planktonic larvae, says that this ability to delay metamorphosis "is possessed by larvae of animals belonging to a number of phyla and may be fairly general, especially for those species which when adult are restricted to specialized environments." He goes on to say, "Apart from a few polychaetes little work has, however, been done on the settling behavior of the larvae of the species living in or on sand or mud bottoms. Many species of invertebrates are restricted in the range of soil types which they inhabit and the waste of larvae, already great from depradations by predators, would be much increased if metamorphosis took place in mid-water followed by chance precipitation onto the bottom. It is of significance, therefore, to find that at least some species when able to metamorphose are capable of distinguishing suitable from unsuitable soils and to postpone metamorphosis for considerable periods of time, if necessary, until a favorable bottom deposit is reached."

However, one consideration deserves mention here, namely that work now in progress on the larvae of the shipworm *Teredo* has shown that although they are capable of surviving as swimming larvae for many days, they will not be able to penetrate wood on which they settle unless they find this within the first day or two. This is probably an extreme case, and most larvae will probably be found to be able to metamorphose, even after a considerable period once they are on the required substratum.

It has been said that a species with pelagic larvae is sure to colonize any available space. It appears though, that the success of such colonization varies greatly from one year to another. It is well known that the spat fall of various molluscs, as well as of some echinoderms and other forms, may have one good year and then several poor ones. The reason for this is not well understood. It has been considered to be due to varying current systems which may, or may not, bring the larvae over the grounds when they are ready to settle. It has also been considered to be caused by varying food availability during the planktonic phase. In this case, however, it appears that most larvae can withstand a reasonable degree of starvation, and that the main effect of shortage of food would be to prolong the pelagic phase, and so expose the larvae to predation for a longer period. With regard to

Figure 9–6. The population densities of two comparable, bottom-living lamellibranchs in successive years in Danish waters. *Abra alba* (broken line) with long pelagic larval life is more variable than *Macoma calcarea* (solid line) which has non-pelagic development. (After Thorson, 1946.)

the current theory, it is known that poor clam beds can often be made to receive a much heavier spat fall if the surface is prepared by ploughing, addition of soil, and other means. Part of the varying spat fall might therefore be due rather to variations from year to year in the nature of the substratum. It is, at least, known that extreme fluctuation in bottom population from one year to another is associated with the possession of pelagic larvae, and that, on the whole, those species which do not have them show a much more uniform population than related species which do (Fig. 9–6). Thorson (1941) has shown, among the prosobranch gastropods, a marked tendency for the higher arctic species to be carnivores rather than herbivores. This is brought out in Table 9–5. Although more of the arctic species are carnivorous, this does not necessarily imply that the total carnivore population is greater. Although no figures are available on this, the situation among the herbivores may well be similar to that shown by Thorson (1950) in which the number of species with planktonic larvae decreases northward. Although this decrease is very marked, the few northern species that do have planktonic larvae are among the most highly successful, as judged by numbers. In the same way, it may prove that, although few prosobranch species are able to function efficiently as herbivores in the far north, those that can do so are highly successful and have but little competition.

TABLE 9–5

The Percentage of Various Feeding Types among Prosobranch Gastropods and the Geographic Variation in Their Relative Values

(Thorson, 1950)

Feeding Type	Den-mark	Faroe Island	S. Ice-land	W. Ice-land	N.W. Ice-land	N. Ice-land	E. Ice-land	N.E. Green-land
Carnivores	28.7	41.8	51.0	42.6	59.5	63.5	64.5	71.1
Herbivores	36.1	41.8	34.7	46.3	35.7	31.7	33.9	24.5
Plankton feeders	4.3	5.4	6.1	3.7	2.4	3.2	1.6	4.4
Commensals and parasites	26.6	9.0	6.1	3.7	0.0	1.6	0.0	0.0
Doubtful	4.3	2.0	2.1	3.7	2.4	0.0	0.0	0.0

Thorson also stated that "it is a general rule that most arctic species in the southern part of their area of distribution prefer larger depths than within their main area of distribution." For example, *Lunatia pallida*, which is a typical arctic shallow-living gastropod is often found at depths of 2000–3000 meters outside the Arctic. Similar changes in vertical distribution are found in the lamellibranchs, *Arca glacialis*, *Pecten groenlandicus*, and *Modiolaria discors*. The brittle star, *Ophiacantha bidentata*, is even more extreme, ranging from shallow arctic waters to more than 4450 meters near the Azores.

THE SUBLITTORAL ALGAL FOREST

Most of the areas of sublittoral bottom which we have discussed so far have been ones with sandy, muddy, and gravel bottoms, on which algal production is not very large. As a result, their fauna is dependent to a considerable extent, for its supply of plant food material, on the phytoplankton and on detritus carried out to them from inshore areas. Except for "grasses," only a relatively small supply of plant material is produced *in situ*. Although it is usual to consider the intertidal zone and the sublittoral zone as separate divisions, it is in many ways better to consider the part of the shores and the shallow water in which plant production is large as one unit. This may then conveniently be subdivided into the part lying between tidemarks or above and the part below low watermark. There are, of course, important habitats lying just below low water but dominated by animals rather than algae, for example coral reefs. These will be considered later. We are concerned here with those belts of extremely heavy algal growth found below low watermark in many parts of the world.

The *Laminaria* forests of northern European waters have received more study than their counterparts in other parts of the world; Kitching (1935, 1941) and Kitching et al. (1934) have explored these forests with the aid of a diving helmet and have studied both their flora and fauna and some of the ecological conditions in them. A few species of large brown algae dominate the vegetations, mainly *Laminaria digitata, L. Cloustoni, L. saccharina, Saccorhiza bulbosa, Alaria esculenta,* and *Himanthalea lorea.* Several of these can extend for a short distance up into the intertidal zone. Among these, *L. digitata* may dominate in both the lower intertidal and the upper sublittoral zone, but it extends out into deeper water only where it can grow as an epiphyte on the fronds of *L. Cloustoni* and so be nearer the surface than it could if attached to the substratum. The main forest, however, tends to consist, at least off the west coast of Scotland where it has been particularly studied, of *L. Cloustoni* with a scattering of *S. bulbosa.* In the shallower water, these grow to a length of about 3 meters, and, if the water is shallower than this, the fronds form a floating canopy just below the surface. In water deeper than this they do not reach the surface. Down to a depth of 6–12 meters, this forest was so dense that a path had to be cleared through it so that the diver could explore it. At greater depths the forest became less dense, but it was too deep for the diver to explore it. *Laminaria saccharina* tended to replace *L. Cloustoni* in the most sheltered localities. These algae are usually attached to solid rock, although, on a sandy bottom, they may grow from a stone that is partly embedded in the bottom. The slope of the rock surface is of great importance in determining the presence of a particular association, the large brown algae being absent from overhangs, where they are replaced by a sponge-tunicate association. On the remaining rock surface, between the stipes of the large algae, there may be an undergrowth of smaller algae such as *Corallina* spp. as well as of encrusting animals such as *Balanus crena-*

tus, Pomatoceros triqueter, and various sponges, bryozoa, and hydroids. The algae themselves support a considerable epiphytic and epizoic flora and fauna on their holdfasts, stipes, and fronds. So dense is the forest that illumination within it is cut to 1 per cent or less of that at the surface. It is interesting to note that with greater depth and corresponding absorption of light by the water, the density of the forest decreases so that the actual amount of light reaching the bottom remains more or less the same. Thus, at a depth of about 4 meters, the algae reduced the light by 98.7–99.4 per cent in an old forest, and by 99.1–99.5 per cent in a dense forest of new growth. On the other hand, in the more open growth at 11 meters, the algae reduced the light by only 82–85 per cent. It is of interest to compare the resulting bottom illumination in such an area, under conditions in which at least some algae can grow, with that in the phytoplankton, whose compensation depth is that at which illumination is reduced to about 1 per cent of its surface value.

Parke (1948) has provided a detailed study of the life history of one of the forest algae, *L. saccharina.* Reproduction of both generations may occur throughout the year, although with seasonal maxima. In the sporophyte generation the growth of the alga is largely conditioned by the time of the year at which it is produced. Those liberated in winter rarely persist to maturity. The bulk of the adult population consists of sporophytes liberated in the spring, but in some sheltered sublittoral areas summer-produced sporophytes may be equally abundant. The life span does not normally exceed 3 years. There is a period of rapid growth from January to June and a period of much slower growth for the remainder of the year. Growth is greater in the second than in the first or third years. Both survival and growth are greatly dependent on habitat. On the whole, a habitat just above low watermark, and involving exposure to the air, is least favorable. A submerged habitat at the same level, that is to say in a pool, is more favorable, and sublittoral habitat is best. Maturity is reached at an age of 8 to 12 months. There is considerable loss of tissue from the end of the frond, the extent of this loss also varying seasonally and with habitat and period of settlement. If part, but not all, the frond is removed, regeneration can take place, and the extent to which this is possible is greatest in the youngest plants.

Black (1948, 1950) and Black and Dewar (1949) have studied the seasonal changes in chemical composition in *L. Cloustoni, L. digitata,* and *L. saccharina.* These are somewhat complicated because of the marked seasonal character of the growth and the loss by fragmentation. In the fronds, in spring, laminarin is absent and mannitol at its minimum, whereas crude proteins, alginic acid, and ash are maximum. In autumn the reverse is true. The stipes vary in a similar way, but to a less extent since they do not suffer loss by fragmentation and they do not contain laminarin at any time. Plants of *L. digitata* and *L. saccharina* from sheltered habitats have a higher laminarin content than ones from greater wave exposure.

Parke (1948) quotes various estimates that have been made of the population density of *Laminaria*. The total stock of *L. saccharina* in the White Sea has been estimated as 1,500,000 metric tons, and the density on the Murman coast as 4.7–5.7 kg. per square meter. The stock in the Barents Sea was 2–8 kg. per square meter. In the Japanese Sea, the population of *L. japonica* is estimated as 4 kg. per square meter, and the same figure is given for *Laminaria* spp. for the Orkney Islands. The fronds grow mainly near the base and fragment from the apex; in exposed habitats the average age of tip tissue in individuals over 6 months old is 5 to 7 months. The stipe and holdfast also are lost at death, which occurs at not more than 3 years. Thus the annual production may be taken as being at least of the same order as the standing crop. Since the dry weight is 10–25 per cent of the wet weight, a *Laminaria* bed may be taken to contribute about a kilogram dry weight of plant material per square meter to the sea annually.

In South Africa and in the Pacific there are comparable forests of giant kelps, some of which grow to a very much greater size than do laminarias. Many of the larger forms are equipped with a float which supports the considerable weight of the stipe, so that the fronds can lie close below the surface. Among the most important Pacific giant kelps are *Macrocystis pyrifera, Nereocystis luetkeana,* and *Alaria fistulosa*. In the first of these the stipes normally attain a length of 30 meters, and ones of up to 300 meters have been reported. Sheldon (1915) quotes a growth rate of 10 inches per day for *N. luetkeana* between March and June, and a growth of about 1 inch per day for the stipe in June–July. Hurd (1916) found that the rate of growth is greater in deep water than in shallow and is apparently controlled by the light intensity, since bright light inhibits growth. An interesting problem is presented by the fact that young plants, starting growth on the bottom, are apparently at an illumination considerably less than that at the compensation point.

In addition to contributing a large source of food to the sea, these algal forests succeed in utilizing a large section of sea bottom which is too dimly lighted to raise any appreciable crop of close-growing algae. By their great size they are able to reach up into the well-lighted upper layers, although their holdfasts are at considerable depths.

They also provide an adequately lighted place of attachment for the mass of smaller epiphytes and epizooids which inhabit them. Finally, they form a very effective breakwater fringing the coast and markedly damping the wave action on the inshore side.

CORAL REEFS

It would be highly artificial to consider separately those parts of the coral reef association lying below low water and those occupying the intertidal zone. On the other hand, until some consideration is given to the conditions on other intertidal areas, it will not be possible to consider the intertidal coral areas in great detail. However, the bulk of the Pacific reefs lie below low watermark and in the Atlantic the corals are hardly ever exposed, so it is legitimate to treat them as essentially a sublittoral community.

Coral reefs form a complete contrast to the area last considered because, although they represent an area of solid bottom, the bottom is of their own formation rather than rock of other origin, and because the overwhelming predominance of algae over animals is often completely reversed. On the reefs, visible algal growth is typically sparse and its place is largely taken by the small symbiotic algal cells or zooxanthellae present in so many of the animals.

As a result of the various reports of the Great Barrier Reef Expedition, we have an extensive knowledge of the ecology of corals in this area of the Pacific. Stephenson (Stephenson et al., 1931) points out that it is at present improper to speak of "a typical coral reef." Those studied on the Great Barrier Reef may, however, be considered as in most ways typical of many Pacific reefs, and many of the deductions drawn from their study would appear to be widely applicable.

Coral reefs are restricted to the warmer oceans of the world, where the winter temperature does not drop much below 20°C. Around Bermuda, their northernmost limit in the Atlantic, winter temperatures drop to about 18°C. and slightly lower along the shore itself. In the neighborhood of Miami, their northernmost limit on the American mainland, the winter temperatures may drop as low as this, but usually not below about 20°C.

Reef growth is also limited by depth to 20–30 fathoms. The figure varies in different localities, and Verwey (1930, 1931) has presented some evidence that there is a correlation with the penetration of light, the reefs extending deeper in more transparent water. This suggests a possible limit set by the depth at which the symbiotic zooxanthellae can find sufficient light for photosynthesis. It is known that individual coral colonies can grow, and apparently thrive in darkness, or after their zooxanthellae have been destroyed by previous subjection to darkness or high temperature. Nevertheless, the colony may well be less efficient in the absence of the zooxanthellae, and it is possible that the effect is sufficient to limit reef formation to depths where photosynthesis is possible.

Figures 9–7, 9–8, and 9–9 show typical areas of the permanently submerged portion of reef area on the Great Barrier Reef (Manton and Stephenson, 1935), and Fig. 9–10 shows an area of Bermuda reef for comparison.

In the three Australian areas, the great dominance of corals is obvious, although in one of them there is some growth of algae and of *Thalassia Hemprichii*. It is clear, from such pictures, that corals are of major importance in the ecology of such reefs. Second to them are lamellibranchs, such as the *Tridacna* shown, and, in some areas, fleshy alcyonaria such as *Sarcophytum, Lobophyton,* and *Sinularia*. By contrast, the Atlantic reefs show a similar paucity of algae but an absence of the fleshy Alcyonaria which are replaced by a heavy growth of gorgonids. It is clear that the ecology of the corals is of prime importance to both.

Ecologically, corals fall into two groups, those from deep water which do not possess zooxanthellae and those from the reef areas which do. The first group includes forms that can tolerate very much lower temperatures than the second, as shown, for instance, by their occurrence in considerable quantities in the deep water in Norwegian fjords. It is true that some corals which are without zooxanthellae do occur within the reef association and that some corals which may or may not contain them are found in the littoral and sublittoral zones of northern waters, but the typical reef coral is characterized by their possession. Reef corals have been shown (Yonge 1930; Yonge and Nicholls, 1930) to be specialized carnivores. Their digestive enzymes include an extracellular proteolytic enzyme and intracellular protease, lipase, and glycolytic enzyme. They do not possess any cellulase and are incapable of digesting phytoplankton or zooxanthellae. This is important since it shows that the role of the zooxanthellae is not that of supplying food material to the corals. The latter are zooplankton feeders, but the rapidity with which such digestion takes place, together with the fact that feeding takes place mainly at night, accounts for the fact that most observers have failed to find any trace of zooplankton in the coelenteron and so have supposed that there is another source of nourishment. Although the corals cannot digest the

Figure 9–7. View from above of a portion of the Great Barrier Reef, with living corals and alcyonarians shown diagrammatically. Dead rock is indicated by
fine stipling, while black represents water over a deeper sandy bottom. (After
Manton and Stephenson, 1935.)

Figure 9–8. View from above of a more sheltered area of the Great Barrier Reef than that shown in Fig. 9–7. The V-shaped objects represent the marine "grass" *Thalassia hemprichii.* (After Manton and Stephenson, 1935.)

Figure 9–9. Side view of the vertical face of a coral head on the Great Barrier Reef. (After Manton and Stephenson, 1935.)

zooxanthellae, there remains the possibility that the latter may excrete sugars or other substances of nutritive value to the corals.   Odum and Odum (1955) have estimated that the ratio of plant protoplasm to animal protoplasm in a reef coral is 3 to 1.   It is thus more plant than animal.   There are large quantities of chlorophyll-containing algae

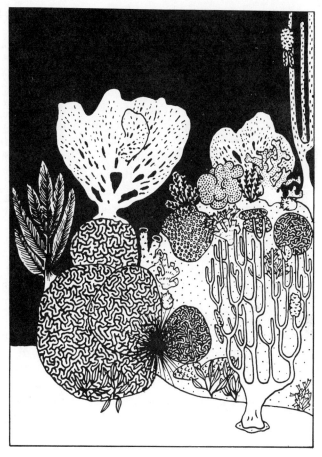

Figure 9–10.   Side view of a part of the outer reef in Bermuda, showing brain corals and gorgonids.

boring in the live skeleton; these algae comprise about two-thirds of the plant material, the zooxanthellae comprising only one-third.

The less specialized corals have large polyps whose tentacles capture the food and pass it to the mouth.   In these corals the ciliated surface of the rest of the colony is concerned mainly with the removal of silt. Many of the more specialized corals have smaller polyps whose tentacles are not long enough to function in this way, and then the ciliated surfaces of both the tentacles and the rest of the surfaces serve the dual purpose of cleansing and conveying food to the mouth. In such cases, ciliary reversal can take place. Most corals expand their tentacles only at night, but some species are found fully expanded in the daytime. It is to be noted that the zooplankton is much more abundant in the waters over the reef at night.

Although not serving directly as a source of food for the corals, the zooxanthellae play an important part in the production of oxygen and in the removal of waste products. However, although zooxanthellae are not able to survive in the absence of corals, the reverse is not the case, and corals that have been depleted of zooxanthellae are quite able to survive. Corals that do not normally contain zooxanthellae, such as *Dendrophyllia,* or ones that have been depleted secrete a considerable amount of phosphorus into the water. Where zooxanthellae are present, they utilize this phosphorus partially or completely. Similar work has not been performed for nitrogen, but it seems likely that the same holds true. The zooxanthellae, which are in close proximity to certain parts of the coral tissues, therefore provide immediate removal of some of the corals' excretory products. They also, during the daytime, produce oxygen in excess of that used by the coral in respiration, although the balance for a full 24-hour period usually shows some excess of respiration over photosynthesis (Yonge et al., 1932) (Fig. 9–11).

Experiments made on the effect of depth on respiration and photosynthesis were less adequate than could have been wished, but they showed, as might be expected, that the balance tipped further toward excess of respiration at greater depths. It would be most interesting to know what the situation is at a depth comparable with the limiting depth for reef formation. The maintenance of the zooxanthellae population within the coral reflects the well-being of the coral itself, as well as that of the algae. When kept in the dark, even when the coral is fed, the zooxanthellae are found to be expelled from the coral tissues. The same thing happens, either in the dark or in light, when the coral is starved. Corals on the reef may be killed by excessively high temperatures. Under experimental conditions, exposure to 40°C. for about an hour killed specimens of *Favia.* It was noted, however (Yonge and Nicholls, 1931), that after a period of unusually high reef temperatures, some corals were dead, whereas others appeared quite healthy but had lost their zooxanthellae. In experiments, exposure of *Favia* to a temperature of 36°C. for 2 hours was found to produce this result. It appears, then, that the upper lethal temperature of zoo-xanthellae is less than that of at least some species of corals.

The statement is frequently encountered in earlier work that corals are unable to tolerate the presence of silt and that this is one of the most potent factors in limiting their distribution within those areas where the temperatures are suitable. Marshall and Orr (1931) found a surprising ability to remove sediment from the surface of the coral. To a large extent this is brought about by ciliary activity, and species

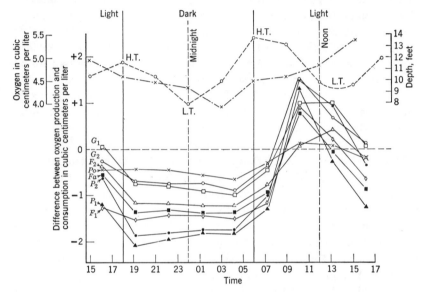

Figure 9–11. The upper lines show the diurnal changes in oxygen concentration (dot-dash) and the depth (broken) of water on the Great Barrier Reef. The lower (solid) lines show changes, for the corresponding period, in the excess of oxygen production over consumption in various corals. *F, Fungia; Fa, Favia; G, Galaxea; P, Psammocora; Po, Porites.* (After Yonge et al., 1932.)

with large polyps are, in general, more efficient at sediment removal than those with smaller polyps. Among the latter, however, those with branched colonies tend to be the most efficient. The expansion of the polyp which usually occurs at night also helps in throwing off sediment. An outstanding coral in this connection is *Fungia*. Its flattened individuals, when adult, lie unattached on the sandy bottom where they must often be buried or even turned over by wave action. They are, nevertheless, able to work their way to the surface, free themselves from the sand, and even turn over when necessary. Ob-servations on the reefs in Bermuda during dredging operations in the construction of an air base there confirmed these results. Although the water was visibly thick with silt for more than a year, the reefs that were not actually buried survived apparently unharmed, although some other forms, such as the urchin *Lytechinus variegatus* and the squirrel fish *Holocentrus* sp., were completely eliminated from the immediate neighborhood. When the amount of silt is large, it has very often been carried down to the sea by rivers and is therefore associated with lowered salinities; it is likely, then, that the limiting factor is salinity rather than silt. Yonge (1940) has brought together various data on the tolerance of corals to varying salinity. Most species can tolerate at least a not-too-prolonged exposure to sea water diluted by one-fifth, and a few have withstood a dilution by one-third for several months, but contact with sea water diluted by a half for 24 hours was fatal to most species. Some Tortugas corals withstood a temporary increase of salinity of a half, and some Hawaiian species an increase of one-tenth for several months. Manton and Stephenson (1935) recorded salinities as low as $17^o/_{oo}$ after rain in pools in which coral was growing.

Where circulation is restricted, as in pools, the oxygen content may fall very low at night without fatal results for the corals. At the same time it may be too low for survival of other animals such as fishes. Corals are, in general, tolerant of considerable lowering of the oxygen saturation of the water in which they live and show little change in their respiratory rate until saturation has dropped below about 50 per cent. Further, those species that are adapted to live in shallow habitats such as pools are more resistant to lowering of the oxygen content of the water than are those characteristic of deeper water (Yonge et al., 1932).

Molluscs play a part second only to that of the corals themselves on many reefs. Certain studies were carried out on the Great Barrier Reef on the ecology of the Tridacnidae which affords an interesting contrast with the corals. Like the latter they contain abundant zooxanthellae and these are concentrated in frilly expansions of the mantle, which is spread widely through the gaping shell when the animal is submerged. Unlike the corals, these clams are adapted for digestion of plant material, and, in fact, obtain practically the whole of their nourishment from the zooxanthellae. The algae reproduce in the tissues of the mantle and are preyed on there by wandering cells which transport them to the digestive tissues of the gut where they are broken down and absorbed. Less is known of the role of zooxanthellae in other reef organisms, but they are recorded in such forms as the foraminiferan *Polytrema*, many sponges, the hydroid *Myrionema*, anemones such as *Stoichactis* and *Actinodendron,* the coralline hydroid *Millepora,* Alcyonacea such as *Sarcophytum* and *Lobophyton,* the gorgonids *Isis* and *Melitodes,* and the colonial tunicates *Trididemnum, Diplosoma,* etc. All the marine sponge symbionts which have been examined have proved to be myxophycean rather than cryptophycean, as are coral zooxanthellae. As such they are very much smaller in size than the coral zooxanthellae, but they may be presumed to play a similar role. De Laubenfels (*in litt.*) cites data pointing to the probability that, unlike the corals, sponges do digest their zooxanthellae. In other groups of coelenterates, it seems probable that such digestion does not take place.

The various theories covering the origin and means of formation of reefs of different types will not be discussed here. They can be found in various works on the subject including the Barrier Reef Reports, Kuenen (1950), Darwin (1897), etc. We are more immediately concerned, however, with the processes of growth and ·breakdown now taking place on the reefs. Habitat has a very great effect on both the rate and the nature of the growth of corals. Yonge (1940) summarizes available data on the rate of growth of reef corals. In the Maldives, upward growth averaged 25.6 mm. per year in young colonies. A similar value was found in Samoa. In the Bay of Batavia, the annual increase in weight ranged from 16.9 per cent in *Favia favus* to 1197.4 per cent for *Montipora ramosa.* Among Atlantic species, *Orbicella annularis* grew upward 5–7 mm. annually on West Indian reefs, and *Acropora palmata* about four times as fast. On the Great Barrier Reef (Stephenson and Stephenson, 1933) branching forms increased in diameter in about 6 months by 33–95 per cent of their initial size, whereas massive colonies grew considerably more slowly. Actual figures are shown in Table 9–5.

TABLE 9–5

Average Percentage Increase in Diameter of Corals on the Great Barrier Reef in a Period of about 6 Months

Branched Forms, %		Massive Forms, %	
Montipora	95	*Porites*	17
Acropora	57	*Favia* and *Coeloria*	10
Pocillopora	43	*Lobophyllia*	10
Psammocora	33	*Symphyllia*	10

There was a wide variation of growth rate in different colonies within the same habitat, and, further, it appears that growth of corals takes place intermittently. It was found that there was a definite tendency for colonies of various species to maintain a more or less circular outline, and that the recorded increase was greater on the lesser diameter of the colony than on the greater diameter. When parts of a colony were broken off, these parts tended to regenerate faster than the rest of the colony. Finally, when a colony was divided into two parts that were thereafter kept in different habitats, both growth and survival were best in the habitat in which that species was normally the more abundant. Some data were also obtained on the growth of newly settled colonies. *Pocillopora bulbosa* attained sizes

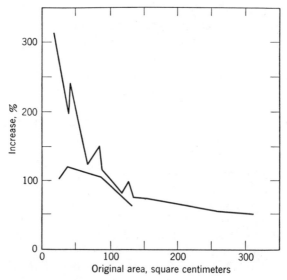

Figure 9–12. The relation of growth to size in the coral *Pocillopora bulbosa*. The upper line is for whole colonies and the lower for ones regenerating after division in half. (After Stephenson and Stephenson, 1933.)

of 11.0 × 10.0 and 14.5 × 9.5 mm. in less than 11 months, and *Porites* 7.0 × 6.0 and 12.0 × 6.5 mm. in 27 weeks.

It appears likely that, at least in some localities, growth is greater at a slight depth than close to the surface. Yonge (1940) quotes examples from the Dutch East Indies where growth was greater below 5 meters than between 3 and 5 meters and much greater than in water shallower than 3 meters. In records from the Andaman Islands, a channel with an original depth of 12 meters was reported to have grown up to 30 cm. in 37 years. Although data are few, there is little doubt that young colonies grow faster than older ones (Fig. 9–12).

It is generally stated that the nature of the habitat has a very great influence on the type of growth of coral present. The wave-exposed regions of the outer edge of the reef contain massive forms or branched forms in which the branches are very thick and stumpy. In sheltered water more foliate and delicately branched forms become more abundant. Opinions differ about whether this is due to selection of the species that are mechanically best designed to tolerate and make use of the conditions present, or whether individual species are modified by the conditions to produce different growth forms in different habitats. The latter view, namely, that the species are highly adaptable within themselves, has been carried to the point of doubting the validity of a large proportion of the generally accepted species and of considering these as growth forms of just a few species. There is general agreement that corals found in regions of considerable wave action are usually more robust than those in more sheltered places. However, there are exceptions, some sheltered species being very robustly built; and at least one very brittle and delicately branched form, *Acropora delicatula*, occurs commonly in the most wave-beaten places. In Stephenson's opinion, the broad trend of growth form in relation to habitat is true, but the suggestion that most of the described species are only habitat forms of a few species is an exaggeration. It is true that very considerable experience is needed in determining the species of corals, but with sufficient experience, this can usually be done.

The upward growth of coral colonies is arrested in the neighborhood of low watermark, the exact level varying with the species and habitat. Since we are dealing here mainly with the sublittoral parts of the reef, the conditions in this low-water zone will be discussed more fully in a later section on intertidal animals.

Along with the constant addition to the reef by growth is a corresponding loss by various causes. Undoubtedly many reefs maintain more or less of a balance between the two while others are either growing or shrinking. Loss of material is continually taking place as a result of wave action. This may break small pieces from the colony or, when the surf is heavy, may detach large coral boulders and wash them up into an intertidal zone too high for survival. Waves may also modify the level of the sandy or muddy bottom, killing any corals that are covered in the process. In addition to the effect of waves on living coral colonies, reefs are continuously being weakened by various boring organisms which reduce their mechanical strength and thus render them less resistant to wave action. Most of these borers avoid living coral, as do encrusting forms such as algae and barnacles. There are a few exceptions such as certain species of the boring lamellibranch, *Lithophaga*. Dead coral, on the other hand, is penetrated by a wild range of boring forms including algae, porifera, lamelli-branchs, cirripedes, polychaetes, and gephyrea. In addition to ac-tively burrowing forms, there are many others that make use of pre-existing burrows or cavities, sometimes enlarging them in the process. The actual coral removed in the process of cutting the burrow is either very finely divided or even, in a few cases such as *Lithophaga*, dissolved by an acid secretion. Larger pieces broken off are not of necessity lost to the reef structure since they may be cemented either by lithotham-nions or by deposition of lime to form coral rock, or they may be ground into smaller particles and form part of the sand floor between the actual coral colonies. It has been said that echinoderms, and particularly holothurians, play a very important part in further grind-ing down this sand in the course of feeding on it. Although this process no doubt takes place, its significance has yet to be evaluated.

From studies of temperate and cold-water invertebrates we have

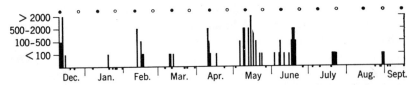

Figure 9–13. Lunar rhythm in the release of planulae by the coral, *Pocillopora bulbosa* or the Great Barrier Reef. (After Marshall and Stephenson, 1933.)

seen that all types of breeding cycle are possible—continuous through-out the year, intermittent throughout the year, and limited to a part of the summer, to part of the winter, or to two periods (spring and fall) with comparable temperatures. In all of these, spawning may be con-tinuous throughout the period or intermittent, often with a lunar rhythm. Studies on the Great Barrier Reef (Fig. 2–4; Stephenson, 1934) show several of these possibilities, and even the few species studied indicate that tropical spawning is not typically a more or less continuous process throughout the year, as had been suggested. Thus, the hydroid *Myrionema* breeds fairly uniformly throughout the year and the coral *Pocillipora* the same, but with a lunar rhythm. Several species breed only in a more or less limited summer period, and two apparently only in the fall. Finally, the urchin *Tripneustes* appears to have two spawning periods, one in the spring and one in the fall. The case of *Pocillopora bulbosa* is particularly interesting since, if the data are to be considered adequate, it indicates a definite lunar rhythm, but with a swing from spawning at new moon in sum-mer to full moon in winter (Fig. 9–13). The significance of this is not known, but it is pointed out that the lowest tides at that locality occur in the summer at full moon and at night, and in the winter they occur at new moon and in the daytime.

The term "coral reef" also embraces structures in which corals play little if any part, and various calcareous algae are the major builders (Taylor, 1950; Setchell, 1926, etc.). "Nullipores," such as *Goniolithon,* can apparently flourish at a greater depth than reef-building corals. They, together with such algae as *Halimeda,* build up a coarse sediment in which animal remains may play only a minor part. Thus, in Funafuti lagoon, down to a depth of about 30 meters, fragments of *Halimeda* comprise 80–95 per cent of the sediment. Such deposits may then become cemented partly by lime deposition and partly by infiltration and overgrowth by *Lithothamnion*-type algae such as *Porolithon.*

In describing Bikini atoll, Taylor comments on the extreme sparsity of larger algae except in places where the bottom is protected from insolation. There was, though, a widespread algal felt of varying thickness, and he lists a number of its constituent species.

10

Organisms

(Continued)

THE INTERTIDAL ZONE—ROCKY SHORES

The exposure of the intertidal zone at low water makes it the most readily explored section of the ocean. This ease is no doubt reflected in the high proportion of study it has received. However, it is a very complex region, so far as variation of ecological factors is concerned, and although this complexity has distinct advantages, it carries with it corresponding disadvantages. Thus, the wide range of variation of certain factors to be found within a short distance facilitates the study of their effects, and of the reactions of various organisms to these changes, whereas the complexity of the interacting factors, and the very fact of their wide differences within short distances, has so far usually defied any complete analysis. As in other habitats, there has been a divergence between study of the communities as wholes and concentration on the ecology of important individual species within those communities. The need for a broad description common to all shores is obvious, as is the need for more detailed pictures of more local conditions. These will, however, never be adequate until there is also an understanding of the ecological characteristics of the individuals comprising the various types of intertidal shore. On the other hand, the particular species that have received detailed study are not always those of most significance on the shore, and even when they are, the part they play both in their community, and also in general shore ecology, has not always been considered.

Stephenson and Stephenson (1949) have discussed the characteristics of zonation which are common to rocky shores in all parts of the world and have suggested a logical system of nomenclature which, if generally adopted, should greatly simplify the present confusion. Although intertidal zonation is generally associated with tidal level, they point out that the operative condition is the meeting of air and water, with a gradation, indicated by the zonation, from completely marine, through intermittently or partially wet to completely land conditions. It is true that this gradation is usually dependent, in the main, on the tides, but it may be modified by wave action, and in some places the latter may far outweigh the tidal effect. Even in a location with no tide and sheltered from all wave action, there will be a zonation of conditions and, as a result, of organisms, in the neighborhood of the water-air interface.

Although one school of thought endeavors to measure the zonation of ecological factors on the shore and to correlate the occurrence or well-being of the various plants and animals with these, Stephenson uses the organisms themselves as an index of the major intertidal zones. An advantage of this method lies in the fact that the presence of particular organisms implies the continuance of conditions within their particular tolerance ranges throughout the period covered by their life span. The physical and chemical measurements necessary to demonstrate this would be impossible with present techniques. Furthermore, we are not restricted to particular species, since there are certain zones which, on all shores, are characterized by certain groups or types of organisms, although with different species from place to place.

Stephenson and Stephenson propose a general nomenclature which is indicated in Fig. 10–1. The main intertidal or littoral zone is to be known as the "midlittoral zone." The zone above high watermark in which there is a transition from marine to land conditions, with an intermingling of the two, is to be known as the "supralittoral zone," and between this and midlittoral, usually in the neighborhood of extreme high watermark, is a connecting region, the "supralittoral fringe." Similarly, in the neighborhood of extreme low water there is an "infralittoral fringe" connecting the midlittoral zone with the permanently submerged "infralittoral zone." The change of the latter from the more usual sublittoral is to avoid confusion with the rather similar supralittoral.

The supralittoral fringe is characterized by the presence of various species of the gastropod *Littorina,* or related genera such as *Tectarius*

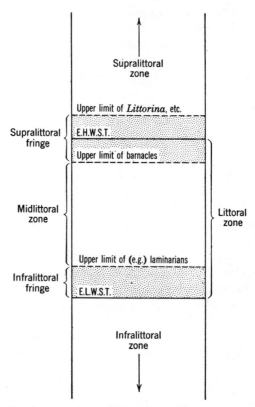

Figure 10–1. Classification of intertidal and neighboring zones: E.H.W.S.T. and E.L.W.S.T. are high and low water of equinoctial spring tides. (After Stephenson and Stephenson, 1949.)

and *Echininus,* and its upper limit coincides with theirs. Its lower limit is the upper limit, at least of any abundance, of the barnacles which characterize the next lower, or midlittoral, zone. Its flora consists of Myxophyceae, lichens of the *Verrucaria maura* type or a mixture of these, and these give the rock a dark coloration which has given rise to its designation as the "black zone."

The midlittoral zone is characterized by the abundance of barnacles of the genera *Balanus, Chthamalus,* and *Tetraclita,* and its lower limit is the point at which they cease to be abundant. However, they are frequently to a large extent replaced by other animals or algae in the lower part of the zone. The characteristic color of this zone tends to be a yellowish brown, which has given it the name of the "yellow zone."

The sublittoral fringe is the region uncovered at spring tides, but not at neaps, into which certain of the typically infralittoral forms can penetrate.

Stephenson shows that this broad scheme of classification is of world-wide application. Although one species will replace another in different localities, it is still possible to distinguish these majors zones on most shores. The great advantage of a classification that is of general application is evident when an attempt is made to correlate the descriptions given by different workers, usually in terms of tidal levels. The use of biological indicator species is common practice in plankton ecology. This is a comparable case, with the difference that type communities are used, and these are not defined in the normal way as an association of particular species, but by groups of varying systematic rank which have been found to characterize the different zones.

Stephenson points out that the observed zonation is ultimately dependent on the relative proportions, at that level, of aerial and aquatic conditions and the concommitant factors. It is true that these factors are complex, but an ultimate understanding of their effect should offer a definition of the observed zonation; attempts to explain local zonation in terms of tides, wave action, etc., are to be accepted as a necessary approach to a solution of the problem from this angle. It has not always, however, been realized that the same factor will vary in significance from one locality to another, and that an explanation of zonation which meets the observed facts well in one place may fail to in another.

There are places where zonation can be observed, even though there is little or no tidal or wave action. There are areas, such as the Baltic, where non-tidal fluctuations of sea level are of greater importance than the very small tidal effect. There are oceanic coasts where the tide is small but the surf is continuously heavy, so that the splash completely masks the tidal effect. The basic fact remains, though, that in most places the tide is the major factor controlling zonation through varying duration of exposure to air and water respectively. Disregarding for the moment the actual factors such as insolation, heating, desiccation, etc., which may directly limit survival, tidal level and

limits of vertical distribution show a marked correlation. If, instead
of tidal level, we consider the duration of exposure to air or water at
the different levels, the correlation becomes even clearer. A simple
case of the relation between the duration of aerial exposure and tidal
level is shown in Fig. 2–34. It will be seen, however, that the duration at a given level varies greatly with the type of tide, i.e., whether
neap or spring. For example, in the locality shown, the level of low
water of extreme neap tides will suffer no aerial exposure on a neap
tide, but it will be exposed for 40 per cent of the tidal cycle on an
extreme spring tide. For typically marine forms, the longest period
on any tide of the year during which they will be exposed to the air
is likely to be a limiting factor, whereas for more aerially adapted

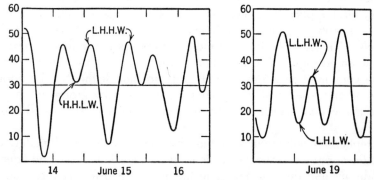

Figure 10–2. Two tidal records for San Francisco, showing marked diurnal inequality: L.H.L.W. = lowest higher low water; H.H.L.W. = highest higher low
water; L.L.H.W. = lowest lower high water; L.H.H.W. = lowest higher high
water. (After Doty, 1946.)

forms it may be the longest period of submergence in the sea. Doty
(1946) has shown how these maximum periods vary with tidal level
on the Pacific coast of North America. The area he considers is one
where there is a very pronounced difference in range between the two
tides of the day, as shown in Fig. 10–2. Figure 2–35 shows his results on the maximum period of submergence in relation to tidal
level, and it will be seen that there are several very sharp steps at
which a small change in level results in as much as a doubling in time
of submergence. If duration of either submergence or exposure is
critical, as seems probable, then these particular levels are likely to
act as limits to the vertical distribution of particular species. That
this occurs is demonstrated in Fig. 10–3 where the upper and lower
limits of a number of Pacific algae are shown. These limits are ones
that have been selected as good indicators of the zones lying within

these critical levels, and there are other species that occupy more than one zone, or whose limits are not these particular levels. However, the correspondence of so many algal limits with these particular levels is striking. With regard to the tidal levels to which Doty refers, it should be noted that, with the marked difference in the two tides of the day, it is necessary to refer to the higher and lower high water of a particular day, and similarly for low water. This is superimposed on the normal highest high waters of spring tides and the lowest high waters of neap tides, or of equinoctial and solstitial tides, as the case may be. The result is of the complicated-sounding terminology of "highest higher high water," "lowest lower high water," etc.

In Doty's work, it is assumed that the greatest duration of immersion or exposure suffered during any one year is significant. Of course one year varies slightly from another in the details of its tides, and the organisms would no doubt show some comparable variation in zonation. It is also assumed that the algae considered have been living at the levels in question for at least a year. For forms with a shorter life span, modifications of this scheme would be necessary in order to allow for the exposures or immersions that they had actually undergone during their life. This might be further modified if their tolerance changed as they grew older, which

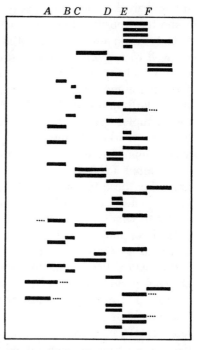

Figure 10–3. Zonation of a number of intertidal algae on the Pacific coast of the United States, showing the tendency for these to end at certain critical levels. *A*, lowest higher high water; *B*, lowest lower high water; *C*, highest higher low water: *D*, lowest higher low water; *E*, mean lower low water; *F*, lowest lower low water. (After Doty, 1946.)

is frequently the case. Yet another important modification lies in the time of day at which the maximum exposure takes place. On some coasts the lowest tides of the year occur always at about the same time of day, and in such cases it may be critical whether this time falls in the middle of the day or morning and evening. In the latter case, insolation would be much less severe. There are other coasts, such as the Great Barrier Reef, where the lowest tides occur at night in the summer but in the daytime in winter. If, as is probable, it is insolation, desiccation, or some similar factor, rather than direct exposure, which is limiting, then the time of day at which the exposure takes place is obviously significant, and a long exposure at a time other than the middle of the day may well prove to be equivalent to a shorter exposure at about noon.

Doty has made a specific study of the tides in one area, and it may be well to explore certain theoretical considerations which would be more widely applicable. There seems little doubt that levels at which there is the most rapid change in conditions during the tidal cycle are particularly unfavorable. This has been shown for the midtidal level for example. Similarly, points at which a slight shift in level results in a very marked change in the period of immersion or exposure, with a concommitant change in duration of associated factors, are likely to be limits to vertical distribution of those species whose tolerance limits for these factors lie within the range of this change. Neglecting the effects of splash and of deviations from predicted tidal levels owing to winds, etc., certain levels may be picked out as theoretically critical for most shores. Extreme low water of spring tides will be a critical upper limit for forms which can tolerate no exposure at all, and a critical lower limit for forms, if there are such, which can tolerate long periods of immersion but require to be exposed at least once a year. Extreme high water of spring tides is a similar critical level. The lowest high water of the year is another critical level, since it represents the transition level from being immersed once on every tide to occasional exposure without wetting for two tidal periods. Where there is a difference between the two tides of the day, the height reached by the high water preceding or succeeding this extreme tide will be another critical level, since above this point there may, on occasions, be exposure for three successive tidal cycles. Where duration of immersion, rather than duration of exposure is critical, there will be similar critical levels at the highest low water of the year and at the low water preceding or succeeding it. These levels are indicated in Fig. 10–4 in which a uniform tidal cycle of 12½ hours has been assumed. It should be noted that the critical levels are in the neighborhood of extreme high- and low-water springs and extreme high- and low-water neaps. Exact correspondence in any one year with average values given in tide predictions is not to be expected. It may be noted that high-water neaps, and to a lesser extent low-water neaps, are well known to be critical levels for the distribution of organisms on many shores, as are extreme high- and low-water springs. There are many organisms that can tolerate periods of many days or weeks of exposure, provided they receive occasional wetting, and similarly there are others that require occasional exposure but can tolerate long periods of immersion.

It is clear, then, that although the concept of critical levels goes far toward explaining observed vertical distribution levels, any generaliza-

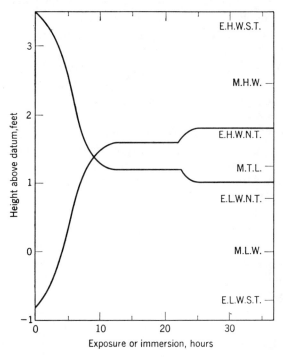

Figure 10–4. Maximum period of exposure and immersion in relation to tidal level at Miami, Florida.

tions from it, or any attempt to predict the levels at a given locality, will lead to a highly complicated analysis. Account will have to be taken of the possible effects of the time of day and the season at which the critical tides occur. The extent of splash varies seasonally in many areas, and this too must be allowed for. For short-lived organisms, or organisms capable of vertical migration, critical tides occurring during their life span or during the immediately preceding period may have to be considered rather than average values made over a period of years. In this connection, reference may be made to the observations of Knight and Parke (1931) on the apparent migration of algae up and down the shore seasonally. This is, of course, not a true migration, but a colonization during one season of a level that cannot be inhabited during the opposite season.

Doty and Archer (1950) have shown experimental evidence in agreement with Doty's critical level theory. They exposed various species of algae for varying periods to sudden changes in temperature and salinity of the order of those they would be expected to undergo when exposed by the tide. They argued that the steps on their critical-level curves involved sudden increments of two- to threefold in the time of exposure. For each species they measured the time of exposure to higher temperature or salinity which just began to injure the alga. According to their theory, a doubling or trebling of the exposure time should then prove fatal. It did so in about half the species. It is pointed out that, in those species for which a negative result was obtained, some other factor might well be the limiting one.

Although these critical levels are tidally determined, it is clear that they will be modified by any factor that tends to produce aquatic or aerial conditions above or below the average water level. Thus wave action will tend to splash water above the average level and will wet levels which, in calm conditions, would have dried out. Similarly, in the Northern Hemisphere a north aspect will reduce insolation and hence desiccation as compared with a south aspect. This situation has been less well studied than the direct tidal relationships. It would appear that a land or an aerial form which is intolerant of salt water would be limited in its downward spread by the highest point reached by splash at any time during the period of its life. Its ability to penetrate downward would be conditioned by the frequency or perhaps the duration of such wetting. Forms requiring to be permanently wet or damp would be able to extend to a higher level where there is always wave action or where the northern aspect always reduces insolation. At mid- and upper levels, there are forms that require wetting at regular or occasional intervals. If regular wave action is always present, their upper limits would be expected to be effectively raised. It is difficult, however, to understand how intermittent wave action would affect forms that require frequent wetting, since these would, if living above their normal limit, be subject to periods of calm weather in which they would not be wet. An example of this is shown in Fig. 2–23 in which the upper limit of the barnacle *Balanus balanoides* rises above mean high water of neap tides by an amount proportional to the degree of wave exposure. It is difficult to see how such a suspension feeder can not only survive at these high levels but actually grow faster there than lower on the shore.

There are many accounts of the zonation of the algae of particular areas, for example those of Colman (1933) and Gislen (1930) for temperate European waters, Stephenson (1939, 1944, etc.) for South Africa, Dakin et al. (1948) for Australia, Dellow (1950) for New Zealand. Although most of these accounts indicate tidal levels and their relations to the vertical distribution of the different species, few of them go further in tracing the direct action of particular intertidal environmental factors. Intertidal algal vegetation is most strikingly developed in temperate waters. In the tropics it is greatly reduced under the influence of excessive insolation and other factors, although toward the poles it tends to be of a more seasonal character because of the removal of much of it by winter ice and by low-salinity water when the ice thaws in the spring. On a temperate shore where the algal vegetation is well developed, much of the shore may be covered by a blanket of brown algae which lies several centimeters thick when left exposed at low tide. Although red and green algae may be abundant, most of the larger forms are brown algae. Figure 10–5 illustrates the zonation of the more important species on a Scottish shore, and Fig. 10–6 shows the actual vertical distributions of the same species in relation to tidal level in the Isle of Man. *Pelvetia canaliculata,* which occupies the top zone between about high water of extreme and mean spring tides, is a comparatively small form only a few centimeters long, but the lower-growing *Fucus spiralis, F. vesiculosus, F. serratus,* and *Ascophyllum nodosum* all grow large, some as much as a meter in length.

Knight and Parke (1950) have described in detail the ecology of two of these, *F. serratus* and *F. vesiculosus*. The growth rate of both is about half a centimeter per week, although this varies under different conditions and tends to be greater in sheltered localities than in those that are wave-exposed. There does not appear to be a marked seasonal variation in growth rate, although the details of growth vary seasonally. Reproductive receptacles began to form in the winter in *F. serratus* and in the spring in *F. vesiculosus*. Release of gametes occurs through the summer in the former and until autumn in the latter. The gas-filled vesicles also show a seasonal rhythm in formation, being produced in the spring, and it is often possible to determine the age of a plant by the number of series of vesicles present. After fruiting, there is a period of heavy defoliation, all those branches which have fruited being cast off down to the point where they join a branch bearing a non-fruiting tip. Figure 10–7 shows a fruiting plant of *F. serratus* and indicates by breaks the sections that will later be cast off. Vegetative growth then occurs from the remaining non-

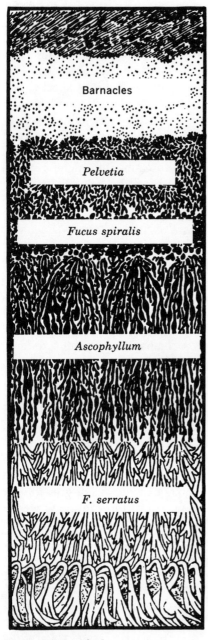

reproductive tips. The proportion of fruiting tips varies locally but may be as high as 100 per cent, leaving nothing for initiation of further vegetative growth. The normal life span is three years, and the mortality rate, excluding very young stages, is about 66 per cent per annum. The amount of branching appears to be greater in

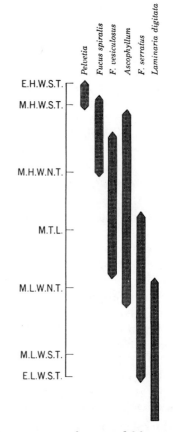

Figure 10–5. Algal zonation on a vertical rock surface on a Scottish shore. (After Yonge, 1949.)

Figure 10–6. The intertidal limits of zonation of the commoner brown algae in the Isle of Man. (After Knight and Parke, 1950.)

wave-exposed localities than in sheltered ones. The eggs settle equally well at all levels on the shore, but a steep slope or smooth surface acts as a deterrent, and strong wave action tends to wash them away. Strong light favors germination, but the value of the increase in this factor at higher levels is offset by the increased effect of desiccation. As a result there may be a considerable population of small plants at the upper limit of distribution, but these may fail to grow to any considerable size. In many areas the presence of a covering of *Enteromorpha* or *Ulva* is a prerequisite to the survival of the small plants, and they will not develop if the rock is bare.

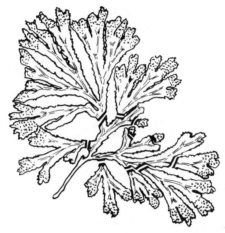

Figure 10–7. A plant of the brown algae *Fucus serratus*, showing the parts which would be lost by fragmentation after fruiting. (After Knight and Parke, 1950.)

The process of winter defoliation of the fruiting parts of the plant is clearly an important factor in the supply of food material to the shore and neighborhood, since it brings great quantities of decaying fragments of algae onto the bottom and within reach of forms that could not feed on the growing plants. However, there are many forms such as the limpet *Patella vulgata* and other gastropods such as *Littorina obtusata* which feed directly on the growing plants. Knight and Parke quote an experiment described by Lodge (1948) in which an area of the shore was completely cleared of limpets, and the previously sparse growth of fucoids gave way to one so dense that it was visible from the air. At the end of the 3 years the limpets had began to return and the algae were regaining their normal abundance.

Hatton (1938) has described the ecology of two further intertidal flucoids of importance. The young plants of *A. nodosum* appear chiefly in the spring and settle less densely, at least on the part of the French coast which he studied, than *F. vesiculosus*. There is an optimum dampness of the substratum for settlement, resulting from its surface roughness, muddiness, or coverage by other algae, but for the first 2 at least there may be excess which is unfavorable. Growth is at a rate of about 15 cm. per year among other algae, but about 11 cm. in the open, and these rates decrease after 3 or 4 years. Growth is also greater at lower levels, and here the difference in rate between isolated plants and those growing among others is decreased. Moderate water movement does not affect the growth rate but does delay

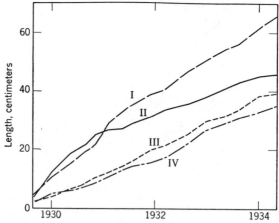

Figure 10–8. The relation of growth to tidal level in the brown alga, *Ascophyllum nodosum*: I, high level; II, intermediate level; III, low level; IV, starting at a high level and then tranferred to a low level. (After Hatton, 1938.)

the appearance of fruiting vesicles, which begins normally at a size of about 8–9 cm. Where water movement is extremely strong, there is mechanical damage to the whole plant. Factors such as north aspect and maintenance of damp around the holdfast of the plant result in increased growth rate (Figs. 10–8, 10–9).

Pelvetia canaliculata, which occupies the highest part of the fucoid belt, also settles mainly in the spring, and its young plants show a much lower mortality rate than the other fucoids. The colonization tends to be uniform where there is a covering of *Catanella opuntia* over the rock's surface but patchy where the surface is bare. With a south aspect, settlement is stronger in the lower part of the *Pelvetia* zone than in the upper. This is a smaller species, and growth is correspondingly less—about 1 cm. per year. It is greater in a damp habitat and on a north aspect and appears to be decreased under the influence of fresh water from rain. The scarcity of this species in wave-exposed localities appears to be due to mechanical action; there are fewer plants where they are rendered brittle by desiccation and more where their attachments are kept damp.

We have so far dealt in some detail with a few species of intertidal algae, choosing those whose ecology is particularly well known; these species together comprise a large fraction of the northern Atlantic algal flora. Chapman (1946) has reviewed much of the field of marine algal ecology up to 1946 and provides a large bibliography

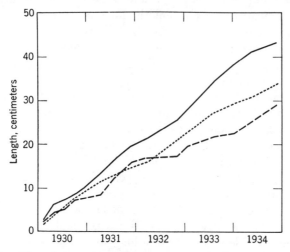

Figure 10–9. The relation of growth to aspect in the brown alga *Ascophyllum nodosum.* Growth was on rocks facing north (solid line), west (dotted line), and south (broken line). (After Hatton, 1938.)

of references to relevant literature. In referring to the two schools, one of which has been primarily concerned with the study and description of communities and their interrelations, and the other with the detailed study of the ecology of particular species, he says "Synecological studies will finally be understood only if they are succeeded by adequate autoecological studies." Since he wrote this, some of the excellent studies of particular species to which we have been referring have appeared.

Chapman points out that geographic distribution is correlated with temperature in the majority of species of algae. In many species there is only a narrow range of temperature tolerance, and in some, such as the Laminariaceae, it is the production of fruiting organs which shows the least tolerance range. Within the tolerance range of a species for such factors as temperature, locally modifying factors may decide whether the species can exist or not. For example, *A. nodosum* and *F. vesiculosus* are absent where wave action is severe, and the presence of water of low salinity may eliminate these and other species. On the other hand, the low salinity may favor the growth of *Enteromorpha* and *Cladophora,* or, under other conditions, of *Fucus ceranoides.* For some algae, such as *Valonia* and *Postelsia,* the strong water movements associated with surf appear to be required. Desiccation is probably a major factor in determining upper limits of algae on temperate shores, and it has been shown that certain algae of the uppermost levels, such as *Bangia fusco-purpurea* and *Urospora penicillus,* are particularly tolerant of both this and high temperature. On tropical shores the effects of heating, during exposure, may prove to be more serious than those of desiccation, and here it has been shown that some algae, such as *Rhodomela crassicaulis,* are particularly tolerant.

Not all temperate shores have a dense growth of intertidal algae, but those that do far surpass the growth in the same zone in warmer waters. There the dense algal growth is almost entirely confined to the sublittoral zone and sublittoral fringe. Tropical intertidal algae are usually in the form of small plants or a felt-like or moss-like covering of the rocks. Further, Rhodophyceae play a relatively much more important part there than in more temperate waters, and calcareous forms are of much greater importance. The work of Stephenson and others on the South African coast affords probably the most detailed series of comparable surveys over a long stretch of coast line throughout which we can trace the zonation of both algae and animals and the variations of these with climate, wave exposure, etc. The southeast coast affords a subtropical flora and fauna, tending in some ways to tropical, while the southern tip is warm-temperate and the adjoining southwest area cold-temperate. Even in the cold-temperate region, the growth of algae above the sublittoral fringe is in no way comparable with that on a really well-grown European or North American shore. Figure 10–10 shows, in a diagrammatic form, the distribution of algae and animals on a rock with fairly heavy wave exposure in the southwest coast cold-temperate region. Above the sublittoral fringe there may be either large patches or scattered plants of *Champia lumbricalis,* and above this a thick encrustation of coralliform *Lithothamnion* with scattered plants of *Aeodes orbitosa.* In more sheltered locations, *Champia,* together with *Gigartina stiriata, G. radula, Iridophycus capensis,* and *Aeodes,* may form extensive sheets (Fig. 10–11). Figure 10–12 illustrates the effect of increasing shelter in

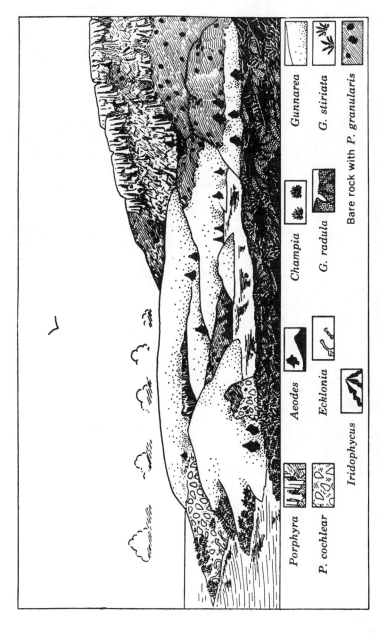

Figure 10–10. Diagram of the zonation on a rocky shore exposed to fairly heavy waves along the west coast of South Africa. (After Stephenson et al., 1940.)

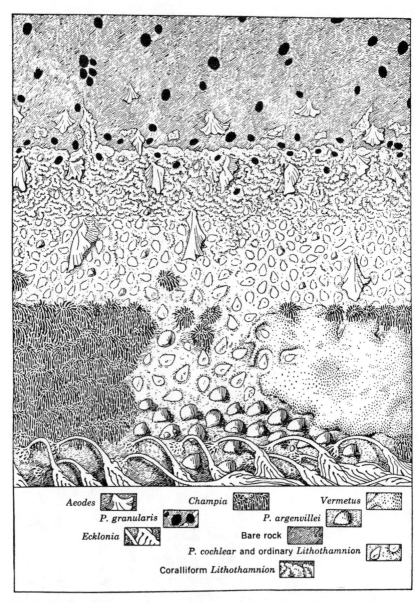

Aeodes   *Champia*   *Vermetus*

P. granularis   *P. argenvillei*

Ecklonia   Bare rock

P. cochlear and ordinary *Lithothamnion*

Coralliform *Lithothamnion*

Figure 10–11. Diagram of the zonation on a more sheltered vertical rock face in South Africa. Limpets (*Patella* spp.) are a prominent feature of the fauna here. (After Stephenson et al., 1940.)

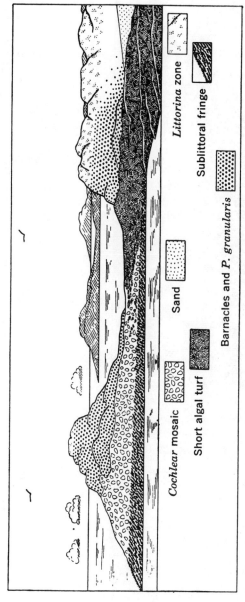

Littorina zone

Sublittoral fringe

Sand

Barnacles and *P. granularis*

Cochlear mosaic

Short algal turf

Figure 10–12. Diagram of the zonation on a sloping rocky shore in South Africa, showing the changes associated with increasing shelter from wave action. (After Stephenson, 1944.)

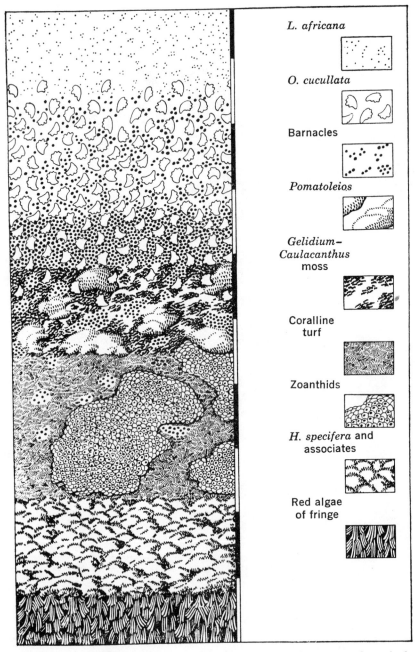

L. africana

O. cucullata

Barnacles

Pomatoleios

Gelidium–
Caulacanthus
moss

Coralline
turf

Zoanthids

H. specifera and
associates

Red algae
of fringe

Figure 10–13. Diagram of the zonation on a rocky slope exposed to fairly heavy waves along the subtropical Natal coast. (After Stephenson, 1944.)

replacing the zone of the limpet *Patella cochlear* by a thick short algal turf in a warm-temperate area on the South coast. Figure 10–13 illustrates conditions on a fairly exposed slope on the subtropical Natal coast.

There is a fringe of various red algae in the sublittoral fringe, and above these is frequently a thick growth of the red *Hypnea specifera*. The upper part of the balanoid zone contains little algal growth, but the lower part contains extensive patches of coralline turf in its lower part and above this of a moss-like growth consisting mainly of *Gelidium reptans* and *Caulacanthus ustulatus*. Many other species

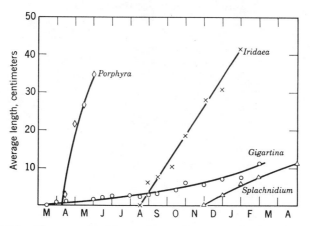

Figure 10–14. The growth of four species of algae on the South African coast. (After Bokenham and Stephenson, 1938.)

may, of course, occur in, or even dominate, these moss-like and turf-like areas according to local conditions. It is noticeable, however that there is a steady decrease in larger algae in the intertidal zone in the warmer waters. A paper by Bokenham and Stephenson (1938) gives the growth of a few species on cleared areas in the temperate section of the South African area studied (Fig. 10–14). Unfortunately there are almost no data of this type from tropical waters.

Although intertidal algal ecology has, in the past, tended largely toward the study of communities and their vertical distribution, that of the animals affords far more information on the characteristics of the particular species. Sessile barnacles comprise a large, and often the major, part of the animal population of rocky shores, and they have been correspondingly well studied both on the shore and as fouling organisms on ships, etc. On temperate European shores, where they have received the most study, the two commonest forms are *B. bala-*

noides and *Chthamalus stellatus*. Papers by Moore (1935, 1936) and
Moore and Kitching (1939) summarize information of their own and
of other workers up to that time. In *B. balanoides* the eggs are shed
into the mantle cavity in the autumn, and are carried there until the
spring when they begin about a 2 months' planktonic existence, first as
nauplii and then as cypris larvae. Settlement of the spat on the shore
is greatest in wave-exposed locations as shown by the figures of Hatton
and Fischer-Piette (1932) given in Table 10–1.

TABLE 10–1

Number of Spat per 100 Sq. Cm.

Locality	Number
Heavy wave exposure	2000
Slight wave exposure	1000
Sheltered	930
Very sheltered	0

TABLE 10–2

Numbers of Spat per 100 Sq. Cm.

Height on Shore	Heavy Wave Exposure		Slight Wave Exposure	
	1930	1931	1930	1931
Above high-water neaps	0	0	30	0
Below high-water neaps	790	560	300	504
Midtide	2325	2017	1207	1262
Low-water neaps	1500	1707	1500	1309

They state also that settlement decreases with increasing height on
the shore, and give the values shown in Table 10–2 for 2 years of
observations. The lower numbers toward high water may be in part
a function of the duration of immersion at that level, but some other
factor is involved since there is not a linear relation between settlement and duration of immersion. Certain conditions are known to
influence the settlement of the cypris. Hatton (1938) has shown that
settlement is greater on a scratched surface than on a polished one.
Settlement is favored by a low light intensity, but not by complete
darkness, and on an area which is a patchwork of dark and shade it is
favored by small, rather than large, dark patches (Smith, 1948). Results of experiments on the effect of currents on barnacles is conflicting, but it appears that continuous currents with a velocity of more
than about 25 cm. per second are unfavorable to settlement, and that

settlement is impossible at current velocities of more than about 50 cm. per second (Doochin and Smith, 1951). It must be remembered that on most shores, water movement is not continuous, and there are slack periods. Strong currents also resulted in smaller growth rates and higher mortality, and both of these effects decreased with increasing barnacle size. Figure 10–15 shows the size of the largest individual at different current velocities for three species of barnacle. The experiment was made over a 28-day period in semitropical waters at Miami, Florida (Smith, in press).

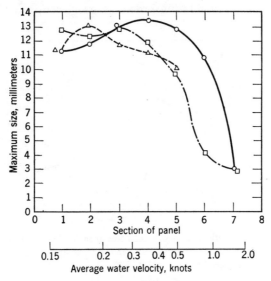

Figure 10–15. The effect of current on the growth of three species of barnacles, *Balanus amphitrite* (circles), *B. improvisus* (squares), *B. eburneus* (triangles). (After Doochin and Smith, 1951.)

Knight-Jones and Stevenson (1950) have shown that the spat of the barnacle *Elminius modestus* settle in greater numbers where there are already other barnacles present, apparently under the influence of some substance secreted into the water. Knight-Jones (1951) has also shown gregariousness in the settlement of the tubicolous polychaete, *Spirorbis*. Not only is settlement greater in the presence of pre-existing *Spirorbis*, but tests with *S. borealis* and *S. pagenstecheri* indicate that it is also specific within a genus. The concept is advanced that this gregariousness at settlement is beneficial to the survival of the species in that the selection of a locality where there are established adults insures that conditions are suitable for survival not only at the time of settlement but that they must also have remained suitable throughout the period covered by the life of the adults there. Thus, a *Spirorbis* settling on *Fucus* near high water would have no way of telling that desiccation would be excessive when the tide fell. Conditions would be much the same as for one settling near low water. At low water, however, there would be surviving adults to attract the settlement of fresh spat. Settlement appears to be mainly in the presence of established specimens of the species and to spread to un-occupied areas only in small proportions unless the larvae are very crowded. The resulting concentrations of the species have the addi-tional advantage of facilitating breeding, gregariousness being typical

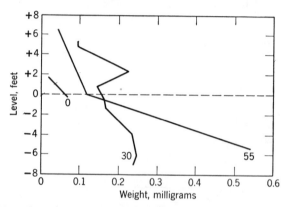

Figure 10–16. The relation of growth of the barnacle *Balanus balanoides* to tidal level and to wave exposure: 0 represents complete shelter, and 55 a high degree of wave exposure. (After Moore, 1935.)

of sessile, hermaphrodite forms. On the other hand, it has been found in some bottom-living lamellibranchs that spat are at a disadvantage when they settle in a dense community of adults. Perhaps because of their relatively higher food requirements, they are unable to com-pete with the adults and suffer a very high mortality.

During their young stages, the spat of *B. balanoides* grow much faster at low levels on the shore than at high ones (Fig. 10–16), and in general grow faster with increasing wave exposure. They also grow very much faster in localities where there is much suspended matter in the water than where it is clear, and this effect is more pronounced toward low water than higher on the shore. After their first year, the same is true in wave-exposed locations or where there is much sus-pended matter, but in clearer water with low wave exposure the op-timum level moves up to the top of their distribution with progressively lower growth rate toward low water. It appears reasonable that the young stages should grow less well in the upper levels since, presumably, their thin shells offer less protection against the increased insolation there. It also seems reasonable that, at all sizes, abundant food supply either as indicated by high sediment content of the water, or as brought to the animal by water movement, should result in increased growth rate. That the increase in growth rate with sediment-laden

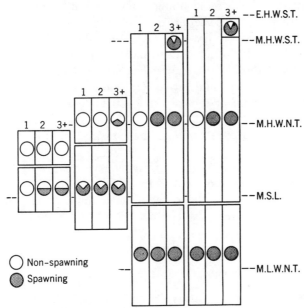

Figure 10–17. The effects of tidal level and wave exposure on the maturation of the gonads of the barnacle *Balanus balanoides.* Age, in years, is shown by the figures at the top of the blocks. The percentage of mature individuals at a given level and age is indicated by the gray area of the circle. With decreased wave-exposure (to the left), and at higher levels, maturation is delayed or may never occur. (After Moore, 1935.)

water is more marked toward low water is in keeping with the greater period of immersion at low levels. However, the shift in clearer, more sheltered, waters to better growth in the upper levels where there is a shorter period of immersion is hard to understand. It has been suggested that there may be some harmful factor associated with immersion, but that its effect is overruled where the food supply is rich by the greater beneficial effect of abundant food supply. This has little support at the moment beyond the facts already given and the fact that intertidal barnacles are rarely found below the level at which they will be exposed at least occasionally. But it is difficult to conceive of any other explanation of why an apparent suspension feeder should, in such habitats, flourish in inverse proportion to the time available for feeding.

Tidal level and wave exposure also control the maturation of the gonads of *B. balanoides* (Fig. 10–17). At the lower levels on a shore with high wave exposure, all individuals mature in their first year. On the same shore, but higher up, they do not mature until their second year, and at their extreme upper limit not until their third year or later. With increasing shelter, this delay in maturation becomes operative at progressively lower levels until, with extreme shelter, those in the lower levels do not mature until their second or third year or even later and those in the upper levels do not mature at all. Mortality rates vary with tidal level. On one area they ranged from 35 per cent per annum at the lowest levels to 3 per cent at the upper ones. This was probably associated, at least in part, with the decrease in numbers of *Purpura lapillus*, their main predator, toward their upper limit.

Chthamalus stellatus occupies a higher level than *B. balanoides*, although they usually overlap. Corresponding with this, the level of maximum settlement is above their lower limit, as shown in Table 10–3 in the figures given by Hatton (1938) and Hatton and Fischer-Piette (1932).

TABLE 10–3

Numbers of Spat per 100 Sq. Cm.

Level	Heavy Wave Exposure		Slight Wave Exposure	
	1931	1932	1931	1932
Just above high-water neaps	21	21	48	60
Just below high-water neaps	270	205	39	42
Midtide	1830	1610	8	19
Low-water neaps	8	5	0	0

These figures show also that the optimum level for settlement of spat is higher on a sheltered shore than on a wave-exposed shore, and that the density of settlement is less with increasing shelter. The same authors give data which show that, in a wave-exposed locality, the growth rate is greatest at the lower levels in the first year, but at the upper levels thereafter. In a more sheltered locality growth is greater at the upper levels at all ages.

Where these two species of barnacles are both abundant, their zonation overlaps, and there is no doubt competition for the available space. However, toward the northern limit of *Chthamalus* its zonation contracts upward, and one locality has been described (Moore and Kitching, 1939) where the lower limit of *Chthamalus* is above the upper limit of *Balanus*, with a small barnacle-free zone between. Here again it is suggested that some harmful factor associated with immersion, accentuated by other generally unfavorable conditions such as low temperature, is operating to restrict *Chthamalus* to that zone where it will undergo the shortest duration of immersion.

Mortality rates at one locality were similar to those of *Balanus*, ranging from 46.5 per cent per annum at their lower limit to 3.3 per cent at their upper. Here again the cause may be the distribution of the predatory *P. lapillus*. Both barnacle species are able to penetrate a

Figure 10–18. Two islands off Lough Ine, Ireland. The barnacle zone is shown as a white strip. The fucoids (dark) progressively replace the barnacles as the degree of shelter increases (to the left).

considerable distance into estuaries and tolerate some lowering of the salinity. In the British Isles, *Chthamalus* is most abundant on oceanic shores, and *Balanus* on the shores of the English Channel and the Irish and North Seas. It was originally suggested that this was correlated with the presence of oceanic or coastal water, but Kitching (1950) has since then suggested that the correlation may be with minimum winter air temperatures. Whatever the cause, however, it has been found that, in the area where one species predominates, that species penetrates further up estuaries, whereas the other and locally rarer species does not pass beyond the mouth. This was described in an earlier chapter as an example of departure from optimum conditions for a species by one factor lowering its tolerance range for another factor. In both species there may also be competition for available space with algae, and particularly in sheltered habitats they may be almost completely excluded by the latter. This encroachment by algae tends to take place from low water upward with increasing shelter, as shown in Fig. 10–18.

We have considered in detail the sedentary, suspension-feeding barnacles of the rocky shore. There are other filter feeders which may play as important a part on at least some shores, although for most of them there is little ecological information. Oysters (*Ostrea, Isognomon,* etc.) and mussel (*Mytilus, Modiolus, Brachydontes,* etc.) may

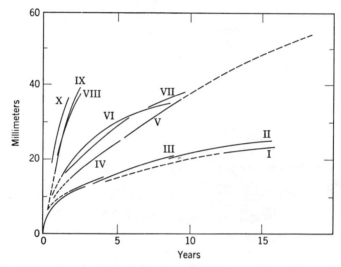

Figure 10–19. Growth of the limpet *Patella vulgata,* in different environments: I, among barnacles, St. Servain; II, among barnacles, Dinard; III, at Ilot de la Petite Conchée; IV, among barnacles, Cancaval; V, under *Ascophyllum,* Dinard; VI, on the fringe of *Ascophyllum* beds, Cancaval; VII, on the fringe of *Ascophyllum* beds, Saint-Enogal; VIII, IX, among barnacles at a high level; X, under *Fucus vesiculosus,* Port-Saint-Hubert. (After Fischer-Piette, 1948.)

be extremely important, and on tropical shores species of *Arca* also. Since both *Mytilus* and *Ostrea* are economically important, there is a wealth of information with regard to them. Reference may be made to such works as those of Tressler (1940, 1951) for a survey of information on oysters and Dodgson (1928) for mussels. On the lower part of the shore ascidians may form extensive sheets, dominating all other forms, as shown in various papers by Stephenson.

A second important group of animals on the intertidal rocks is comprised of the various gastropods, some of them predators and others feeding on the larger algae or on the algal and diatom film on the rock surface. A few gastropods are filter feeders and may be locally very important.   An example of this is the sheets of vermetids which may take the place on many tropical rocks of the barnacles and filter feeding tube worms of other shores.   Morton (1951) gives an excellent account of the New Zealand forms.   Three main groups occur among the forms that graze the surface film—limpets and members of the families Littorinidae and Neritidae.

Limpets belong to unrelated groups of the gastropods, the genera *Patella* and *Acmaea* being aspidobranchiates and the externally similar genus *Siphonaria* being pulmonates.   Much less is known of the ecology of the pulmonates.   There has been much discussion about the validity of the three common species of *Patella* on the northern European shores.   However, *P. vulgata* is the commonest, and the following remarks refer to this form. The limpets occur abundantly on rocky shores from about extreme low water to high water of neap tides.   According to Orton (1929) this is their upper limit, where they are exposed to insolation, but they extend higher under the influence of either shade or splash.   Settlement of young is greater with moderate wave exposure than in shelter (Fischer-Piette, 1948), but their mortality in the first year is correspondingly greater in the more wave-exposed habitat.   Growth is widely variable and is in general most rapid where the population density is least.   It is higher than normal where there is a high organic content in the water, as in estuaries or near sewer outfalls, where there is a current, or where there is a fucoid cover on the rocks (Fig. 10–19).   Longevity is, in general, inversely proportional to rate of growth.   Shells of limpets from the upper levels are relatively considerably taller than those from near low water and have a much thicker apical region (Fig. 10–20).   There is evidence that the shell shape is correlated with desiccation, those limpets which inhabit high levels where they tend to dry out maintaining a more contracted posture and secreting new shell, as a result, in the form of a more acute cone.   Near low water or in pools, the animals expand more freely and produce a more flattened shell as a result (Orton,

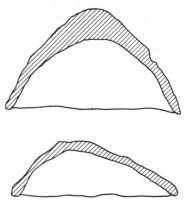

Figure 10–20. Sections of the shells of the limpet *Patella vulgata,* showing the relation of shell shape and thickness to tidal level. The upper shell was from high water, and the lower from low water in the Isle of Man.

1933; Moore, 1934). The food of limpets consists largely of algal and diatom film scraped from the rock surface, though they are also known to eat the larger fucoids. The latter fact may account for their greater growth rate on fucoid-covered rocks than on more open surfaces. At present there is no adequate explanation of why they should flourish particularly in water with a high organic content. Limpets, except in the smaller stages, characteristically inhabit a scar on the rock surface to which they return after a feeding excursion. There is disagreement about just when they make these feeding excursions, and the conditions no doubt vary locally, but feeding is probably restricted in general to the period when they are covered by water or to that part of the period of exposure before desiccation becomes serious. According to Hatton (1936) periodic exposure of the young is essential, and those adults found living permanently immersed in pools have migrated there after an initial stage of growth on the open rock.

For South African shores there is considerable information on the many species of Patellidae occupying the intertidal zone. Stephenson (1939) gives data on their distribution. With regard to zonation, the relative levels of the commoner species are as follows:

P. granularis

P. oculus and *P. granatina*

P. longicosta

P. cochlear

P. argenvillei

P. patriarcha and *P. compressa*

Although some species extend over the entire coast studies, others are limited to the colder western or to the eastern shores, or some to an intermediate region. Several exhibit a more or less regular variation in size with locality. Data for *P. granularis* are shown as an example in Fig. 10–21.

On the Pacific coast of North America, Test (1945) has made a survey of the niches occupied by the various species of *Acmaea*. Of the seventeen species present only one is estuarine—*A. depicta,* which lives on *Zostera*. Three species, *A. digitalis, A. scabra,* and *A. conus,* inhabit the upper levels and feed on the surface algal and diatom film. These three are apparently competitors for space, having very similar ecological requirements. A number of species occupy intermediate intertidal levels. Of these, *A. persona* is specialized in inhabiting the underside of ledges in dim light. It has been shown to be negatively phototropic. *Acmaea fenestrata* is restricted to surfaces of rocks whose bottoms rest in sand. During the period of low water, this species moves down the rock surface until it is below the level of sand surface. The remaining species of the intermediate levels may be divided according to the nature of the food taken. *Acmaea asmi* feeds solely on the microscopic film which it finds growing on another gastropod, *Tegula funebralis*. *Acmaea pelta* feeds on most available species of larger algae, although with certain preferences. It may occur either on rock or on the algae themselves and is mainly limited by its requirement of shelter from wave action, either in the form of rock surfaces or of a breakwater of algae. *Acmaea testudinalis scutum* in the northern part of the coast and *A. limatula* in the south both require a rock substratum and are restricted in diet to more delicate algae, such as *Ulva, Iridaea,* and *Enteromorpha.* Of species with still

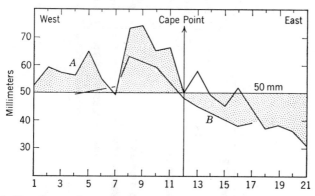

Figure 10–21. Geographic variation in the adult shell size of the South African limpet *Patella granularis.* (After Stephenson, 1939.)

more restricted diets, *A. insessa* is found only on *Egregia Menziesii* on which it feeds, and *A. instabilis* on *Laminaria Andersonii* and *A. paleacea* on the eel grass, *Phyllospadix torrevi.* *Acmaea triangularis* is found only among the coralline alga *Amphiroa tuberculosa,* on which it feeds. Two species are restricted to very low levels where there is only brief exposure. Of these, *A. mitra* is restricted to patches of moss-like red algae on which it feeds, and *A. ochracea* to permanently submerged rocks which are free from larger algae. Certain inter- and intraspecific trends occur among these various limpets that appear to be correlated with environmental conditions. Thus, the forms living near high water have taller shells, as in *P. vulgata.* Those living in lowered salinity have thinner shells, and those in chemically polluted water are taller, with smaller apertures. Those exposed to heavy wave action tend to have thicker or more sculptured shells, except where they live on an alga instead of on rock. For these limpets it is suggested that the flexibility of the alga affords protection from the wave shock. Such specimens also have reduced openings, apparently correlated with the limited size of the available surface of attachment.

One notable characteristic in this area was the degree to which the various *Acmaea* matched their background in coloration and pattern

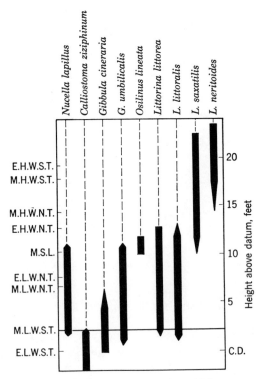

Figure 10–22. Zonation of the commoner intertidal gastropods on English shores. (After Bokenham et al., 1938.)

variations occurring even within a single species according to habitat. In some other gastropods, such as *Purpura*, similar observations have been made, but the color variations have been shown to be a direct response to the diet rather than an adaptation to the background. In the case of the *Acmaea*, however, this seems to be ruled out, and there seems to be no acceptable alternative to the suggested explanation that the phenomenon is due to the selective removal of nonmatching individuals by predators; the main predators are oyster catchers, rodents, raccoons, fish, and probably crabs.

Abe (1931, 1933) has reported on the habits of certain Japanese *Acmaea* which congregate in the summer in groups of 30 to 40. They disperse for the winter, the young ones moving away first. Some, but not all, return to the same group the following year. The young ones were found to move about at all times, whereas the adults were active only at night.

There are, of course, very many gastropods which are present in significant numbers on one shore or another, and it would be impossible to consider them all. However, two groups are of particular importance and wide distribution. These are the Littorinidae and the

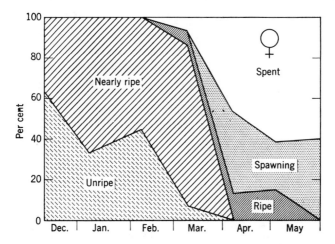

Figure 10–23. The progress of spawning in the female of the intertidal gastropod *Littorina littorea.* (After Moore, 1937.)

Neritidae, and ecological information is largely confined to the former. On temperate European shores there are four common members of the family. *Littorina neritoides* is a very small form living at a very high level on the rocky shore. *Littorina rudis* (*L. saxatilis*) lives somewhat lower (Fig. 10–22) and *L. littorea,* a yet larger form, lower still. The latter two species extend also to a softer substratum. *Littorina obtusata,* which lives on the lower half of the shore, occurs typically on fucoids.

Of the four species, *L. littorea* is the best known. It has received particular study since it occurs on both sides of the Atlantic and is of some local importance economically. Spawning occurs in the south of England in the spring (Fig. 10–23) and after a planktonic phase, the young appear on the shore in May and June. Shell growth proceeds most rapidly during the summer, and the females grow faster than the males. This sexual difference in growth rate has also been demonstrated in the Indian species *L. scabra* and *L. obesa* (Sewell, 1924) and in the American *L. angulifera* (Lenderking, 1952). More rapid growth in the females appears to be rather widespread in marine invertebrates. Tissue growth follows similar lines except that, after

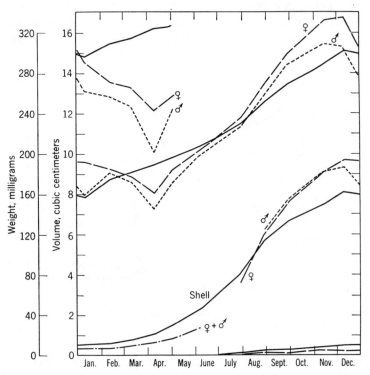

Figure 10–24. Growth of the intertidal gastropod *Littorina littorea*. The solid line shows shell growth, and the dotted and broken lines show male and female tissue growth. There is a slight sexual difference. The mature individuals, over a year old, show a marked decrease in tissue weight during the spawning period. (After Moore, 1937.)

sexual maturity, there is a drop in body weight at the time of spawning (Fig. 10–24). Spawning first occurs 2 years after hatching on some grounds but not until 3 years later on others. Mortality rates were estimated as 94 per cent per annum for the first 2 months after settlement and 66 per cent for the rest of the first year. After the first year it dropped to 57 per cent. On another ground the rate for individuals over 15 months old was estimated as only 23 per cent per annum (Moore, 1937). The lower limit of distribution seems to be fairly constant at about low water of spring tides, but the upper limit varies locally. It does not usually exceed mean high water of neap tides unless elevated by splash, and it frequently does not attain this level if there is insufficient algal cover on the rocks. There is evidence of a variation in vertical distribution with age, the smallest and largest individuals tending to be more restricted than the medium-sized ones (Moore, 1940).

Lysaght (1941) has studied the high-level *L. neritoides*. The center of abundance of this species is about high water of spring tides,

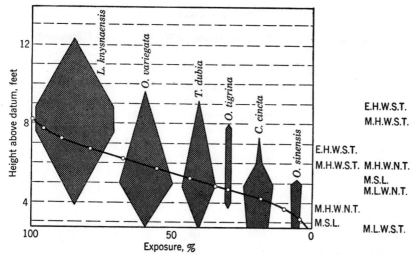

Figure 10–25. The zonation of the commoner gastropods on the South African shore. The superimposed curve shows the relation of percentage exposure to tidal level. Of the two sets of tidal levels on the right, the outer set has been elevated to provide correction for the effect of splash. (After Broekhuysen, 1940.)

although young ones extend further down the shore than older ones. It tends to shelter in crannies and small pools at this level, such shelter being necessary for survival. The species is most abundant where there is considerable wave action. It also appears to be favored by a barnacle cover on the rocks and to be rare or absent where algae are abundant. In this species also the larvae are planktonic and are released only when the animal is wet by sea water. Correlated with this, egg capsules are found in the sea close to the habitat of the adults mainly at the time of spring tides when the animals would have been immersed at high tide.

Broekhuysen (1940) has contributed a valuable study of the ability of certain South African gastropods to withstand desiccation and the relation of this ability to their normal tidal level. These gastropods include the high-level *Littorina knysnaënsis*. Figure 10–25 shows the vertical distribution of the species concerned and the percentage of the average tidal cycle during which the various levels are exposed. The latter does not take into account the effect of splash or wash, but the tidal scale on the extreme right shows what allowance should be made at the locality in question. Table 10–4 shows the minimum water loss from desiccation that killed any individuals, and the loss required to kill practically all.

TABLE 10–4

Relation of Survival to Level in South African Intertidal Gastropods

(Broekhuysen, 1940)

Species	Maximum Percentage of Water Loss at Which Death Occurred		Minimum Percentage of Water Loss at Which Practically All Were Dead	
	At Room Temperature	At 39–40°C.	At Room Temperature	At 39–40°C.
Oxystele sinensis	3	3	9	9
O. tigrina	7	4	11–12	7
Cominella cincta	10	8	13	11
O. variegata	12	10	21	16
Thais dubia	15	13	24	20
Littorina knysnaënsis	15	14	29	25–26

It is apparent that the order agrees well with that observed for zonation on the shore, those species which can tolerate most water loss living at the highest levels. *Oxystele tigrina,* the one exception, is characterized by living in pools, whereas the others live on the open rock; it is thus less liable to desiccation. However, when rate of loss of water by desiccation was measured, there was found to be little correlation between the level inhabited and the rate of water loss. Only in *L. knysnaënsis,* the highest-living, was there a markedly lower loss than in the other species. Finally, in Table 10–5, the vertical distributions of the different species are expressed as percentages of exposure in the average tidal cycle. Where there is a marked center of distribution, this also is indicated. In the last column, the time necessary to kill them, under shore conditions of desiccation, is expressed also as percentages of the average 12.5-hour cycle.

Here again there is reasonable agreement except in *O. tigrina* for which allowance has to be made because of its normally wet habitat.

Experiments were also made on the effects of high temperature when the animals were immersed in water as shown in Table 10–6, and here again the agreement was good. Unfortunately there are no

TABLE 10–5

Relation of Survival to Level in South African Intertidal Gastropods

(Broekhuysen, 1940)

Species	Tidal Levels Expressed as Percentage Exposure on Average Tide		Lethal Exposure Expressed as Similar Percentage
	Range	Optimum (when there is one)	
Oxystele sinensis	0– 45	—	12–>60
Cominella cincta	0– 90	c. 35	32–>60
O. tigrina	10– 95	—	20– 48
O. variegata	<5–100	c. 35	48–>100
Thais dubia	<5–100	c. 35	>56–>100
Littorina knysnaënsis	10–100	95–100	>100

TABLE 10–6

Relation of Survival to Temperature in South African Intertidal Gastropods

(Broekhuysen, 1940)

Species	Temperature at Which Activity Stopped, °C.	Lowest Temperature at Which Death Occurred, °C.	Temperature at Which All Snails Were Dead, °C.
Oxystele sinensis	35.4–>39.0	38.0 (80% alive)	39.6
Cominella cincta	36.3– 38.0	38.9 (67% alive)	c. 39.5
O. tigrina	36.8–>38.3	38.9 (90–100% alive)	40.5
Thais dubia	36.0– 39.4	41.2 (80–90% alive)	41.7
O. variegata	37.2–>41.5	41.5 (80% alive)	42.1
Littorina knysnaënsis	35.7– 40.7	47.4 (90–100% alive)	48.6

comparable data on the effects of air temperature, and it is probably during the period of exposure to air that the highest temperatures would be encountered.

Mattox (1949) gives some comparable data for the survival of Puerto Rican intertidal gastropods. In his experiments, the animals were kept dry in the laboratory, and some survived for a surprising time without food or water (Table 10–7).

Broekhuysen (1940) also gives a table, part of which is included in Table 10–8, showing a similar tendency for higher living forms to have a higher lethal temperature among intertidal molluscs in general.

TABLE 10–7

Relation of Survival to Level in Puerto Rican Intertidal Gastropods

(Mattox, 1949)

Species	Upper Limit, height in feet above low water	Survival Dry in Laboratory
Thais patula	0	9 days
Neritina virginea	1.5	12 days
Nerita tessellata	2.2	17 days
N. versicolor	3.5	36 days
N. peloronta	4.5	11 weeks
Littorina ziczac	6.0	7 months
Tectarius tuberculatus	8.0	12 months
T. muricatus	20.0	17 months

Purpura lapillus affords an example of a carnivorous intertidal gastropod. This species is a temperate form in the North Atlantic, but other species of the genus are found throughout the world in similar habitats. Breeding occurs throughout the year but mainly in winter and spring (Moore, 1936, 1938). The yolky eggs, 300 to 1000 in number, are enclosed in a horny capsule which is attached to the rock surface, often in a cranny. From 6 to 31 capsules are produced at a time. Most of the ova in the capsule are unfertilized and serve as food for the 5 to 40 larvae which finally hatch. These do so at an advanced stage with a well-formed shell and are able to crawl readily. Although small, they inhabit much lower levels on the shore than the adults (Fig. 10–26) and feed mainly on the small tubicolous polychaete *Spirorbis*. At a height of about 8–10 mm. they show a tendency to climb upward and simultaneously to change to the adult diet of barnacles, mussels, etc. At different localities there is a variation of as much as ten times in growth rate and also in the nature of the relation between growth rate and age. The reason for this is not understood, but it is suggested that it is correlated with both food and wave exposure. At sexual maturity, increase in shell size ceases, and the lip of the shell is thickened internally, considerably reducing the size of the aperture. Although a number of other species are known to be attached and eaten by *Purpura*, the two most abundant items in its diet are barnacles and mussels. Variations in diet have been shown to be correlated with various shell characteristics. Thus an increase in the proportion of *Mytilus* to barnacles in the diet is asso-

TABLE 10–8

Level	Species	Lethal Temperature, °C.	Locality
Sutlittoral	*Venus mercenaria*	45.2	St. Andrews, N.B.
	Yoldia sapotilla	34.8	St. Andrews, N.B.
	Musculus niger	34.5	St. Andrews, N.B.
	Pandora trilineata	33.5	St. Andrews, N.B.
	Astarte undata	33.5	St. Andrews, N.B.
	Cardium pinnulatum	33.2	St. Andrews, N.B.
	Crenella glandula	32.8	St. Andrews, N.B.
	Saxicava rugosa	32.8	St. Andrews, N.B.
	Leda tenuisulcata	32–31	St. Andrews, N.B.
	Musculus discors	31.9	St. Andrews, N.B.
	Cardita borealis	31.6	St. Andrews, N.B.
Lower intertidal zone	*Littorina littorea*	44–41	St. Andrews, N.B.
	Littorina littorea	46.6	Halifax
	Mactra solidissima	37	St. Andrews, N.B.
	Modiolus modiolus	36.3	St. Andrews, N.B.
	Zirfaea crispata	35.5	St. Andrews, N.B.
	Oxystele sinensis	39.6–39.0	False Bay, S.A.
	Cominella cincta	39.4–39.0	False Bay, S.A.
Midtidal zone	*Littorina saxatilis*	43.2–42.3	St. Andrews, N.B.
	Littorina palliata	42.5–41.8	St. Andrews, N.B.
	Oxystele variegata	42.1–41.5	False Bay, S.A.
	Thais dubia	41.7–41.2	False Bay, S.A.
	Oxystele tigrina	40.5–40.0	False Bay, S.A.
Upper intertidal zone	*Littorina knysnaënsis*	48.6–47.9	False Bay, S.A.
	Macoma fusca	42.3	St. Andrews, N.B.
	Mytilus edulis	40.8	St. Andrews, N.B.
	Mya arenaria	40.6	St. Andrews, N.B.

ciated with a slight increase in the size at which sexual maturity occurs, and this in turn with a greater amount of thickening of the shell lip at maturity and with certain changes in the shape of the shell. An increase in the proportion of *Mytilus* is also associated with an increase in the spiral angle of the shell, but with a decrease in the apical angle, and these in turn are reflected in changes in the shell weight. Sexually mature individuals also constitute a smaller proportion of

Mytilus-fed populations than of barnacle-fed populations. Perhaps most striking, though, is the correlation between shell color and diet (Fig. 10–27). Barnacle-fed individuals are white, unless stained by algal infection of the shell or some similar condition. Both the shell and the tissues of *Mytilus edulis* are strongly pigmented, and this pigment appears to be passed through the *Purpura* which feeds on them and is laid down in its own shell. In some species the pigment may even be laid down in the yolk of any eggs produced and so passed on to the developing larvae, whose larval shells will then be pigmented.

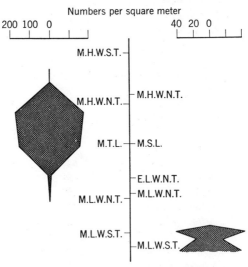

Figure 10–26. The zonation of the gastropod *Purpura lapillus* on two shores in Scotland, showing the marked difference in level between the adults (left) and the young (right). (After, Moore, 1938a.)

The pigment so passed on may be brown or black or mauve pink. Earlier authors have claimed that the dark color of many of the *Purpura* found among *Mytilus* has a protective value, as does the white color of those living on the light-colored barnacles. Whether or not this is true, the direct cause is one of diet and not of selection by predators of the more readily visible specimens. In the same way, a generally observed correlation between the color of the *Purpura* and wave exposure is explained by the fact that, in many areas at least, *Mytilus* tends to replace barnacles on the rocks in wave-exposed localities. On the other hand, there is some suggestion that shells with yellow coloration are more abundant at localities with medium wave exposure, that this may not be a direct effect of diet. There are always some uncolored individuals in a *Mytilus*-fed population of *Purpura,* and in some localities there may be no colored ones at all. It has been shown recently that there are local differences in genetic make-up, and that the pigment in the diet can only be transmitted to the shell of the *Purpura* when the necessary genetic characteristics are present. The habits of *Purpura* tend to isolate it in distinct communities and to favor the development of genetic differences between these.

Purpura lapillus plays an important role as a predator on the shore. Although there are no exact data on its food requirements, the 21–35

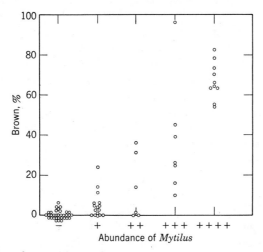

Figure 10–27. The correlation between the percentage of brown-pigmented shells in populations of the gastropod *Purpura lapillus* and the abundance of the mussel *Mytilus edulis.* Each circle represents one locality. (After Moore, 1937.)

per cent mortality per annum observed in *B. balanoides* at the lower levels on the shore was probably caused mainly by *Purpura,* this rate is probably greatly exceeded where *Purpura* are present in large numbers, and not deliberately removed, as they were on the area in question. The account given by Fischer-Piette (1935) of cyclic changes in the *Balanus-Mytilus* relations on a French shore demonstrate the ability of *Purpura* to modify whole communities. It is interesting to note that in this instance *Purpura,* previously barnacle-fed, apparently had to learn the technique of attacking *Mytilus,* and although the latter provided a larger, and presumably more economical, meal for them, they continued to take *Balanus* by preference until driven by its scarcity to make the change in diet. Boring of the

Mytilus shells, by *Purpura*, is performed entirely by radula action, without the assistance of any acid secretion. Barnacles appear to be opened by bursting apart their opercular plates, possibly after the animal has been partially narcotized by the action of some secretion of the *Purpura*.

Purpura requires a rocky substratum and can, with difficulty, cross a stretch of soft bottom. Because of this, and because it does not have a planktonic larval stage, rocks which are otherwise suitable but are isolated by sand are frequently not colonized. Rocks overhanging deep water are also poorly populated by this species, apparently because when they are washed off the rocks by wave action they are unable to return to their normal habitat. In certain areas they are preyed on rather extensively by gulls, and it is stated that they are often completely eliminated from the neighborhood of gull nesting areas. Their tolerance of lowered salinity is only slight, and they do not penetrate far up estuaries. The principal limitation to geographical distribution appears to be temperature. To the north they appear to be limited approximately by the presence of ice in winter, although Gislén (1930) states that, in the Gullmar Fjord, they descend below low water in winter, presumably to avoid ice action and low salinity. Their southward extension appears to be limited by maximum summer temperatures, and the summer air temperatures at their southern limit on both sides of the Atlantic are in the neighborhood of the 35.0–35.5°C., quoted by Gowanloch (1927) as their lethal limit.

As an example of the still more active intertidal forms about which there is available a useful amount of information, we may take the shore crab *Pachygrapsus crassipes*. Hiatt (1948) has made a valuable study of this species, in which he compares it with two related forms from the same shores, *Hemigrapsus nudus* and *H. oregonensis*. On the Pacific coasts of North America, *P. crassipes* occurs typically on rocky shores devoid of loose stones and throughout the intertidal zone. It inhabits crevices and pools, coming out at night to forage. In bays and estuaries it may be found in the crevices between boulders but not underneath rocks bedded on sand or mud. Since there is a tendency in such habitats for the larger boulders to lie lower on the shore, and there are more mud-free crevices available at this level than higher up, *P. crassipes* tends to be restricted here to the lower levels. *Hemigrapsus nudus* and *H. oregonensis*, on the other hand, which normally occupy a rather lower zone than *P. crassipes*, here invert their relationship, living higher on the boulder-covered shore. This choice of level is associated with their better ability to withstand sandy and muddy conditions. Finally, a few *P. crassipes*, living in estuaries and bays, inhabit holes at about high watermark where the muddy foreshore meets the vegetation cover of *Salicornia,* etc. In this habitat they are restricted completely to the upper zone of the shore. With the differences in habitat of these three species of crab are associated certain anatomical and physiological adaptations. *Hemigrapsis oregonensis* is associated typically with a muddy substratus. The water entering its gill chambers is filtered through a thick mesh of fine setae on the branchiostegite and the dorsal side of each coxa, and the mastigobranch of the third maxilliped is exceedingly plumose, thus adapting it particularly for sweeping the gill surfaces free from silt. *Hemigrapsis nudus* inhabits, typically, a sandy substratum, and the filtering setae are less numerous but much stiffer; this would appear to afford a more efficient strainer for larger particles. *Pachygrapsus crassipes,* which usually avoids both mud and sand and lives in crannies or pools on bare rock, has fine setae, but they are much reduced in quantity. The gills of land crabs are usually reduced in number. Thus *Uca minax, U. pugnax,* and *U. pugilator* have 12 instead of the normal 18. *Pachygrapsus crassipes* has the full number, but *H. oregonensis* and *H. nudus* have only 16. All three show a reduction in relative gill volume, compared with fully marine crabs, as shown in Table 10–9.

TABLE 10–9

Gill Volumes of Crabs

(Hiatt, 1948)

Species	Habitat	Gill Volume as Percentage of Body Volume
Cancer antennarius	Low tide and below	5.0
C. magister	Below low tide	4.4
Pugettia productus	Intertidal and below	3.72
Hemigrapsus nudus	Lower intertidal	2.77
H. oregonensis	Intertidal	2.4
Pachygrapsus crassipes	Upper intertidal	2.36

In a laboratory test of ability to withstand desiccation, *H. oregonensis* were all moribund in 6 hours and dead in 10. *Hemigrapsus nudus* and *P. crassipes* were much more tolerant, none being moribund until 13 hours. Most survived for 18 hours, but all were dead in 24 hours. These three species, therefore, show differences from one another which are more or less in agreement with their different requirements for substratum and tidal level. All are to be considered as intermediate between marine and fully adapted terrestrial crabs. Other changes also are usually associated with the evolution of a land habitat in crabs. One change is in increased agility, and with this is frequently associated a relative increase in leg length. A comparison of the high level *P. crassipes* with the lower-living *H. nudus* bears this out, the total lengths of the second ambulatory leg having a ratio of 1.13:1 in the two species, and the dactylus a ratio of 1.15:1. Another terrestrial adaptation is in the nature of osmoregulation. *Hemigrapsus oregonensis* and *H. nudus* have more highly developed osmoregulation toward lowered salinity than does *P. crassipes*. This

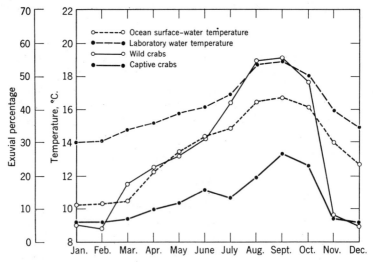

Figure 10–28. The relation between frequency of molting and water temperature in the Pacific intertidal crab, *Pachygrapsus crassipes*. (After Hiatt, 1948.)

is in agreement with their greater abundance under estuarine conditions. On the other hand, the osmoregulation of *P. crassipes* toward raised salinity is greater than in the other species, which accords with its higher tidal level and the increased desiccation to which it is subject.

Molting in *P. crassipes* varies in frequency with the temperature, as it has been found to do in other species of crabs. Figure 10–28 shows this clearly. There is, typically, a winter period of inhibited ecdysis (Fig. 10–29). Molting also takes place more frequently in the younger crabs, and their relative increase in size at the molt is greater. Growth is similar in the two sexes up to the time of sexual maturity, but thereafter the females grow more slowly than the males. In addition, they suffer a more prolonged intermolt period than normal during the period when they are carrying eggs.

Copulation and egg production normally occur once each year, although probably twice in some individuals. The eggs are carried by the female for 26 to 31 days, and the subsequent planktonic phase

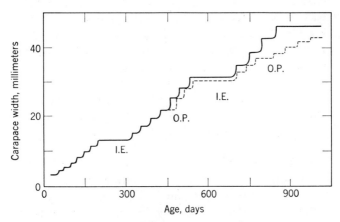

Figure 10–29. Growth of the crab *Pachygrapsus crassipes*, showing the periods of inhibited ecdysis in winter (I.E.) and during the ovigerous period of the females (O.P.). The solid line indicates both sexes before maturity, thereafter males; the dotted line indicates females. (After Hiatt, 1948.)

occupies about 35 days. Young crabs are markedly more active than older ones. This is reflected in their relatively long legs as shown in Table 10–10. They also have relatively larger eyes, but Hiatt is of

TABLE 10–10

Leg and Eye Lengths in *Pachygrapsus*

(Hiatt, 1948)

Carapace Breadth	Ratio of Length of Second Walking Leg to Length of Carapace	Ratio of Length of Eye to Length of Carapace
3.7	1.82	0.23
9.1	1.75	0.17
15.2	1.80	0.13
20.5	1.71	0.11
24.0	1.66	0.10
31.1	1.68	0.09
37.6	1.58	0.08
45.8	1.59	0.07

the opinion that this does little to enhance their visual perception, for relatively less of the eye is flattened so that it is not possible for them to concentrate as large a mass of visual elements on a given object as the adults can.

Although they are general scavengers, taking live or dead animal matter when available, the principal diet of *P. crassipes* is algae. The greater part of this is obtained by scraping the algal felt or film from the rocks, although they may also bite pieces from larger algae. They sometimes attack gastropods, removing them, with varying success, from their shells. Hiatt records watching *Pachygrapsus* pursuing a *Ligia,* and even of one stalking and catching a fly. *Hemigrapsus nudus,* on the other hand, feeds mainly on detritus which is a relatively minor item in the diet of *P. crassipes.* This diet also is in agreement with the preferred habitat of *H. nudus*—a soft substratum. *Pachygrapsus crassipes* may be active during the daytime, although its activity is mainly confined to pools, whereas at night it travels over the exposed rock surfaces. Their daytime activity in pools is greatest on sunny days, and less when the sun is obscured, but Hiatt states that this variation is actually conditioned by the water temperature and that activity is markedly decreased below 65°F.

11

Organisms—Rocky Shores

(Continued)

On all shores there is a more or less constant process of denudation, with subsequent replacement of the flora and fauna. This usually takes place on a small scale and in patches, although, under the influence of ice or of very severe wave action, it may be fairly wholesale. Occasionally, too, catastrophic changes such as unusual flooding by fresh water may produce such denudation. This may occur regularly every spring in some localities such as arctic fjords. On a small scale, though, it is a normal process, limpets grazing small areas of rock clear of algae, barnacles and mussels dying and falling off to leave vacant space, and, for that matter, new barnacles and mussels growing and themselves providing a fresh surface for attachment of other organisms.

The process of recolonization has received considerable study, particularly because of its bearing on the growth of fouling organisms on ships, piles, etc. The first phase in colonization is almost invariably a surface film of bacteria and diatoms (Bokenham and Stephenson, 1938; Wilson, 1925 etc.), although for some attachment surfaces this may be preceded by a period during which chemical or other change takes place which renders the surface tolerable to the colonizers. Under natural conditions, exposure of a completely new rock surface is probably of comparatively rare occurrence, and such denudation does not involve loss of the initial diatom film. Following the diatom film phase, there is sometimes a profuse growth of hydroids, although this does not always occur. Following or sometimes replacing this is a dominance of algal felt, composed of *Enteromorpha, Ectocarpus,* or other forms. This in turn affords shelter to the earlier stages of *Fucus* spp. or other larger algae, and the presence of the algal felt, if not essential for the colonization by the larger forms, at least greatly facilitates their settlement and subsequent growth.

Settlement of barnacles, mussels, ascidians, or other animals may occur at various stages of this algal succession, and the details will vary according to local conditions. Further, where the species involved have a limited breeding season, the specific details will vary according to the larvae available for settlement at the time when space for them is available. This will of course vary locally but the calendar for LaJolla, California (Coe, 1932), given in Table 11–1, may be taken as an example.

Denuding of rock surfaces by wave action or ice is likely to occur principally at specific seasons in any one locality, and to this extent the species recolonizing them will be fairly constant and predictable. The continuous process of denudation by removal of sessile forms by predation and other causes will result in a varying succession according to the time at which it takes place. It is probably true that for most such cleared areas there will be immediate competition for the available space. It must be remembered, however, that such a cleared space is not suitable for immediate settlement by all members of the climax community, and the succession which actually takes place may be a slow one, with return to the original flora and fauna only after several years, if at all. An example of this is given by Moore and Sproston (1940), in which, after 4 years, a rocky foreshore in the English Channel did not yet support a fauna and flora completely comparable with that of neighboring older shores. In the case cited by Fischer-Piette (1935) in which the balance between mussels, barnacles, and *Purpura* went through a cyclic change, the entire cycle took about 4 years to reach completion. In the case quoted by Knight and Parke (1950), in which limpets were cleared from a stretch of shore and the resulting increase in fucoids was studied, after 3 years the limpets were only beginning to return. It must be remembered that the depopulation of a surface is rarely complete. Frequently it involves removal of all

TABLE 11–1

Colonization of Test Blocks at La Jolla, California

(Coe, 1932)

Month	Sea Temperature, °C.	Organisms Colonizing Concrete Blocks during Month
January	14	Algae dominant and hydroids very abundant: *Ectocarpus granulosus, E. Mitchelli, E. confervoides, E. cylindricus, Leathesia difformis, Scytosiphon lomentarius, Herpetosiphonia verticellata. Obelia dichotoma, Plumularia setacea.* Also present: *Nereis agassizii, Caprella scaura, Pecten latiauritus.*
February	14	Algae and hydroids dominant, with sometimes a few barnacles.
March	14–15	Very similar, with the addition of some tubicolous polychaetes: *Eupomatus, Serpula, Spirorbis.*
April	16	Hydroids dominant, algae abundant. Some *Bugula* and other bryozoa. Considerable numbers of *Balanus tintinnabulum* and some *Ostrea lurida.*
May	17	*Obelia dichotoma* dominant, *Ectocarpus* and other algae abundant (including *Corallina gracilis*). Numerous barnacles, oysters, and bryozoa (*Bugula neritina, Crisia geniculata, Membranipora membranacea*).
June	18	Hydroids abundant but bryozoa dominant: *Bugula neritina, B. eburnea, Crisia geniculata, C. franciscana, C. pacifica, Scrupocellaria diegensis, Thalmoporella, Hippothoa.* Various ascidians common: *Molgula verrucifera, Ascidia californica, Didemnum carnulatum, Distaplia occidentalis.*
July	20	Similar to above except for scarcity of hydroids and algae.
August	21	Similar.
September	19	Similar, but the number of species present decreasing toward the end of the month.
October	18	Algae and hydroids increasing again. Some settlement of oysters, barnacles, and bryozoa.
November	16	Hydroids and algae dominant. A few barnacles and oysters.
December	15	Algae (principally *Ectocarpus*, with some *Leathesia* and *Herposiphonia*) and hydroids (*Obelia*) dominant. Practically nothing else.

macroscopic forms. At other times, however, the removal is more selective. For instance, wave action may remove the larger algae but leave small forms and certain animals. Or a particularly hot summer or cold winter may selectively kill some species while leaving others.

It has been possible, in a limited space, to select only a few types of organisms typical of the intertidal rocky shore and to summarize what is known of their ecology. It is clear that many more would have to be considered before a picture that was at all adequate could be built up, but at present the information is lacking for a great majority of the forms. The most, then, that will be possible, will be to trace some general trends in the effects of known intertidal factors on known organisms. To begin with, the nature of the rock surface may affect the settlement of sessile forms such as algae and barnacles, through the firmness of the holdfast which it affords them, and a soft surface such as chalk may, for this reason, be poorly populated. The degree of dissection of the surface will affect its moisture retention as well as the shelter which it affords to young animals and plants. Similar protection from insolation and desiccation may, however, be given by a covering of algae, and so we find such forms as young plants of *Fucus* flourishing best where such cover is provided. The extent to which this algal cover varies with tidal level, wave exposure, etc., is often reflected in the density of colonization of those forms to which it affords protection. Since it also affords an important item in the food supply of many herbivores it may be reflected in their distribution also.

Wave action is beneficial to many forms, in part, at least, because it brings more food within their reach. By its splashing action it keeps wet a greater extent of the intertidal zone than is possible in a sheltered locality. Wave action thus tends to extend the area available for successful colonization by many forms which require to be wet at frequent intervals. The food-providing effect of waves is reflected in the enhanced growth of such suspension feeders as barnacles in exposed localities. Its wetting action is reflected in the elevation of their upper limit on wave-exposed shores. There is, on the other hand, a harmful effect in the mechanical damage caused by waves, as well as the limitations on free movement which they impose on motile forms. The latter may result in decrease in the time available to them for feeding. Through a combination of these various effects of waves we can trace a sequence of interconnected effects on the flora and fauna of a rocky shore. Extreme wave action restricts the population of fucoids, probably by direct mechanical action. Settlement of barnacles spat is favored by wave action, as is their subsequent growth. The absence of the abrasive neighboring algae further favors them. Finally, the wave action may be sufficient to restrict or even eliminate their principal predator, *Purpura.* If mussels take the place of the barnacles at their particular levels, these too may be favored by the same factors. The growth of smaller algae will be less hindered than that of the larger forms, so there will still be ample food available for such herbivores as can live there. These include such forms as limpets and chitons, whose holdfast is secure, whereas others such as *Littorina* are more likely to be excluded.

The significance of tidal levels lies largely in the duration of exposure and immersion associated with them, and these in turn govern the severity of such factors as desiccation and insolation, exposure to high or low air temperatures, as well as the availability of water for food supply to filter feeders, for release of larvae, etc. Correlated with these we find the forms that live higher on the shore tending to be thick-shelled, or avoiding the light when they are young and their shells are thin. They also tend to be tolerant of higher temperatures than those living lower on the shore and to be better able to resist desiccation. Correlated with the increase in desiccation to which they are liable, they have better osmoregulatory systems to combat increased salinity in the body fluids, as well as mechanisms such as decreased gill area to restrict water loss. The effect of tidal level in duration of immersion, and the resulting time available for filter feeders to obtain food, is not well understood, and the barnacles, for which there is the best information, present anomalous results. Forms living in the upper levels may have their reproductive cycle so timed as to liberate eggs or larvae at the time of the highest spring tides; or, when they live above the reach of these, they may descend to the water to liberate them.

Polar shores differ from the temperate ones just described mainly in the effect of winter ice. Some effect is produced by mechanical action, scraping the algae and animals from the rocks. The fauna and flora is therefore restricted to forms which are either annual, and present only in summer, or else are able to migrate down to below the level of the ice during the winter. The ice also acts by sealing off the oxygen supply from the animals and by its freezing action. In addition, when it melts in the spring, it may form a surface layer of comparatively fresh water on the sea, at which time only the forms that can tolerate low salinities can survive in the intertidal zone. Finally, the shortness of the season during which there is an adequate food supply of phytoplankton in polar waters has favored the forms that produce eggs and larvae which are supplied with yolk and are thus independent of a planktonic food supply. Such larvae are produced in relatively smaller numbers and have less power of dispersal, but the settlement of spat produced by them tends to fluctuate less from one year to another than that from planktonic larvae. A few forms which do have planktonic larvae and are able to time their breeding to coincide sufficiently closely with the time of phytoplankton outburst are, however, among the most successful of the polar invertebrates. Some others, of course, do not breed in polar waters but are maintained as a population by an influx of planktonic larvae from more favorable areas.

On a tropical shore, insolation is almost certainly the major limiting factor, and it has been suggested that its effect in raising the temperature of organisms may be more significant than either actinic action or action producing desiccation. Large algae are little represented in the intertidal zone except at its lowest levels in the sublittoral fringe. Algal felt may be well developed, and, as with the fucoids of temperate shores, may be more extensive in a sheltered locality than at high wave exposure. It is rather generally assumed that tropical growth rates are much higher than temperate ones, but at present there is little evidence to support this. It has also been suggested that breeding seasons might be expected to extend throughout the year in the tropics, instead of being limited to particular seasons as they are in temperate waters. The observations that are available do not support this, limited seasons being, apparently, about as common as they are elsewhere. On the other hand, with the more uniform phytoplankton of the tropics, it might be expected that there would be less concentration of breeding seasons in the spring-summer period in the tropics than there is in cooler waters where phytoplankton production is more markedly seasonal. As yet there is not sufficient evidence to verify this possibility.

INTERTIDAL SAND

The fauna and more particularly the flora of sand are more limited in numbers of species, since only a relatively small number of forms are adapted to the special conditions. Only a comparatively small number of algae inhabit sandy bottoms, and few of these the intertidal zone. On most sandy beaches there is very little macroscopic vegetation between tidemarks, and where there is, this is more likely to be composed of some of the "sea grasses" such as *Zostera, Halodule,* and *Cymodocea.* (These are not true grasses.) There is considerable knowledge of the biology of *Zostera* from the work of Ostenfeld

(1908, 1918, etc.). In addition, the epidemics which have greatly reduced its abundance over a wide geographical range (Butcher, 1934) have called forth further intensive study. *Zostera* may form a moderately close growth over intertidal and sublittoral sands. The leaves stand up from a rooted creeping rhizome, and Petersen (1914a) gives the production per plant as about ten during the summer and five during the winter. There is progressive loss of the older leaves. A rich growth may represent as much as 6000 gm. per square meter. This is given as wet weight, and the equivalent dry weight would be about 960 gm. The annual productivity is probably slightly more in weight than the standing crop. *Zostera* grows under a rather wide range of conditions, including normal to low salinity and varying wave exposure. It is found on both sand and mud, but not on a hard substratum. The various species of marine grasses also span a wide range of temperature conditions, and those growing in shallow water in the tropics may have to withstand an extremely high temperature.

Fauré-Fremiet (1951) demonstrated a rhythm in the diatom *Hantzschia amphioxys* on the sandy beach. This species appears at the surface during the low-tide period, forming patches similar to those of *Convoluta*. There was a tide-controlled phototropism which reversed after a time, so that the diatoms came to the surface and later retreated downward. Comparable cases are quoted in *Convoluta roscoffensis,* dinoflagellates, chrysomonads, etc.

Although representatives of many animal phyla are found inhabiting sand, the groups that are quantitatively most important are the lamellibranchs, polychaetes, and certain crustacea. We have little quantitative information on the microfauna of sand, but this may be very rich in harpacticoid copepods, rotifers, nematodes, etc. Remane (1933) gives a valuable account of these.

The lamellibranchs have received particular attention on account of the economic value of some of the species, and a survey of these may be found in Tressler (1940). One of the most abundant of the intertidal lamellibranchs of some European shores is *Tellina tenuis*. Stephen (1928) records these with a density as high, on one occasion, as 7588 per square meter, with a normal density, at one locality, of 3000–4000. They are most abundant somewhat below low water-mark and decrease in numbers both deeper and toward high water. This quantitative distribution is illustrated both in total populations and in the numbers of spat settling, as shown in Table 11–2. On the other hand, their growth rate is greatest at higher levels on the shore, and it appears that there is a correlation between density of population and growth. This correlation is illustrated in Fig. 11–1.

TABLE 11-2

Total Population and Number of Spat (in October) in Relation to Tidal Level, in Kames Bay, Scotland

(Based, in part, on Stephen, 1928)

Station	Level	Total Population per square meter	Number of Spat per square meter	Mean Size in October, millimeters	
				One-Year Group	Three-Year Group
1	High-water neaps	0	0	—	—
1a		56	80	—	—
2		528	80	9.5	14.5
3		820	504	8.5	14.0
4		1892	420	7.5	12.0
5	Low-water springs	3288	408	7.0	11.0
6	L.W.S.T.—4 feet	(6150)*	(1600)	6.0	9.5
7	L.W.S.T.—10 feet	(545)	(3140)	—	—
8	L.W.S.T.—22 feet	0	(527)	—	—

* A different collecting method was used for the sublittoral samples, and the correction factor used leaves them not strictly comparable. These samples are indicated by parentheses.

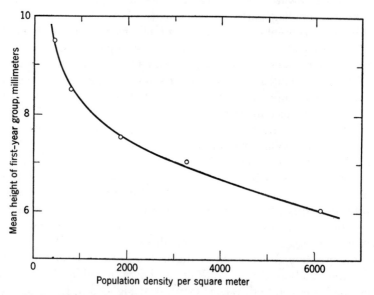

Figure 11-1. The relation of growth to population density in the lamellibranch *Tellina tenuis* in a Scottish intertidal sand. All levels have been combined. (Modified from Stephen, 1940.)

As Thorson (1946) has pointed out, animals with a planktonic larva tend to vary widely in the amount of spat settlement in different years. This is clearly demonstrated by *Tellina tenuis*. As shown in Table 11–3, 1926 was an exceptionally favorable year for it in the Clyde, and

TABLE 11–3

Spat Fall of *Tellina tenuis* at Kames Bay, Scotland, in Successive Years

Date	Number of Spat per square meter	Spat in Population, %
24 Sept. 1926	2620	80
7 Nov. 1927	1088	36
28 Sept. 1928	854	28
20 Sept. 1929	232	17
27 Aug. 1930	1628	76

this year group dominated the population for several years. Even a moderately successful spat fall, however, does not of necessity imply good survival. This is shown by the fates of the 1927 and 1928 groups. Of these, the former was slightly the more successful from the point of view of density of settlement, but the spring of 1928 was apparently unfavorable, and the group practically died out, with the result that, thereafter, the 1928 group was better represented relatively in the population.

The relation between growth rate and both population density and tidal level is of particular interest. *Tellina tenuis* is not an unselective filter feeder, as are certain other intertidal lamellibranchs, but picks up detritus with the aid of its extensible siphon (Fig. 11–2). It is possible that it achieves the major part of its feeding

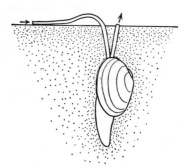

Figure 11–2. The lamellibranch *Tellina tenuis, in situ* in the sand, showing the position of the siphons and the direction of their water currents. (After Holme, 1950.)

as the advancing tide sweeps a line of detritus up the shore. If this were true, the duration of immersion would be of less significance than it would for a filter feeder. Rather, feeding conditions should be optimal where the detritus line remained longest, that is to say around high and low watermark. However, since some feeding takes place throughout the period of immersion, this should favor low, rather than high, water levels. The fact that growth is faster at high levels suggests, therefore, that growth is regulated by something other than food supply. Holmes (1950*a*) has shown that, except in a highly crowded population, *T. tenuis* tends to keep away from its neighbors, possibly being stimulated to move apart by siphonal contact. This suggests that there is a benefit to the individual in having the region it can reach with its siphon, and so clear of available detritus, free of rivals.

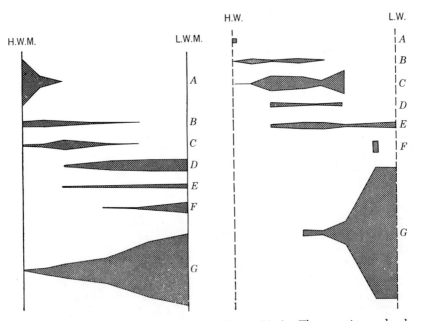

Figure 11–3. The zonation and relative abundance of the fauna of intertidal sand in Scotland: A, *Nereis diversicolor*; B, *Nerine foliosa*; C, *Eteone flava*; D, *Nephthys caeca*; E, *Venus gallina*; F, *Tellina fabula*. (After Stephen, 1929.)

Figure 11–4. The zonation and relative abundance of an intertidal muddy sand in Scotland: A, *Nereis diversicolor*; B, *Macoma baltica*; C, *Cardium edule*; D, *Scoloplos armiger*; E, *Nephthys caeca*; F, *Travisia forbesii*; G, *Tellina tenuis*. (After Stephen, 1930).

Tellina tenuis is typically an inhabitant of clean sand and is replaced to a considerable extent by other lamellibranchs, such as *Macoma baltica* and *Cardium edule* in a more muddy habitat. Both of these live at a higher level on the shore than does *T. tenuis*. There is a similar change in the associated fauna of polychaetes, crustacea, etc. This is illustrated in the two examples shown in Figs. 11–3 and 11–4, the former from a sandy area and the latter from a muddy area. The center of abundance of *C. edule* is in the middle and the upper half of the shore, except where variations in the nature of the substratum modify this. Like *T. tenuis,* however, the individuals living at the higher levels are the largest, as shown in Table 11–4.

On the other hand, growth of *C. edule* is greater at lower levels, as indicated by Table 11–5.

TABLE 11–4

Size Distribution of *Cardium edule* in Relation to Level, Barra, Scotland

(From Stephen, 1930.)

	Size, cm.					
Station	0–1	1–2	2–3	3–4	4–5	5–6
1. *c.* H.W.	0	0	0	0	1	3
2.	1	0	0	1	7	1
3.	0	0	0	0	1	0
4.	0	5	2	1	0	0
5.	0	0	3	1	0	0
6.	13	7	0	0	0	0
7. *c.* L.W.	9	5	0	0	0	0

TABLE 11–5

Size of *Cardium edule* at Successive Winter Rings, in Relation to Tidal Level

(From Stephen, 1930)

Tidal Level	First Ring, mm.	Second Ring, mm.	Third Ring, mm.
Near H.W.M.	19.3	25.2	29.3
Quarter tide	20.5	27.8	30.5
Half tide	22.4	30.4	30.5
Near L.W.M.	27.3	—	—

The texture of the substratum may modify growth rate, shell weight, and shell shape. Swan (1952) has demonstrated this experimentally in *Mya arenaria.* Battle (1932) has demonstrated a marked lunar rhythm in the spawning of *M. baltica* (Fig. 11–5) as well as in another intertidal lamellibranch, *M. arenaria.* It is suggested that heating of the mud flats, on which they occur, is greatest during neap tides when the flats are exposed during the middle of the day. Low water of spring tides, in that locality, occurs morning and evening. If this heating is the factor concerned in maintaining the tidal rhythm, then it would appear that the higher temperatures trigger the onset of spawning. This begins during first quarter neaps and continues through full moon springs and third-quarter neaps.

Another typical sand inhabitant whose ecology is comparatively well known is the lugworm *Arenicola marina*. This worm occupies a wide zone from about high water of neap tides to below low water (Fig. 11–6). It is most abundant in muddy, rather than clean sand, or in pure muds. Related species of the same area, such as *A. ecaudata* and *A. branchialis* tend to favor a more gravely habitat, although *A. marina* may occur there also. It inhabits a burrow (Fig. 11–7) which is generally described as U-shaped but is more typically L-shaped (Wells, 1945, 1949). The burrow comprises a head shaft, gallery, and tail shaft. The head shaft may be open but more typically contains loose sand, and at intervals this is further loosened by either pumping action of water or movements of the head end of the worm. The sand from this section supplies the food of the worm which, when feeding, lies in the bottom section of the gallery. The gallery curves upward at the tail end and communicates with the surface by the tail shaft through one or more openings. At intervals, the worm retreats tail first up this section and liberates the rod-shaped sandy excreta at the surface. During the high-tide period, when the burrow is covered with water, there is a circulation of water in at the tail shaft and out at the head shaft. This is maintained by pumping action of the worm.

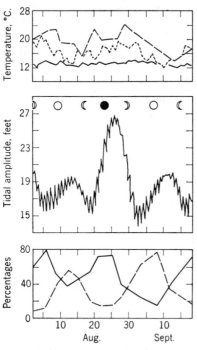

Figure 11–5. Lunar rhythm in the spawning of the lamellibranch *Macoma baltica*. The upper graph shows temperatures of the air (dotted line), mud flat (broken line), and water (solid line). The middle section shows the phase of the moon and the tidal amplitude. The bottom section shows the percentages of mature individuals (solid line) and of spent individuals (broken line). (After Battle, 1932.)

The circulation of water provides sufficient oxygen for respiration during the high-tide period. At low tide, if the burrow is in suffi-

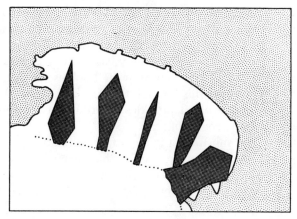

Figure 11–6. The intertidal distribution of the polychaete *Arenicola marina* on a sandy beach in the Isle of Man. The part of the beach covered by the lowest kite is considerably more muddy than the rest. (After Pirrie et al., 1932.)

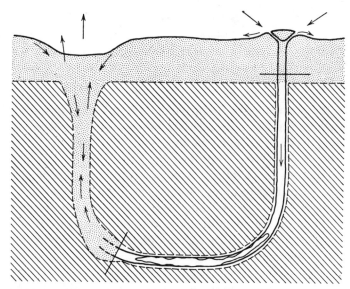

Figure 11–7. Diagram of the arrangement of the burrow of the polychaete, *Arenicola marina*. The shading indicates the distribution of oxidized and un-oxidized sand, the cross line the boundary between head shaft, gallery, and tail shaft, and the arrows the direction of water currents. (After Wells, 1945.)

ciently well-drained sand, it may be filled with air, thus providing the needed oxygen. If, however, the burrow retains water, this may become depleted of oxygen, both by the respiration of the worm and because the surrounding sand frequently has a strong reducing action. In such conditions the worm may trap air bubbles around its tail at the time when it extrudes this through the tail shaft during defecation. The hemoglobin of the blood provides a further mechanism for survival during anaerobic conditions.

The nature of the substratum is important in relation to the ability of *Arenicola* to inhabit a given area. Chapman (1949) has shown the inability of the worm to burrow in sand of more than a certain hardness. Chapman and Newell (1949) have shown a correlation

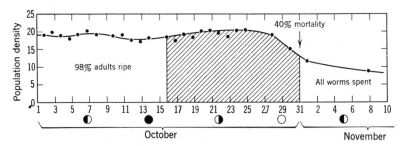

Figure 11–8. The population density of the polychaete *Arenicola marina* on a stretch of shore, showing the sharp decrease in numbers following spawning. The spawning period is indicated by hatching. (After Newell, 1948.)

between the abundance of *Arenicola* and the thickness of suitable substratum where the latter is underlain by an unsuitable clay.

Breeding has been shown in the Whitstable area to be of very limited duration covering a fourteen-day period between the new- and full-moon period in October. Accompanying this breeding period, there is a sharp drop of about 40 per cent in the population of adult worms (Fig. 11–8). Newell interprets this as due to mortality and cites evidence of abundant dead worms found at this time. It is not impossible, however, that some migration of the adults might be concerned. Spawning occurs in the burrows, the genital products being expelled to the surface where fertilization occurs. Genital products have been found in ripple marks in the neighborhood of the burrows, and there is no suggestion that the worms might leave their burrows to spawn near the water surface. However, swimming of the adults, although not associated with spawning, has been observed. Chapman and Newell (1949) prepared sand-filled pits on the shore, isolating from the surrounding area by clay that burrowing worms were unlikely to cross. The figures given in Table 11–6 indicate a definite repopulation of these patches by large worms which, it would seem, must have swum there.

There has been considerable discussion about the nature of the larvae of *Arenicola,* but Newell appears to have shown that they are not planktonic unless lifted by currents or wave action. The adults are moderately tolerant of lowered salinity and no doubt gain considerable protection from temporary lowering of the salinity of the overlying water by their burrowing habit. However, Nicol (1935) records them living in salt marsh pools whose salinity averaged $15^0/_{00}$ and rarely fell below $8^0/_{00}$.

TABLE 11–6

Repopulation by *Arenicola marina*

Numbers per square yard*

Date	Patch I	Patch II
18 Aug. 1948	0	2
24 Sept.	1	4
24 Oct.	0	3
21 Nov.	0	4
5 Dec.	0	5
16 Jan. 1949	4	6
18 Feb.	4	9
16 April	15	12

*Indicated by surface casts.

Other polychaete worms besides *Arenicola* may be abundant in the intertidal sands, and many of these do not form regular burrows. For example, in Kames Bay, Scotland, whose *T. tenuis* population has been described earlier, Stephen (1929) records maximum populations per square meter as follows: *Travisia forbesii* 142, *Nephthys caeca* 36, *Scoloplos armiger* 35, together with 10 other species occurring in smaller concentrations. Some of these worms are deposit feeders, whereas others are carnivorous, praying largely on other polychaetes and on crustacea. Crustacea also play an important role on the sandy shore. From the same Kames Bay area Elmhirst (1931) records concentrations up to 106 per square meter for the amphipod *Bathyporeia pelagica,* and 116 for *B. guilliamsoniana,* with 18 other species in smaller numbers.

Many of the intertidal Crustacea are inactive at low tide but swim actively when the tide is high, or in some species, only when the night tide is high. In addition to these there may be a heavy invasion of the intertidal zone, particularly on the night high tide, by Crustacea which retreat below low water for the rest of the tidal cycle. For example, a night haul at the water's edge in the Isle of Man, which theoretically filtered about 100 cubic meters of water, produced 630 shrimps (*Crangon vulgaris*), 9072 mysids (*Schistomysis spiritus*), 280 gammarid amphipods, 336 specimens of the isopod *Eurydice pulchra*, and 280 of the amphipod *B. pelagica*. Another similar haul produced about 200,000 *Schistomysis*. Of these, the mysids, at least, must have come from below low water.

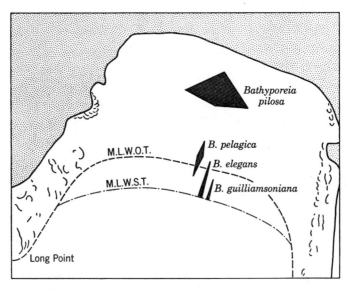

Figure 11-9. The zonation of four species of the amphipod *Bathyporeia* on a sandy beach in Scotland. (After Watkin, 1939.)

Watkin (1939, 1941) has examined the Crustacea obtained during the night tide in the intertidal zone in Kames Bay, in Scotland. The method used was to take a townetting at the edge of the tide, usually between about 10 p.m. and midnight. This was done on various occasions throughout the year and at various states of the tide. In the first place, it was found that there were two types of fauna present. The first of these was, during the low-water period, an inhabitant of the sublittoral zone, invading the intertidal zone only with the inflowing water. Shrimps, mysids, and cumaceans were included in this group. A second group was composed of those forms whose normal habitat was in the intertidal sand, into which they burrowed during the low-tide period. It was strikingly shown that these latter forms did not, when swimming, depart far from the zone in which they normally occurred. As an example of this, Fig. 11–9 shows the distribution of four species of the amphipod *Bathyporeia* in Kames Bay, as determined from samples sieved at low water. Table 11–7 shows the

TABLE 11–7

Average Numbers of *Bathyporeia* per Haul in Relation to Stage of Tidal Cycle

(Modified from Watkin, 1939)

Hours from High Water	B. pilosa	B. pelagica	B. elegans
0	61	0	0
1	33	1	0
2	14	3	1
3	8	17	1
4	35	2	1
5	1	3	14
6	0	1	5

average numbers per haul of the three commonest species in relation to the stage of the tidal cycle. As might be expected, *B. pilosa*, which is mainly restricted to the upper part of the beach, is taken only or for the most part while swimming, when that part of the beach is covered. The two lower-living species, *B. pelagica* and *B. elegans*, however, were taken at the water's edge only as the tide reached their level; they did not move up the beach in any numbers as the tide passed their normal habitat.

As might be expected, there is evidence of a lunar periodicity in the concentration of this night plankton, numbers tending to be greatest in two periods before new and full moon. It is not clear whether this periodicity is associated with differences in range between spring and neap tides or whether it is more closely connected with the time of night at which the tide rises (Fig. 11–10). There is also some evidence that, although those forms migrating in from below low water tend to be predominantly immature, the swimming intertidal inhabitants comprise a more mature population than the burrowing ones. Further, among these swimming individuals, the ratio of males to females is much higher than in the burrowing population. In other words, of the permanent intertidal inhabitants, mature individuals swim more than immatures, and males more than females, whereas it is the immatures of the sublittoral forms that invade the intertidal zone during high water. These data are shown in Table 11–8.

In general, the instability of the sand on wave-exposed beaches greatly limits their fauna, with the result that, in many places, they are comparatively barren. A few forms have, however, adapted themselves to such conditions and may be very abundant in the sand, even under conditions of almost constant wave action. One of these is the small lamellibranch, *Donax variabilis*, which occurs in great numbers near low watermark on the southern Atlantic coasts of the United

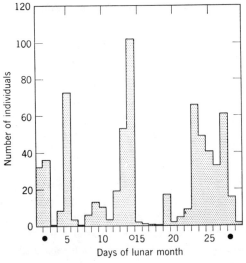

Figure 11–10. Lunar rhythm in the occurrence of the amphipod *Bathyporeia* in the night plankton over a sandy beach. (After Watkin, 1939.)

States. These are constantly being washed out of the sand by the waves but immediately burrow under the surface again. Mori (1938) describes how a Japanese form, *D. semignosus,* moves up and down the beach with the tide, timing its periodic emergences from the sand so as to be swept up the beach by the waves on the rising tide and down again on the falling tide. Another inhabitant of wave-beaten sands is the anomuran crustacean, *Emerita analoga,* of the Pacific coasts from Oregon to Panama. This is a small, crab-shaped animal which digs into the sand until only its antennae are exposed (MacGinitie, 1938). Except under very still conditions, feeding is accomplished by orientation of the crab up the beach so that the antennae can trap food particles carried down the beach by the wash of the retiring waves. If the *Emerita* are washed out of the sand by the

TABLE 11–8

Comparison between Proportion of Adults and Proportion of Males in *Bathyporeia* Populations

(Modified from Watkin, 1939)

Species	Percentage Adults		Percentage Males among Mature Individuals	
	From Sand during Low Tide	From Water during High Tide	From Sand during Low Tide	From Water during High Tide
B. pilosa	49	56	40	71
B. pelagica	17	70	13	86
B. elegans	28	42	27	63
B. guilliamsoniana	45	75	40	100

waves, they burrow again rapidly. As the tide rises or falls, the crabs follow so as to be located continuously in the region of wave wash. The curious point is that, by some unknown mechanism, the animals from a wide area all move simultaneously. The mass movements occur at intervals of an hour or so. These are two examples from a comparatively small number of animals which are adapted to withstand, and apparently to require, wave action in their sand habitat.

ESTUARIES

The predominant characteristic of estuarine conditions is that the salinity of the water is less than that of normal sea water. The organism living there must be adapted in one way or another to tolerate this. Further, the salinity varies markedly during the tidal cycle and with the seasons, so that a simple adaptation to live at a constant lower salinity is of little value. Secondary factors are the temperature of the water, which is likely to exhibit wider tidal and seasonal fluctuations than that of the sea, the usually high silt content, and the current flow. The increased silt content brings with it a decrease of illumination, which adversely affects plant growth, and smothering effects, such as the clogging of the gills of animals and the covering of hard surfaces so that settlement of spat may be difficult. Against this must be set the beneficial effect of the large food supply which it provides. Estuaries are usually sheltered from wave action, but this effect is offset by the tidal currents. Although currents may be of benefit in bringing food, oxygen, etc., within the reach of the forms requiring them, they result also in instability of the areas of soft bottom which they affect. Finally, in many estuaries, there is the problem of pollution by trade and other effluents which may be much more severe than it can ever be in the open sea. Here direct toxic action of the effluents, reduction in oxygen content of the water, and smothering action

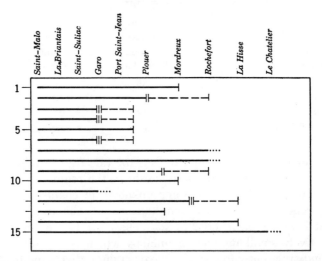

Figure 11–11. Penetration into La Rance estuary of a number of species between high and low water of neap tides. Salinities decrease toward the right. A dotted horizontal line indicates an upper limit not due to salinity or of unknown cause. A single vertical line indicates a limit because of salinity, a double line indicates a winter retreat down the estuary, and a triple line indicates a retreat under conditions of abnormal salinity. 1, *Mytilus edulis;* 2, *Patella vulgata;* 3, *Gibbula umbilicalis;* 4, *Trochocochlea lineata;* 5, *Littorina littorea;* 6, *Purpura lapillus;* 7, *Chthamalus stellatus;* 8, *Balanus balanoides;* 9, *B. Perforatus;* 10, *Actinia equina;* 11, *Lichina pygmaea;* 12, *Ascophyllum nodosum;* 13, *Fucus serratus;* 14, *F. platycarpus;* 15, *F. vesiculosus.* (After Fischer-Piette, 1931.)

may all be important. Although there are many studies of the comparative penetration of organisms into various estuaries, there is less information on the biology of the particular species involved. Fischer-Piette (1931) has provided a demonstration that salinity is the actual factor involved in setting the upper limitation of penetration of many estuarine species, a fact that has been generally assumed without adequate proof. LaRance estuary, in France, during the period when he studied it, first had a series of normal years and then suffered 1 or 2 years of unusually heavy rainfall when salinities were much below normal. Figures 11–11 and 11–12 show the normal upper limits of a number of species in the estuary and the extent to which these moved seaward during the years of lowered salinity. In a later paper (1933) Fischer-Piette followed the fauna through a succeeding particularly dry period when salinities rose above normal and showed a similar movement of some species farther up the estuary. For such a shift to occur, the species in question must not only respond to the salinity change but must also have powers of dispersal which will permit the shift; it is possible that some species were not able to move in

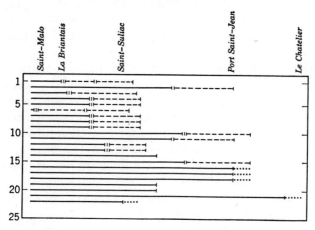

Figure 11–12. The penetration of species living below low water of neap tides into La Rance estuary (symbols as in Fig. 11–11) 1, *Morchellium argus;* 2, *Circinalium concrescens;* 3, *Amaroucium nordmani;* 4, *Polysyncraton lacazei;* 5, *Didemnum aspersum;* 6, *D. maculosum;* 7, *Trididemnum cereum;* 8, *Ascidiella aspersa;* 9, *Botryllus schlosseri violaceus;* 10, *B. schlosseri,* other varieties; 11, *Distomus variolosus;* 12, *Dendrodoa grossularia;* 13, *Molgula manhattensis;* 14, *Tapes decussatus;* 15, *T. aureus;* 16, *T. pullastra;* 17, *Venus verrucosa;* 18, *Volsella barbata;* 19, *Mytilus edulis;* 20, *Pecten maximum;* 21, *Chlamys varia;* 22, *Anomia ephippium.* (After Fischer-Piette, 1931.)

accordance with improved salinity conditions. With lowered salinities, forms are killed if they are unable to move away from the unfavorable conditions. Fischer-Piette was able, also, to demonstrate that the observed changes were not caused by differences in temperature in the different years.

Fischer-Piette was also able to show that a number of the estuarine species were unable to live as high in the estuary during the low-salinity period in winter as they were in the higher salinities of summer. However, from the salinity data which he presents, it does not appear that they retreat far enough down the estuary in winter to maintain the same salinity minima that are found at their upper limits in summer. Thus, in the midtide zone, *Patella vulgata* and *Balanus perforatus* have an upper limit in the estuary in summer at Rochefort, where the lowest salinities are about $20^0/_{00}$. The salinity minima at their upper limits are about 6 and $3^0/_{00}$ respectively in winter.

This is rather surprising, in view of the usual interrelation of low-salinity tolerance and temperature. In general, lower salinities can be tolerated at summer temperatures (Broekhuysen, 1936). Broekema (1941) also records this for the shrimp *Crangon crangon*. It is of interest to note that, just as Broekhuysen found the developing eggs of *Carcinus* unable to tolerate as low salinities as the adults, so Fischer-Piette found the eggs of the gastropod *Purpura lapillus* less tolerant than the adults.

The forms discussed by Fischer-Piette are mainly those occurring on rocky substrata and those kept reasonably free from deposits of silt by tidal currents. It is somewhat rare to find an adequate series of such habitats along an estuary. More work has been done on the inhabitants of the estuarine muds, and here their reaction to salinity is undoubtedly complicated by such other factors as the effect of the varying nature of the substratum and their ability to retreat into burrows and so avoid adverse salinities and other unfavorable conditions. Spooner and Moore (1940) have described the vertical and horizontal distribution of the larger members of the mud fauna of the Tamar estuary. Disregarding those fresh-water forms which penetrate the upper part of the estuary, they group the fauna under three headings as shown in Table 11–9.

Although there is no marked variation in tidal range with penetration up the estuary, it is noticeable that the more marine species tend to concentrate in the lower levels of the shore, whereas the more estuarine tend to concentrate above midtide level. Theoretical considerations in Chapter 6 suggested that a protected marine species, that is, one that could cut itself off from lowered salinity and was limited only by the occurrence at some part of the tidal cycle of water of suitably high salinity, would be restricted to the lower levels of the shore as it penetrated the estuary. Although the results from the Tamar estuary do not show that such species inhabit a lower level in the estuary than they do on the open shore, it does suggest that only those forms which, under marine conditions, live at low levels are able to penetrate the estuary. The concentration of the typically estuarine species in the upper levels, as well as in the central reaches of the estuary, agrees most closely with the theoretical distribution of an unprotected estuarine form which requires water of intermediate salinity

TABLE 11–9

Species	Relative Penetration up Estuary, km.*	Tidal Zonation in Estuary

A. Essentially marine species, with only limited estuarine penetration

Species	Relative Penetration up Estuary, km.*	Tidal Zonation in Estuary
Abra prismatica	2	At low water only
A. nitida	4	At low water only
Ampharete grubei	4	Lower half of tidal zone
Melinna palmata	8	Lower half of tidal zone
Phyllodoce maculata	6	? scattered
Cereus pedunculatus	6	? scattered
Lanice conchilega	c. 9	Around low water only
Scoloplos armiger	2–6	Very patchy distribution, but only above midtide
Carcinus maenas juv.	c. 28	Scattered
Littorina littorea	11	Throughout tidal zone, with indications of maximum below midtide
L. saxatilis	10	Concentrated above midtide
Cardium edule	13.5	Scattered

B. Essentially estuarine species which, however, are also common in normal marine habitats

Species	Relative Penetration up Estuary, km.*	Tidal Zonation in Estuary
Nephthys hombergi	13.5	Mainly in lower half of tidal zone
Macomá balthica	15	Scattered throughout tidal zone

C. More or less strictly estuarine species

Species	Relative Penetration up Estuary, km.*	Tidal Zonation in Estuary
Hydrobia ulvae	18.5	Marked concentration from midtide upward
Corophium volutator	c. 27	As far as known, maximum in upper half of tide zone
Cyathura carinata	15 ?	Concentrated, and almost confined, above midtide
Scrobicularia plana	18.5	Concentrated above midtide
Nereis diversicolor	c. 24	Concentrated above midtide throughout range, except at extreme seaward end

* The entire range of estuarine influence is 30.5 km.

at all times and is limited by the occurrence, at any part of the tidal cycle, of water above or below its salinity tolerance limits.

There are various genera whose species form a sequence with increasing tolerance of lowered salinity, and with corresponding estuarine distributions. Amphipods form an important part of the bottom fauna of most estuaries, and among these the genus *Gammarus* and closely related genera are prominent. Spooner (1947) and Segerstråle (1947) have described the distribution of a series of these in European estuaries. Of the species of *Marinogammarus*, *M. pirloti* and *M. stoerensis*, though marine, are most abundant where there is fresh-water seepage down the shore. *Marinogammarus obtusatus* and *M. finmarchicus* penetrate only slightly into estuaries, and only *M. marinus* and *M.*

Figure 11–13. The seventh peraeopod of the amphipod *Gammarus zaddachi*, showing the increase in hairiness in the forms from less saline habitats. Subspecies *zaddachi* (left) lives in almost fresh water, and subspecies *salinus* (right) at the seaward end of the estuary. (From Spooner, 1947.)

olivii do so to any considerable extent. Within the genus *Gammarus*, the species *locusta* is typically marine, although penetrating a certain distance into estuaries, where it tends to be restricted around high water. This would be in agreement with the theoretical distribution of an unprotected marine form. *Gammarus locusta* is stated to tolerate a lower limit of about 5–6 $^o/_{oo}$ in the Baltic. Near its upper limit of estuarine penetration its growth tends to be stunted, and in certain areas of permanently lowered salinity it has given rise to a dwarf race. *Gammarus zaddachi* is the typical form of the estuary proper, and it has been divided into three subspecies, *Gammarus zaddachi oceanicus* at the seaward end of its range, *G. z. salinus* in the middle, and *G. z. zaddachi* at the upper end. The last of these can tolerate fresh water, at least for a time, whereas the other two cannot. There is a progressive increase in hairiness toward the fresher-water forms in this series of subspecies, as shown in Fig. 11–13. One other species of *Gammarus*, *G. duebeni*, is usually not associated with estuaries, but rather with areas of marked fresh-water seepage on the shore. We have, therefore, within the genus *Gammarus* and a closely related genus, a complete range of species or subspecies with preferences for all types of estuarine salinities as well as other species with preference for non-estuarine lowering of salinity.

A similar series, this time from more tropical areas, is provided by the gastropods of the family Neritidae (H. D. Russell, 1941). On the Atlantic coasts of America, *Nerita peloronta*, *N. versicolor*, and *N. tes-*

sellata are all marine, although with an ability to tolerate slight decreases of salinity in the vicinity of river mouths; the tolerance of the three species increases in the order in which they are listed. Also fully marine is *Smaragdia viridis*. *Puperita pupa* and *P. tristis* are both marine but inhabit tide pools in the upper levels, where they are subject to wide salinity fluctuations. *Nerita fulgurans*, although found in fully marine habitats, becomes abundant only in brackish waters, but usually ones where the salinity is not very low. *Neritina virginea* is found in brackish water, typically at the mouths of rivers and creeks. *N. meleagris* and *N. piratica* are brackish-water forms, and *N. zebra* and *N. reclivata* range from brackish to fresh water. Finally, *Fluvinerita tenebricosa*, *Neretina clenchi*, *N. punctulata*, and *Neritilia succinea* are all fresh-water forms. In other tropical areas a similar series may be found, and in the western Pacific the series may be extended to include the terrestrial *Neritina cornea*.

TABLE 11–10

Average Survival Time in Days of *Carcinus maenas* in Relation to Temperature and Salinity

Salinity, $^0/_{00}$	Temperature, °C.	Survival
7	0.6	14
7	12	40
15	0.6	30
15	9.7	permanent

Although salinity is apparently the significant factor in these examples, it must be remembered that its effect is frequently greatly modified by temperature. Evidence on the nature of the effect is somewhat conflicting, and it appears at present that it varies from one species to another. For example, Broekhuysen (1936) showed that in the typically estuarine crab *Carcinus maenas*, a lower salinity could be tolerated when the temperature was high than when it was low (Table 11–10). Development of the eggs, also, took place at a lower limiting salinity at high temperatures than at lower temperatures (Table 11–11).

In contrast with these results, Amemiya (1928) showed that, for the oyster *Ostrea gigas*, at a lower temperature the optimum and lower limits of salinity were lowered, but the maximum was raised, thus increasing the tolerance range at the lower temperature (Table 11–12).

A large part of the fauna of an estuary consists of burrowing forms, among which polychaetes and lamellibranchs predominate. Such forms must be able to tolerate the almost invariably muddy conditions. Since many burrowing animals show rather marked limitation to particular types of mud or sand, it is not surprising that many of them also show a patchy distribution within that part of the estuary which they inhabit. Further, the region near and below low water tends, as has been pointed out, to suffer stronger scour from tidal flow than the upper tidal area, a fact which is reflected in its generally scanty burrowing fauna. The surface of the mud is inhabited by various Crustacea, mainly isopods and amphipods, as well as by such gastropods as *Hydrobia* and *Littorina*. Both of the latter may be very patchy in their distribution, which is frequently associated with varying surface

TABLE 11–11

Minimum Salinity for Development of Eggs of *Carcinus maenas* in Relation to Temperature

Temperature, °C.	Minimum Salinity, ‰
10	26
16.3	20

TABLE 11–12

Salinity Tolerance of *Ostrea gigas* in Relation to Temperature

Temperature, °C.	Salinity Tolerance, ‰		
	Minimum	Optimum	Maximum
16	c. 6	17–26	c. 37
23–26	c. 8	20–26	c. 36

texture; large accumulations are frequently found where there is grass, weed, or dead shell. Thamdrup (1935) has provided comparative information on the respiration of various estuarine, mud-living species. To begin with, for four of these on which data are available, the respiratory rate in air is considerably less than that in water. The values range from 26.0 to 51.5 per cent.

The highest rates are found in the small forms, *Hydrobia, Corophium,* and *Pygospio,* all of which are from a markedly estuarine habitat, living on or near the mud surface. *Macoma, Cardium,* and *Littorina,* with slightly lower rates, are also surface or shallow forms but are more marine in habitat. Next in rate are *Nereis* and *Nephthys,* both deeper-burrowing forms. After them lie *Mytilus* and *Scrobicularia,* the former a surface form but the latter a deep-burrowing form, and finally the lowest rates are found in *Mya* and *Arenicola,* both deep-burrowing and typically marine forms. The extra expenditure of energy involved in osmoregulation for an estuarine form might be expected to result in a higher rate of oxygen consumption there than in a marine habitat. Further, deep-burrowing forms tend to be better protected from salinity changes than unprotected forms. Thamdrup's results, in general, agree with this hypothesis but are clearly too few to constitute a proof of its general application. Table 11–13 also

TABLE 11–13

Relation of Respiratory Rate to Temperature

Respiratory Rate, mg. per kg. of wet tissue per hour*

Species	At 2°C.	At 10°C.	At 20°C.	At 28°C.
Nereis diversicolor	24	79	138	90
Nephthys hombergi	(16)	100	136	—
Pygospio elegans	16	205	500	750
Arenicola marina	9	21	48	25
Hydrobia ulvae	35	180	490	930
Littorina littorea	42	100	169	262
Mytilus edulis	42	84	128	80
Cardium edule	30	91	188	?
Macoma baltica†: *A*	30	95	221	305
B	35	76	125	295
Scrobicularia plana	32	62	40	174
Mya arenaria	15	32	57	75?
Corophium volutator	130	600	870	1040

* Without shells.

† Early (*A*) and late (*B*) in spawning period.

shows that in *Pygospio, Hydrobia, Littorina, Scrobicularia,* and *Corophium* the respiratory rate increased up to the highest temperature tested, indicating that, in this respect at least, their optimum temperature is at least as high as 28°C. *Nereis, Arenicola, Mytilus,* and *Cardium,* on the other hand, showed an optimum below 28°C., and *Cardium* actually failed to survive the two days at this temperature during which the tests were made. Of the forms with the higher optimum temperature, the first three inhabit the upper levels of the intertidal zone and are surface or shallow-living forms. *Scrobicularia,* according to Thamdrup, is a southern form. The forms with the lower optimum temperature are either deep-burrowing or else live low in the intertidal zone where less extreme temperatures are encountered.

Two other important constituents of the estuarine fauna are those forms that invade the intertidal area during the low-tide period and those that do so at the high-tide period, retreating into the channel at low tide. The former group, in northern waters, is composed mainly of wading birds, and these may be present in very large numbers. Some of these, such as the plover, feed mainly on forms such as Crustacea. Yet others, such as ducks, may sift through the mud for molluscs and other animals, and still others with long bills, such as the curlew, probe deep into the mud to obtain such forms as burrowing polychaetes. As on marine shores, other predators may be locally important, for instance rats and raccoons. Of the animals that come into the intertidal zone during the period of high water, there are various fish, as well as numbers of larger Crustacea, such as crabs and shrimps. There is evidence that some of the crabs may migrate up and down the estuary seasonally, but it is unlikely that they move much with the tide. On the other hand, many of the shrimps and fish regularly move in and out, at least to some extent, with the tide. This of course insures them less salinity variation than they would meet if they were to remain at the same place throughout the tidal cycle.

TABLE 11–14

Growth of *Pleuronectes flesus* in the Tamar Estuary and in Sweden

(Hartley, 1940)

Length, cm.

Age in Years	Plymouth		Ystad, Sweden		
	1936	1937	1929	1930	1931
$1\frac{1}{2}$	9.5	11.5	8.4	9.1	10.3
$2\frac{1}{2}$	15.5	16.0	14.4	12.7	17.4
$3\frac{1}{2}$	(19.0)	19.5	18.8	19.5	21.8

In view of the rather detailed study available on the invertebrate fauna, and of the buoy flora of the Tamar estuary, in the south of England, the work of Hartley (1940, 1947) on the fishes of the area makes an ideal complement. His work was concerned mainly with the flounder, *Pleuronectes flesus*, which is the most typically estuarine of the flatfishes of the region, often living for a time in fresh water. Spawning occurs in the sea. Young flounders below about 7 cm. in length were not obtained, possibly because they do not move into the estuary below this size but more probably because they do not inhabit the same locations in which the older ones were being fished. Table 11–14 shows the growth in successive years in the Tamar area, with corresponding figures from Sweden for comparison.

During the winter, feeding practically ceases, and with it growth. The correlation of these is shown in Fig. 11–14. The condition factor used here is obtained from the formula:

$$K = \frac{100 \times W}{L^3}$$

where W is the weight in grams and L is the length in centimeters.

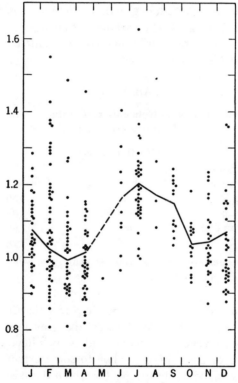

Figure 11–14. Seasonal variation in condition factor in flounders in the Tamar estuary. (After Hartley, 1940.)

Crustacea form more than 80 per cent of the food of the flounder, with the shrimp *C. vulgaris* 32 and 42 per cent in two different years, and mysids 43 and 52 per cent. Both of these comprise forms that normally retreat to the channel during the low-tide period. In con-

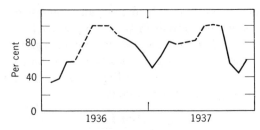

Figure 11–15. Seasonal variation in the percentage of flounders in the Tamar estuary whose stomachs contain food. Dotted lines are based on small samples. (After Hartley, 1940.)

tradistinction to the flounder, the dab, *Pleuronectes limanda*, feeds mainly on small Crustacea when young but changes to a diet in which polychaetes predominate as it grows larger. This change is demonstrated in Table 11–15.

TABLE 11–15

Variation in Proportion of Polychaetes to Crustacea with Size of Fish in *Pleuronectes limanda*

(Hartley, 1940)

Length of Fish, cm.	Polychaetes, %	Crustacea, %
0–4	0	100
5–9	37	63
10–14	67	33
15–	72*	28

* The two together are taken as 100 per cent since other food constitutes only a minor fraction of the total.

Of the various estuarine fish, there are a few that have no competitors for food. As an example of these, the gray mullet *Mugil chelo* and *M. auratus* are vegetable feeders and as such have no competition. A second group of fish, although they to some extent share the food of other species, take mainly species for which there is no competition. As an example of these, the dab, *Pleuronectes limanda*, once it has outgrown the crustacean diet of its young stages, feeds mainly on the polychaete *Sabella pavonina*. It has little competition for this species, and should the supply be short it is able to supplement its diet with such other forms as shrimps. A third group, including the plaice *Pleuronectae platessa,* have a wide range of food organisms, and thus a wider range of alternative foods. Thus, although only three species of polychaete were recorded in the food of the dab, and of these, *Sabella* constituted 93 per cent, ten species of polychaetes were recorded for the diet of the plaice, and the most abundant of these polychaetes, *Nephthys*, constituted only 21 per cent. There remain those fish for example the flounder, which have a more or less limited diet, and which have a number of competitors for this prey. It is particularly striking that, among all the fish studied, none makes any great use of the molluskan fauna in its diet. It is true that most of the bivalves, when full grown, are both too thick-shelled and too deep-burrowing to be available, but there are both the younger stages of these and also such small gastropods as *Hydrobia ulvae*, and these appear to be largely neglected. One predator of the fish requires special mention, namely the shag, *Phalacrocorax graculus*. This is a fish-eating bird, 40 per cent of whose diet is flatfish (Steven, 1933). Since these birds feed more than once during the day, and can easily swallow a 200-gm. fish, they must take a considerable toll.

12

Review

It was pointed out in the introduction that, in the whole field of ecology, there are very few general laws or principles that have been enunciated. Of those that are generally accepted, some are of only limited application and others do not apply to marine forms. In the present state of our knowledge, attempts to regiment ecological observations into a set pattern have too often resulted in obscuring vitally important points. Nevertheless, some orderliness of treatment is necessary if the steadily increasing array of information available is not to become completely indigestible.

Broadly speaking, there are two principal gradients of conditions that have proved useful in classifying marine organisms and their environments. The first of these is the gradient from tropical to polar conditions and the second is the vertical gradient from the supralittoral zone to the abyssal. These two gradients may be considered as coordinates on a graph in which the major types of marine environment may be arrayed. Many other gradients might, of course, be chosen, but these are the two that seem to be the most generally useful, particularly when they are modified to express certain environmental characteristics associated with them.

The two gradients, latitudinal and vertical, are widely used on land, but with rather different implications about the environment factors associated with them. This is particularly true of the vertical gradient. In the sea the major basic factor in both gradients is illumination, with temperature differences as the resulting operative factor in the latitudinal gradient. The tropical regions receive heavy insolation throughout the entire year, with little seasonal variation. In temperate regions, the summer level of insolation is almost as high as in the tropics, but it drops very markedly in winter. In polar regions the summer level is lower, and in winter it is so small that little photosynthesis can take place. Solar radiation heats the water, or, in the intertidal zone, the organisms themselves. There is, therefore, a latitudinal gradient of temperature, the values decreasing poleward. There is also a latitudinal gradation in the range of seasonal variation in temperature, this being maximal, in the western North Atlantic, about 40°N., and decreasing poleward and equatorward.

Except in the circumantarctic seas, there is a general circulation in the waters of the major ocean basins, clockwise in the Northern Hemisphere and counterclockwise in the Southern. The sea water heats or cools comparatively slowly, so that the water currents carry to the various parts of the continental margins temperature characteristics that may be very different from those that would prevail were the water masses stationary. In the Northern Hemisphere, warm water travels far up the eastern margins of the continents and cold water similarly streams down their western margins from the Arctic. So far as temperature is concerned, then, the latitudinal grid is distorted, with the isotherms tending to cross the lines of latitude diagonally. This is seen for the North Atlantic in Fig. 12–1.

Solar radiation incident at the water surface is more closely dependent on latitude. Once the light enters the water, however, its rate of penetration depends on the extinction coefficient of the water. Since this varies widely from place to place and with no simple geographic pattern, subsurface illumination shows little relation to the simple latitudinal grid. As a broad generalization, it may be said that light penetration decreases from ocean waters toward the coast and from the tropics toward the poles. The latter, combined with the poleward decrease in incident illumination, results in a wide difference in submarine illumination in polar and tropical waters.

The total annual productivity of different parts of the ocean differs less widely than was once believed. Most local differences are unrelated to any simple geographical pattern, although areas of high productivity attributable to upwelling do tend to occur on the western margins of continents. Again, two broad generalizations may be made. The depth of water column in which there is sufficient light for photosynthesis, and so for plant growth, decreases poleward, so there is a more extensive productive zone in the tropics. The seasonal variation in phytoplankton production is great in polar waters, but

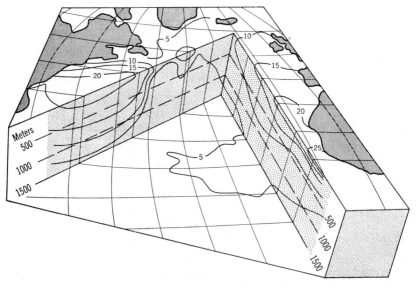

Figure 12–1. Diagrammatic sections of the North Atlantic, showing the great differences in surface temperature at the same latitude on the two sides. The varying relation of temperature to depth is also shown.

very slight in the tropics. In the latter, therefore, animals dependent on the plankton for their source of food are insured a fairly constant supply, whereas in polar waters they have to be able to make the most of a brief season of rich feeding. Finally, there is one other factor affecting the poleward ends of the latitudinal gradient, namely the presence of ice. Apart from any temperature effects, this reduces illumination and oxygen supply restricts movement and mechanically damages tissues. There is a gradient in the length of time during which ice is present, and this approximates the temperature gradient already referred to.

The other major gradient is the vertical one, from the top of the littoral zone down to abyssal ocean troughs. Three major primary factors are involved here, pressure, temperature, and illumination. The increase in pressure with depth is, for biological purposes, the same in all parts of the ocean. Pressure and depth gradients may therefore be considered as identical. Temperature in general decreases with increasing depth, but the rate of this decrease varies widely. In very deep water, except in certain basins, temperatures everywhere approach within a few degrees of zero (centigrade). The temperature range from top to bottom may therefore be only 2 or 3°C. in polar seas, and 20 or more degrees in the tropics. Where the range is at all extensive, the rate of change of temperature with depth increases upward, with a maximum somewhere below the surface, at the thermocline. Seasonal variation in temperature also decreases, generally, downward and is biologically negligible below a depth of a few hundred meters.

The heating effect of solar radiation is lost very close to the surface. More slowly absorbed wavelengths, suitable for photosynthesis, penetrate further, and light sufficient for vision penetrates further still. Nevertheless, by far the greater part of the vertical range of the oceans is without illumination of external origin in any significant quantities. Within the illuminated zone, though, the intensity of the light is of prime importance. In general, light decreases exponentially downward, and the loss is more rapid at the two ends of the spectrum than in the blue-green region.

The compensation depth, below which plant respiration outweighs photosynthesis, is rarely much deeper than a hundred meters and usually less. The whole life of the oceans is ultimately dependent on organic production within this zone. Dead material rains down from it, undergoing progressive breakdown into soluble products as it falls. The greater the depth of the water, the greater the loss of particulate organic matter before it reaches the bottom. There is therefore a gradient of available food, and so of the population it can support, decreasing toward greater depths.

Having outlined this simplified latitudinal-vertical grid and shown how it is distorted to fit some of the major ecological factors, the next step is to consider how the distribution of particular organisms fits the grid. Before doing so, however, it is necessary to review the effects of the factors on the organisms.

The distribution of an organism in relation to a particular factor is rarely simple. The species does not usually occur in abundance right up to the region where that factor attains lethal values and then stop, although this does happen sometimes. For example, the presence of ice, which scrapes attached organisms from intertidal rocks, is an all-or-nothing factor. Intertidal barnacles, for example, may occur right up to the edge of ice influence and there cease abruptly. More usually, changing temperature, salinity, etc., approach lethal values only gradually, and through stages in which the effective success of the organism is progressively lessened. It has been found that there is a correlation between the upper lethal temperatures for different species and the maximum temperatures to which the species are normally exposed, but it has also been found that these maxima are well below the lethal values. The success of a species requires that none of the relevant conditions surrounding it pass specific limiting values. Even within these limits, though, the combined effects of several moderately unfavorable conditions may be sufficient to exclude the species. Thus, a species living at a non-optimal temperature, but one it is well able to tolerate when it has no competitors, may be unable to compete there with a species for which the temperature is more nearly optimal. We have an example in oxygen limitation in deep-sea fish of the genus *Chauliodus*. *Chauliodus sloanei sloanei* occurs over a wider range of oxygen concentrations than does *C. danae* but is excluded by competition with the latter within the range of 53–75 per cent saturation.

To take a more complex situation, the growth of phytoplankton is controlled primarily by nutrient salt concentration, temperature, and illumination, all three interacting in their effects. Still other factors may also play a part. It is known that various species differ in their optima for at least temperature and illumination. It is hardly to be expected, then, that the distribution of such species can be defined in terms of a single obvious factor. Even this statement does not represent the full complexity of the picture, however. Most eggs and larvae have smaller tolerance ranges than their adults. Many are so different morphologically from the adults that they require an entirely separate set of environmental conditions. This is obviously true of sessile forms whose larvae are planktonic. A species is likely, then, to be differently limited at various stages in its life cycle. For example, temperatures necessary for gonad maturation may differ from those for spawning, and these again from the temperatures best suited for development of the larvae, growth of the adult, etc. Hutchins has shown how, in some species for which temperature is the major limiting factor, this may act through control of the survival of the adult at one distributional margin and through control of breeding at another margin.

With such complexity in the control of distribution and of relative success within the region of occurrence of each species, it seems surprising that it is possible to make any ordered classification of organisms and communities in relation to their environment. Yet it is apparent that, both in broad view and in detail, there are many species and groupings of species which are clearly associated with particular types of environment.

To begin with, most plants require light for photosynthesis and so are restricted to a small upper section of the vertical gradient. Within this section, they exhibit a grouping related to the light intensity, red algae tending to dominate at greater depths and browns and greens higher up. Flowering plants overlap their upper limit and extend inland beyond the limits of marine influence. Again, among floating plants, small size is universal except for *Sargassum*, and there is an assemblage of diatoms, dinoflagellates, etc., comprising the phytoplankton, differing widely in constitution from the attached plants of the coastal regions.

Among animals such broad generalization can rarely be made, since most of the groups are widely adapted to different conditions. The air-breathing marine mammals, birds, and reptiles are, however, like the plants, restricted to a small vertical range, although for a different reason. The fishes, primitive chordates, and invertebrate phyla range through almost all the major types of marine environment. It is only in some of the smaller subdivisions of environmental classification that special adaptability of certain groups becomes apparent. Further, these organisms tend to be represented by a lower order of classification, that is genera or species, which are characteristic of such particular environments.

There can be no question that certain genera of animals are peculiarly adapted to certain limited types of environment, and different species of such genera tend to occur wherever such environments are found throughout the seas. For example, on intertidal rocks, barnacles of the genera *Balanus* and *Chthamalus* occur on most shores from the edge of ice influence to the tropics. So do gastropods of the genus *Littorina*. These genera are comparatively sparsely represented below low water. Again, Peterson has characterized certain sublittoral sand communities by the abundance in them of the lamellibranch *Macoma baltica*. This was in Danish waters. Similar sands are typically inhabited by *M. calcarea* in the Arctic and by *M. nasuta* in the North Pacific. His *Venus* community, containing *V. gallina* in Danish waters, is paralleled by *V. fluctuosa* in east Greenland, *V. verrucosa* in the Mediterranean, and yet another species of the same genus in the Persian Gulf (Thorson, 1950).

In the plankton the group of chaetognaths has attained major importance among the predators, whereas outside this habitat only one genus, containing three species, is known. Copepods are probably the most important planktonic herbivores, and the biggest proportion of these belong to the Calanoidea. Yet on the bottom, and particularly in the interstices of sediments, it is harpacticoid copepods that predominate.

Within smaller habitat subdivisions, different species of a genus may be characteristic of different conditions. Thus, *Sagitta elegans* and *S. setosa* are respectively characteristic of two different water masses that may occur in the mouth of the English Channel. Two species of lichen of the genus *Lichaena* are characteristic of high-water rock surfaces on the French coast, one in wave-exposed situations and the other in shelter. There are, thus, many "indicator" species whose presence may be taken to imply certain more or less limited environmental conditions.

Where two or more species have similar requirements or limitations, these will usually tend to occur together. Thus the species of *Sagitta* just referred to tend to be associated with particular species of medusae and siphonophores. A close association also occurs when one species is dependent on another or derives peculiar benefit from it, giving a series through commensalism to parasitism. It is not surprising, then, that many types of habitat are typified by a community of species, some of them specific in their requirements and others more or less overlapping into other types of habitat.

Many attempts have been made to arrange these communities in an orderly array, and a good survey of the subject, so far as bottom communities are concerned, has been made recently by Jones (1950). It is fairly generally agreed that there are two gradients on which habitats can most usefully be classified. The first of these is vertical, i.e., intertidal, continental shelf, abyssal, etc., with various subdivisions of these. The second is according to substratum, i.e., rock, gravel, sand, mud, etc. Their vertical gradient corresponds with that already used at the beginning of this chapter. Their substratum gradient is an alternative to the latitudinal gradient suggested here.

The principal reason for this difference in choice lies in the different requirements of the auto- and the synecologist. A bed of eel grass, *Zostera marina,* in northern waters, and one of turtle grass, *Thalassia testudinum,* or of manatee grass, *Cymodocea manatorum,* in the tropics, may for many purposes be considered as similar. Each requires a soft substratum near low water and plays a similarly important role in stabilizing substratum. Each contributes a similar important supply of detritus to the neighboring sea bottom, and each harbors a similar peculiar assemblage of molluscs, crustaceans, etc. In other words, a sea grass community is an entity, recognizable as such, wherever it is found. We have seen, similarly, how a *Venus* or *Macoma* community may be recognized as world-wide, although with a geographic change in the actual species concerned. In general, temperature does not enter this picture, and temperature is the most important variable in the latitudinal gradient.

The autecologist, on the other hand, is concerned with a particular species, rather than with a characteristic group of forms. For a single species, temperature is probably the most important single controlling factor. An individual is very closely responsive to even small changes of temperature. A species may contain physiologically adapted races which, among them, may span a wider temperature range than an individual could tolerate. The possible range of these species is thereby extended. The community, retaining its essential characteristics, but varying in its specific make-up, may be even less dependent on temperature control, and so more world-wide in distribution. Much the same series could be found in respect to illumination or other factors. It appears, then, that the factors important in controlling the community may differ considerably from those important for the species or individual.

In the introductory chapter, reference was made to the possibility that a community may be something more than the sum of its constituents. The question was left unanswered. The fact that the factors controlling the community differs from those controlling the individual species seems to be a definite indication that such is the case. If this is so, how can the autecologist's study of individuals ever adequately describe communities as they occur under natural conditions? This part, at least, of the original question can be answered. The community is an assemblage of more or less replaceable units. Within limits, alternative species or physiological races may be substituted to meet changing conditions. Within these limits, the essential character of the community does not change as a whole. When the autecologist knows the characteristics of all the possible replacement units in a given community, then he will know all the possible manifestations of that community.

There is one final point deserving emphasis. The ocean is not stable, nor are its communities and individuals. The existence of a community is the resultant of a wide array of interacting forces. Diurnal, seasonal, and other changes in the environment are constantly varying these forces and so modifying the life of the individuals which constitute the community. The reaction of each species to a change in its environment may be different, as may the rate at which it can react. Thus phytoplankton may, in a few days, show a population change in response to improvement in conditions for growth. The herbivores which feed on the phytoplankton, because of their slower rate of growth, take weeks or months to react similarly to the improved food supply. Fish, which in turn feed on the herbivores, may take a year or more for a similar reaction, at least to the point where it is reflected in an improvement in commercial fish catches. At no time, then, are we dealing with a really stable climax condition. On the contrary, we are dealing with an unstable system which is in a constant process of readjustment.

The understanding of the forces and processes involved in this system constitutes ecology; it is still in its infancy. The science has, in some of its aspects, suffered from the overcollection of data to the point where the mass of material tends to become indigestible. One of the present urgent needs is that there be, along with investigations in the vast field of exploration which is obviously open, more reviewing and coordinating of the existing information. This has been attempted here from the special point of view of the needs of a student in the field. It is to be hoped that more workers will produce critical reviews of their own specialized fields in marine ecology.

Appendix

Genera Referred to in the Text*

Division Mycophyta (Fungi)
  Class Schizomycetes
    Order Eubacteriales
      Family Enterobacteriaceae
        1. *Bacillus*
  Class Ascomycetes
    Order Saccharomycetales
      Family Saccharomycetaceae
        2. *Saccharomyces*
Division Lichenes (Lichens)
  Class Ascolichenes
    Order Sphaeriales
      Family Verrucariaceae
        3. *Lichina*
        4. *Verrucaria*

Division Phycophyta (Algae)
  Class Chlorophyceae
    Order Chlorococcales
      Family Hydrodictyaceae
        5. *Hydrodictyon*
      Family Oöcystaceae
        6. *Chlorella*
    Order Ulvales
      Family Ulvaceae
        7. *Enteromorpha*
        8. *Ulva*
    Order Cladophorales
      Family Cladophoraceae
        9. *Cladophora*
        10. *Urospora*

* The serial number of the genus given in the index refers to its position in the following scheme.

Order Siphonales
Family Codiaceae
11. *Halimeda*
Order Siphonocladiales
Family Valoniaceae
12. *Valonia*
Class Chrysophyceae
Order Chrysomonadales
Family Chromulinaceae
13. *Chromulina*
Family Prymnesiaceae
14. *Prymnesium*
Class Bacillariophyceae
Order Centrales
Family Biddulphiaceae
15. *Bacteriastrum*
16. *Biddulphia*
17. *Ditylium*
Family Discaceae
18. *Actinoptychus*
19. *Asteromphalus*
20. *Coscinodiscus*
21. *Melosira*
22. *Porosira*
23. *Skeletonema*
24. *Stephanopyxis*
25. *Thalassiosira*
Family Soleniaceae
26. *Chaetoceros*
27. *Guinardia*
28. *Lauderia*
29. *Leptocylindrus*
30. *Rhizosolenia*
31. *Schroederella*
Order Pennales
Family Achnanthiaceae
32. *Achnanthes*
Family Fragillariaceae
33. *Asterionella*
34. *Fragillaria*
35. *Thalassiothrix*
Family Naviculaceae
36. *Navicula*
Family Nitzschiaceae
37. *Bacillaria*

38. *Hantzschia*
39. *Nitzschia*
Class Dinophyceae
Order Gymnodiniales
Family Gymnodiniaceae
40. *Gymnodinium*
Order Desmomonadales
Family Prorocentraceae
41. *Prorocentrum*
Order Peridiniales
Family Ceratiaceae
42. *Ceratium*
Class Phaeophyceae
Order Ectocarpales
Family Ectocarpaceae
43. *Ectocarpus*
Order Chordariales
Family Chordariaceae
44. *Leathesia*
Order Desmarestiales
Family Desmarestiaceae
45. *Desmarestia*
Order Punctariales
Family Asperococcaceae
46. *Scytosiphon*
Order Laminariales
Family Laminariaceae
47. *Alaria*
48. *Costaria*
49. *Egregia*
50. *Hedophyllum*
51. *Laminaria*
52. *Lessoniopsis*
53. *Macrocystis*
54. *Nereocystis*
55. *Postelsia*
56. *Pterygophora*
Order Fucales
Family Durvillaeaceae
57. *Splachnidium*
Family Fucaceae
58. *Ascophyllum*
59. *Fucus*
60. *Pelvetia*
61. *Pelvetiopsis*

Family Himanthaliaceae
   62. *Himanthalea*
Family Sargassaceae
   63. *Cystoseira*
   64. *Sargassum*
Class Myxophyceae
Order Hormogonales
Family Nostocaceae
   65. *Anabaena*
   66. *Nostoc*
Family Oscillatoriaceae
   67. *Oscillaria*
   68. *Phormidium*
Class Rhodophyceae
Order Bangiales
Family Bangiaceae
   69. *Bangia*
   70. *Porphyra*
Order Corallinales
Family Corallinaceae
   71. *Corallina*
Order Nemalionales
Family Acrochaetiaceae
   72. *Rhodocorton*
Family Chaetangiaceae
   73. *Gloiopeltis*
Order Gelidiales
Family Gelidiaceae
   74. *Caulacanthus*
   75. *Gelidium*
Order Cryptonemiales
Family Corallinaceae
   76. *Calliarthron*
   77. *Goniolithon*
   78. *Lithothamnion*
   79. *Porolithon*
Family Dumontiaceae
   80. *Pikea*
Family Grateloupeaceae
   81. *Aeodes*
   82. *Prionitis*
     [= *Zanardinula*]
Family Nemastocaceae
   83. *Schizymenia*

Family Squamariaceae
   84. *Hildenbrandia*
Order Gigartinales
Family Gigartinaceae
   85. *Chondrus*
   86. *Endocladia*
   87. *Gigartina*
   88. *Iridophycus*
   89. *Rhodoglossum*
Family Hypneaceae
   90. *Hypnea*
Family Phyllophoraceae
   91. *Ahnfeltia*
   92. *Gymnogongrus*
Family Rhodophyllidaceae
   93. *Catanella*
Family Solieriaceae
   94. *Agardhiella*
Order Rhodymeniales
Family Rhodymeniaceae
   95. *Champia*
   96. *Halosaccion*
   97. *Plocamium*
   98. *Rhodymenia*
Order Ceramiales
Family Ceramiaceae
   99. *Antithamnion*
   100. *Ceramium*
   101. *Microcladia*
   102. *Ptilota*
   103. *Trailiella*
Family Dasyaceae
   104. *Dasyopsis*
Family Delesseriaceae
   105. *Delesseria*
   106. *Membranoptera*
Family Rhodomeliaceae
   107. *Chondria*
   108. *Herpesiphonia*
   109. *Laurencia*
   110. *Lophosiphonia*
   111. *Odonthalia*
   112. *Polysiphonia*
   113. *Rhodomela*

Division Spermatophyta
(Seed Plants)
Class Monocotyledones
Order Hydrocharitales
Family Hydrocharitaceae
114. *Thalassia*
Order Naiadales
Family Cymodoceaceae
115. *Cymodocea*
Family Zosteraceae
116. *Zostera*

Phylum Protozoa
Class Sarcodina
Order Amoebina
117. *Amoeba*
Order Foraminifera
118. *Polystrema*
Order Radiolaria
119. *Podocanelius*
Class Ciliata
Order Hydroida
120. *Paramecium*
Phylum Coelenterata
Class Hydrozoa
Order Hydroida
120. *Amphinema*
122. *Catablema*
123. *Gossea*
124. *Monocaulus*
125. *Myrionema*
126. *Obelia*
127. *Plumularia*
128. *Ptychogena*
Order Hydrocorallina
129. *Millepora*
Order Trachylina
130. *Aglantha*
131. *Bougainvillea*
132. *Cosmetira*
133. *Laodicea*
134. *Liriope*
135. *Melicertum*
136. *Octorchis*
137. *Phialidium*

138. *Sarsia*
139. *Slabberia*
140. *Staurophora*
141. *Turritopsis*
Order Siphonophora
142. *Agalma*
143. *Cupulita*
144. *Diphyes*
145. *Muggiaea*
146. *Physalia*
147. *Physophora*
148. *Stephanomia*
Subclass Scyphozoa
Order Discomedusae
149. *Cyanea*
Class Anthozoa
Subclass Alcyonaria
Order Alcyonacea
150. *Lobophyton*
151. *Sarcophytum*
152. *Sinularia*
Order Pennatulacea
153. *Virgularia*
Subclass Zoantharia
Order Actiniaria
154. *Actinia*
155. *Actinoden-
dron*
156. *Cereus*
157. *Metridium*
158. *Stoichactis*
Order Madreporaria
159. *Acropora*
160. *Coeloria*
161. *Dendrophyllia*
162. *Favia*
163. *Fungia*
164. *Galaxea*
165. *Lobophyllia*
166. *Montipora*
167. *Orbicella*
168. *Pocillopora*
169. *Porites*
170. *Psammocora*
171. *Symphyllia*

Class Ctenophora
  172. *Martensia*
  173. *Pleurobrachia*
Phylum Platyhelminthes
 Class Turbellaria
  174. *Convoluta*
  175. *Gunda*
Phylum Chaetognatha
  176. *Sagitta*
Phylum Bryozoa
 Class Ectoprocta
  177. *Bugula*
  178. *Crisia*
  179. *Hippothoa*
  180. *Membrani-*
    pora
  181. *Schizoporella*
  182. *Scrupocellaria*
  183. *Thalamopo-*
    rella
Phylum Annelida
 Class Polychaeta
 Polychaeta Errantia
  184. *Aricia*
  185. *Glycera*
  186. *Heterocirrus*
  187. *Nephthys*
  188. *Nereis*
  189. *Notomastus*
  190. *Odontosyllis*
  191. *Perinereis*
  192. *Phyllodoce*
  193. *Pygospio*
  194. *Scoloplos*
  195. *Tomopteris*
 Polychaeta Sedentaria
  196. *Ampharete*
  197. *Arenicola*
  198. *Eupomatus*
  199. *Lanice*
  200. *Melinna*
  201. *Pomatoceros*
  202. *Sabella*
  203. *Serpula*
  204. *Spirorbis*

  205. *Terebellides*
  206. *Travisia*
Phylum Mollusca
 Class Amphineura
  207. *Chaetoderma*
  208. *Chiton*
 Class Gastropoda
 Order Prosobranchiata
  209. *Acmaea*
  210. *Aporrhais*
  211. *Buccinum*
  212. *Calliostoma*
  213. *Cominella*
  214. *Echininus*
  215. *Fissurella*
  216. *Fluvinerita*
  217. *Gibbula*
  218. *Helcion*
  219. *Hydrobia*
  220. *Littorina*
  221. *Murex*
  222. *Nassa*
  223. *Natica*
  224. *Nerita*
  225. *Neritilia*
  226. *Neritina*
  227. *Nucella*
  228. *Osilinus*
  229. *Oxystele*
  230. *Patella*
  231. *Polynices*
  232. *Puperita*
  233. *Purpura*
  234. *Tectarius*
  235. *Tegula*
  236. *Thais*
  237. *Trochocochlea*
  238. *Trochus*
  239. *Truncatella*
  240. *Turitella*
  241. *Urosalpinx*
 Order Opisthobranchiata
  242. *Acera*
  243. *Clione*
  244. *Limacina*
  245. *Philine*

Class Lamellibranchiata
 246. *Abra*
 247. *Anomia*
 248. *Arca*
 249. *Astarte*
 250. *Cardita*
 251. *Cardium*
 252. *Chlamys*
 253. *Corbula*
 254. *Crenella*
 255. *Cultellus*
 256. *Cyprina*
 257. *Hippopus*
 258. *Leda*
 259. *Lithophaga*
 260. *Macoma*
 261. *Mactra*
 262. *Modiolaria*
 263. *Modiolus*
 264. *Montacuta*
 265. *Mya*
 266. *Mytilus*
 267. *Nucula*
 268. *Ostrea*
 269. *Pandora*
 270. *Pecten*
 271. *Portlandia*
 272. *Psammobia*
 273. *Saxicava*
 274. *Scrobicularia*
 275. *Solen*
 276. *Syndosmya*
 277. *Tapes*
 278. *Tellina*
 279. *Teredo*
 280. *Tridacna*
 281. *Venus*
 282. *Volsella*
 283. *Yoldia*
 284. *Zirfaea*
Class Cephalopoda
Order Octopoda
 285. *Octopus*
 286. *Vampyro-*
  teuthis

Order Decapoda
 287. *Illex*
 288. *Loligo*
Phylum Echinodermata
Class Echinoidea
 289. *Brissopsis*
 290. *Diadema*
 291. *Echinocar-*
  dium
 292. *Echinus*
 293. *Eucidaris*
 294. *Lytechinus*
 295. *Spatangus*
 296. *Strongylo-*
  centrotus
 297. *Tripneustes*
Class Asteroidea
 298. *Asterias*
 299. *Astropecten*
 300. *Luidia*
Class Ophiuroidea
 301. *Amphiura*
 302. *Ophiacantha*
 303. *Ophiocomina*
 304. *Ophioglypha*
 305. *Ophiothrix*
Class Holothuroidea
 306. *Elpidia*
 307. *Myriotrochus*
 308. *Pelopathides*
Phylum Arthropoda
Class Crustacea
Subclass Branchiopoda
 309. *Artemia*
 310. *Chiroceph-*
  alus
 311. *Daphnia*
 312. *Evadne*
Subclass Ostracoda
 313. *Candona*
 314. *Herpetocypris*
Subclass Copepoda
 315. *Anomalocera*
 316. *Calanus*
 317. *Centropages*
 318. *Ctenocalanus*

386. *Doliolum*
387. *Salpa*
Subphylum Craniata
   Class Pisces
      Subclass Elasmobranchii
388. *Scyllium*
      Subclass Teleostii
389. *Bathophylus*
390. *Chauliodus*
391. *Conger*
392. *Cottus*
393. *Crenilabrus*

394. *Gasterosteus*
395. *Holocentrus*
396. *Lepadogaster*
397. *Lepomis*
398. *Lopholatilus*
399. *Pagellus*
400. *Pleuronectes*
401. *Pterophryne*
402. *Syngnathus*
Class Aves
403. *Phalacrocorax*

References

Abe, N. (1931). Ecological observations on *Acmaea dorsuosa* Gould. *Sci. Repts. Tôhoku Imp. Univ.* [4], **6**, 403–428.

—— (1933). The colony of the limpet (*Acmaea dorsuosa* Gould). *Sci. Repts. Tôhoku Imp. Univ.* [4], **8**, No. 2, 169–187.

Alexander, W. B., Southgate, B. A., and Bassindale, R. (1932). The salinity of the water retained in the muddy foreshore of an estuary. *J. Marine Biol. Assoc. United Kingdom*, **18**, No. 1, 297–298.

Allee, W. C., Finckel, A. J., and Hoskins, W. H. (1940). The growth of goldfish in homotypically conditioned water; a population study in mass physiology. *J. Exptl. Zool.*, **84**, No. 3, 417–443.

Allee, W. C., Emerson, A. E., Park, O., Park, T., and Schmidt, K. P. (1949). *Principles of Animal Ecology*, pp. 1–837. Saunders, Philadelphia.

Allen, E. J. (1899). On the fauna and bottom deposits near the thirty-fathom line from the Eddystone grounds to Start Point. *J. Marine Biol. Assoc. United Kingdom*, **5**, No. 4, 365–542.

Allen, E. W., Bates, S., James, M. C., and Nickerson, G. W. (1949). Regulation and investigation of the pacific halibut fishery in 1948. *Rept. Internat. Fisheries Comm.*, No. 14, 1–30.

Allen, W. E. (1928). Quantitative studies on inshore marine diatoms and dinoflagellates collected in Southern California in 1924. *Bull. Scripps Inst. Oceanog. Tech. Ser.* **1**, No. 15, 347–356.

Amemiya, I. (1928). Ecological studies of Japanese oysters with special reference to the salinity of their habitats. *J. Coll. Agr. Tokyo Imp. Univ.*, **9**, No. 5, 333–382.

Andersson, M. (1942). Einige ernährungsphysiologische Versuche mit *Ulva* und *Enteromorpha*. *Kgl. Fysiograf. Sällskap. Lund Förh.*, **12**, No. 4, 42–52.

Andrews, E. A. (1940). The snail, *Neritina virginea* L., in a changing salt pond. *Ecology*, 21, 335–346.

Atkins, W. R. G. (1922). The influence upon algal cells of an alteration in the hydrogen ion concentration of sea water. *J. Marine Biol. Assoc. United Kingdom*, 12, No. 4, 789–791.

———— (1945). Autotrophic flagellates as the major constituent of the oceanic phytoplankton. *Nature*, 156, No. 3963, 446–447.

Atkinson, R. (1948). Leach's petrel. *New Naturalist*, 110–114.

Awerinzew, S. (1911). Ueber die Pigmente von *Strongylocentrotus droebachiensis*. *Arch. zool. exptl. et gén.* [5], 8, No. 1, 1–8.

Bachrach, E., and Lucciardi, N. (1932). Influence de la concentration en ions hydrogène (pH) sur la multiplication de quelques Diatomées marines. *Rev. algol.*, 6, 251–261.

Baerends, G. P. (1947). The rational exploitation of the sea fisheries with particular reference to the fish stock of the North Sea. (Translated by Hahn, J., 1950.) *Spec. Sci. Rept. U. S. Fish Wildlife Service*, No. 13, 1–102.

Baley, E. C. C. (1935). The kinetics of photosynthesis. *Proc. Roy. Soc.* [B], 117, No. 804, 218–239.

Baranov, F. (1918). *On the Question of the Biological Basis of Fisheries.* Moscow.

———— (1925). *On the Question of the Dynamics of the Fishing Industry.* Moscow.

Barker, H. A. (1935). Photosynthesis in diatoms. *Arch. Mikrobiol.*, 6, No. 2, 141–181.

Bartholomew, J. (1950). *The Advanced Atlas of Modern Geography*, pp. 1–108, and 1–47. Meiklejohn, London.

Battle, H. I. (1932). Rhythmic sexual maturity and spawning of certain bivalve mollusks. *Contribs. Can. Biol. and Fisheries*, 7, A, No. 17, 255–276.

Beadle, L. C. (1931). The effect of salinity changes on the water content and respiration of marine invertebrates. *J. Exptl. Biol.*, 8, No. 3, 211–227.

Beebe, W., and Crane, J. (1939). Deep-sea fishes of the Bermuda oceanographic expeditions. Family Melanostomiatidae. *Zoologica N. Y.*, 24, No. 6, 65–238.

Biebl, R. (1938). Trockenresistenz und osmotische Empfindichkeit der Meeresalgen verschrieden tiefer Standorte. *Jahbr. wiss. Botan.*, 86, No. 3, 350–286.

Bigelow, H. B. (1926). Physical oceanography of the Gulf of Maine. *Bull. U. S. Bur. Fisheries*, 40 (Report for 1924), No. 2, Doc. 969, 511–1027.

Bigelow, H. B., Lillick, L. C., and Sears, M. (1940). Phytoplankton and planktonic protozoa of the offshore waters of the Gulf of Maine. Part I. Numerical distribution. *Trans. Am. Phil. Soc.*, 31, 149–191.

Bigelow, H. B., and Sears, M. (1939). Studies of the waters of the continental shelf, Cape Cod to Chesapeake Bay. III. A volumetric study of the zooplankton. *Mem. Museum Comp. Zool. Harvard*, 54, No. 4, 183–378.

Black, W. A. P. (1948). Seasonal variation in the chemical composition of some of the sublittoral seaweeds common to Scotland. Part I. *Laminaria cloustoni*. Part II. *Laminaria digitata*. *J. Soc. Chem. Ind. London*, 67, 165–172.

———— (1950). The seasonal variation in weight and chemical composition of the common British Laminariaceae. *J. Marine Biol. Assoc. United Kingdom,* **29,** No. 1, 45–72.

Black, W. A. P., and Dewar, E. T. (1949). Correlation of some of the physical and chemical properties of the sea with the chemical constitution of the algae. *J. Marine Biol. Assoc. United Kingdom,* **28,** No. 3, 673–699.

Black, W. A. P., and Mitchell, R. L. (1952). Trace elements in the common brown algae and in sea water. *J. Marine Biol. Assoc. United Kingdom,* **30,** No. 3, 575–584.

Blegvad, H. (1929). Mortality among animals of the littoral region in ice winters. *Rept. Danish Biol. Sta.,* **35,** 49–62.

——— (1933). Plaice transplantations. *J. conseil, Conseil permanent intern. Exploration mer,* **8,** No. 2, 161–180.

Bogorov, B. G. (1946). Peculiarities of diurnal vertical migrations of zooplankton in polar seas. *J. Marine Research Sears Foundation,* **6,** No. 1, 25–32.

Bokenham, N. A. H., and Stephenson, T. A. (1938). The colonization of denuded rock surfaces in the intertidal region of the Cape Peninsular. *Ann. Natal Museum,* **9,** No. 1, 47–81.

Bokenham, N. A. H., Neugebaur, F. L. M., and Stephenson, T. A. (1938). The vertical distribution of certain intertidal marine gastropods in False Bay, with notes on the development of two of them. *Ann. Natal Museum,* **9,** No. 1, 113–137.

Borden, M. A. (1931). A study of the respiration and the function of haemoglobin in *Planorbis corneus* and *Arenicola marina*. *J. Marine Biol. Assoc. United Kindom,* **17,** No. 3, 709–738.

Braarud, T. (1944). Experimental studies on marine plankton diatoms. *Avhandl. Norske Videnskaps-Akad. Oslo I Mat. Naturv. Kl.,* **1944,** No. 10, 1–16.

Broekema, M. M. (1941). Seasonal movement and the osmotic behaviour of the shrimp *Crangon crangon* L. *Arch. néerl. zool.,* **6,** No. 1, 1–100.

Broekhuysen, G. J. (1935). The extremes in percentages of dissolved oxygen to which the fauna of a *Zostera* field in the tidal zone at Nieuwdièp can be exposed. *Arch. néerl. zool.,* **1,** No. 3, 339–346.

——— (1936). On development, growth and distribution of *Carcinides maenas* (L.). *Arch. néerl. zool.,* **2,** No. 2, 257–399.

——— (1940). A preliminary investigation of the importance of desiccation, temperature and salinity as factors controlling the vertical distribution of certain intertidal marine gastropods in False Bay, South Africa. *Trans. Roy. Soc. S. Africa,* **28,** No. 3, 255–292.

Brotskaja, V. A., and Zenkevich, L. A. (1939). Quantitative evaluation of the bottom fauna of the Barents Sea. *Trans. Inst. Marine Fish. U. S. S. R.,* **4,** 99–126.

Brown, D. E., Johnson, F. H., and Marsland, D. A. (1942). The pressure temperature relations of bacterial luminescence. *J. Cellular Comp. Physiol.,* **20,** No. 2, 151–168.

Bruan, A. F., Greve, S., Mielche, H., and Sparch, R. (Editors) (1956). The Galathea deep sea expeditions, 1950–1952, pp. 1–296. Macmillan, New York.

Bruce, J. R. (1926). The respiratory exchange of the mussel (*Mytilus edulis,* L.). *Biochem. J.,* [1], **20,** No. 8, 829–846.

——— (1928). Physical factors on the sandy beach. Part I. Tidal, climatic and edaphic. *J. Marine Biol. Assoc. United Kingdom,* **15,** No. 2, 535–552.

Buchsbaum, R. (1938). *Animals Without Backbones,* pp. 1–371. Univ. Chicago Press, Chicago.

Burkenroad, M. D. (1948). Fluctuation in abundance of Pacific halibut. *Bull. Bingham Oceanog. Coll.,* 11, No. 4, 81–129.

Butcher, R. W. (1934). *Zostera.* Report on the present condition of ell grass on the coasts of England, based on a survey during August to October, 1933. *J. conseil, Conseil permanent intern. exploration mer,* 9, No. 1, 49–65.

Caldwell, J. M. (1949). Beach erosion. *Sci Monthly,* 69, No. 4, 229–235.

Cattell, McK. (1936). The physiological effects of pressure. *Biol. Revs. Cambridge Phil. Soc.,* 11, No. 4, 441–476.

Caullery, M. M. (1929). Effects des grands froids sur les organisms de la zône cotidale dans les Boulonnais. *Bull. Soc. zool. France,* 54, 267–269.

Chapman, G. (1949). Thixotropy and dilatancy of marine soil. *J. Marine Biol. Assoc. United Kingdom,* 28, No. 1, 123–140.

Chapman, G., and Newell, G. E. (1949). The distribution of lugworms (*Arenicola marina* L.) over the flats at Whitstable. *J. Marine Biol. Assoc. United Kingdom,* 28, No. 3, 627–634.

Chapman, V. J. (1941). *An Introduction to the Study of Algae,* pp. 1–387. Cambridge Univ. Press, London.

―――― (1946). Marine algal ecology. *Botan. Rev.,* 12, No. 10, 628–672.

Chase, F. A. (1940). Plankton of the Bermuda oceangraphic expeditions. IX. The bathypelagic caridean crustacea. *Zoologica N. Y.,* 25, Part 2, No. 11, 117–209.

Chu, S. P. (1942). The influence of the mineral composition of the medium on the growth of planktonic algae. Part I. Methods and culture media. *J. Ecol.,* 30, No. 2, 284–325.

―――― (1943). The influence of the mineral composition of the medium on the growth of planktonic algae. Part II. The influence of the concentration of inorganic nitrogen and phosphate phosphorus. *J. Ecol.,* 31, No. 2, 109–148.

―――― (1946). The utilization or organic phosphorus by phytoplankton. *J. Marine Biol. Assoc. United Kingdom,* 26, No. 3, 285–295.

Clarke, F. W., and Wheeler, W. C. (1922). The inorganic constituents of marine invertebrates. *Dept. Int., U. S. Geol. Survey, Prof. Paper,* 124, 1–62.

Clarke, G. L. (1933). Diurnal migration of plankton in the Gulf of Maine and its correlation with changes of submarine irradiation. *Biol. Bull.,* 65, No. 3, 402–436.

―――― (1936). On the depth at which fish can see. *Ecology,* 17, No. 3, 452–456.

―――― (1936a). Light penetration in the western North Atlantic and its application to biological problems. *Rappt. et Proc. verb. conseil permanent intern. explanation mer,* 101, 2, No. 3, 1–14.

―――― (1940). Comparative richness of zooplankton in coastal and offshore areas of the Atlantic. *Biol. Bull.,* 78, No. 2, 226–255.

Clarke, G. L. and Backus, R. H. (1956). Measurements of light penetration in relation to vertical migration and records of luminescence of deep-sea animals. *Deep Sea Res.,* 4, 1–14.

Clarke, G. L., and Wertheim, G. K. (1956). Measurements of illumination at great depths and at night in the Atlantic ocean by means of a new bathyphotometer. *Deep-Sea Research,* 3, No. 3, 189–205.

Cloud, P. E. (1952). Facies relationships of organic reefs. *Bull. Am. Assoc. Petrol. Geologists,* 36, No. 11, 2125–2149.

Clowes, A. J. (1938). Phosphate and silicate in the Southern Ocean. *"Discovery" Rept.,* 19, 1–120.

Coe, W. R. (1932). Season of attachment and rate of growth of sedentary marine organisms at the pier of the Scripps Institution of Oceanography, La Jolla, California. *Bull. Scripps Inst. Oceanog. Tech. Ser.,* 3, No. 3, 37–86.

———— (1946). The means of dispersal of bathypelagic animals in the North and South Atlantic Oceans. *Am. Naturalist,* 80, No. 793, 453–469.

Cole, W. H. (1929). The relation between temperature and the pedal rhythm of *Balanus. J. Gen Physiol.,* 12, No. 5, 599–608.

Collier, A., Ray, S. M., Magnitzky, A. W., and Bell, J. O. (1953). Effects of dissolved organic substances on oysters. *Bull. U. S. Bur. Fisheries,* 54, No. 84, 166–185.

Colman, J. (1933). The nature of the intertidal zonation of plants and animals. *J. Marine Biol. Assoc. United Kingdom,* 18, No. 2, 435–476.

Cooper, L. H. N. (1937). The nitrogen cycle in the sea. *J. Marine Biol. Assoc. United Kingdom,* 22, No. 1, 183–204.

Cooper, L. H. N., and Milne, A. (1938). The ecology of the Tamar Estuary. II. Underwater illumination. *J. Marine Biol. Assoc. United Kingdom,* 22, No. 2, 509–527.

———— (1939). The ecology of the Tamar Estuary. V. Underwater illumination. Revision of data for red light. *J. Marine Biol. Assoc. United Kingdom,* 23, No. 2, 391–396.

Copeland, J. J. (1936). Yellowstone thermal Myxophyceae. *Ann. N. Y. Acad. Sci.,* 36, 1–232.

Cornish, V. (1934). *Ocean Waves and Kindred Geophysical Phenomena,* pp. 1–164. Cambridge Univ. Press, London.

Coulthard, H. S. (1929). Growth of the sea mussel. *Contribs. Can. Biol. and Fisheries,* 4, No. 10, 121–136.

Crozier, W. J., and Arey, L. B. (1919). On the ethology of *Chiton tuberculatus. Proc. Natl. Acad. Sci. U. S.,* 5, 496–498.

Dakin, W. J. (1934). The plankton calendar of the continental shelf of the Pacific coast of Australia at Sydney compared with that of the Irish Sea. In *James Johnstone Memorial,* pp. 164–174. Liverpool Univ. Press, Liverpool.

Dakin, W. J., Bennett, I.. and Pope, E. (1948). A study of certain aspects of the ecology of the intertidal zone of the New South Wales coast. *Australian J. Sci. Research [B]* 1, No. 2, 176–230.

Damant, G. C. C., (1937). Storage of oxygen in the bladders of the seaweed *Ascophyllum nodosum* and their adaptation to hydrostatic pressure. *J. Exptl. Biol.* 14, No. 2, 198–209.

Dannevig, H. (1895). The influence of temperature on the development of the eggs of fishes. *13th Ann. Rept. Fishery Board Scotland,* 147–152.

Darwin, C. (1897). *The Structure and Distribution of Coral Reefs,* 3rd ed., pp. 1–344. New York, Appleton and Co.

Darwin, G. H. (1898). *The Tides,* pp. 1–378. Houghton, Boston.

Davis, F. M. (1923). Quantitative studies on the fauna of the sea bottom. No. 1. Preliminary investigations of the Dogger Bank. *Fish invest. London* [2], 6, No. 2, 1–54.

———— (1925). Quantitative studies on the fauna of the sea bottom. No. 2. Results of the investigations in the southern North Sea. *Fish. Invest. London* [2], **8**, No. 4, 1–50.

Dawes, B. (1930). Growth and maintenance in the plaice (*P. platessa* L.). Part I. *J. Marine Biol. Assoc. United Kingdom*, **17**, No. 1. 103–174.

———— (1931). Growth and maintenance in the plaice (*P. platessa* L.). Part II. *J. Marine Biol. Assoc. United Kingdom*, **17**, No. 3, 877–947.

Dawydoff, C. (1928). *Traité d'Embryologie comparée des Invertébrées*, pp. 1–930. Masson et Cie, Paris.

Day, J. H. (1951). The ecology of South African estuaries. Part I. A review of estuarine conditions in general. *Trans. Roy. Soc. S. Africa*, **33**, No. 1, 53–91.

Delf, E. M. (1932). Experiments with the stipes of *Fucus* and *Laminaria*. *J. Exptl. Biol.* **9**, No. 3, 300–313.

Dellow, V. (1950). Inter-tidal ecology at Narrow Neck Reef, New Zealand. *Pacific Sci.*, **4**, No. 4, 355–374.

Delphy, J. (1917). Influence des agents climactériques sur les variations de fauna. *Bull. Museum natl. hist. nat., Paris*, **23**, 78–82.

Dodgson, R. W. (1928). Report on mussel purification. *Fish. Invest. London* [2], **10**, No. 1, 1–498.

Doochin, H., and Smith, F. G. W. (1951). Marine boring and fouling in relation to velocity of water currents. *Bull. Marine Sci. Gulf and Caribbean*, **1**, No. 3, 196–208.

Doty, M. S. (1946). Critical tide factors that are correlated with the vertical distribution of marine algae and other organisms along the Pacific coast. *Ecology*, **27**, No. 4, 315–328.

Doty, M. S., and Archer, J. G. (1950). An experimental test of the tide factor hypothesis. *Am. J. Botany*, **37**, No. 6, 458–464.

Drewes, K. (1928). Über die Assimilation des Luftstickstoffs durch Blaualgen. *Zentr. Bakteriol. Parasitenk Abt. II*, **76**, 88–101.

Edwards, G. A., and Irvin, L. (1943). The influence of temperature and season upon the oxygen consumption of the sand crab, *Emerita talpoida* Say. *J. Cellular Comp. Physiol.*, **21**, No. 2, 169–182.

Ehrke, G. (1929). Die Einwirkung der Temperatur und des Lichtes auf die Atmung und Assimilation der Meeresalgen. *Planta*, **9**, No. 3, 631–638.

———— (1931). Über die Wirkung der Temperatur und des Lichtes auf die Atmung und Assimilation einiger Meeres- und Süsswasseralgen. *Planta*, **13**, Nos. 2/3, 221–310.

Einarsson, H. (1945). Euphausiacea I. Northern Atlantic species. *"Dana" Rept.*, **27**, 1–185.

Ekman, S. (1953). *Zoogeography of the Sea*, pp. 1–417. Sidgewick and Jackson, London.

Ellis, M. M. (1947). Toxicity of phenyl-mercuric lactate for fish. *Spec. Sci. Rept. U. S. Fish Wildlife Service*, **42**, 1–6.

Elmhirst, R. (1931). Studies in the Scottish marine fauna.—The crustacea of the sandy and muddy areas of the tidal zone. *Proc. Roy. Soc. Edinburgh*, **51**, Part 2, No. 21, 169–175.

Encyclopedia Brittanica, World Atlas (1947), pp. 1–154. Hammons, New York.

Eriksen, A., and Townsend, L. D. (1940). State Pollution Comm., State of Wash. Poll. Series 2.

Evans, R. G. (1947). The intertidal ecology of selected localities in the Plymouth neighborhood. *J. Marine Biol. Assoc. United Kingdom,* **27,** No. 1, 173–218.

Fauré-Fremiet, E. (1951). The tidal rhythm of the diatom *Hantzschia amphioxys. Biol. Bull.,* **100,** No. 3, 173–177.

Federighi, H. (1931). Studies on the oyster drill (*Urosalpinx cinerea* Say). *Bull. U. S. Bur. Fisheries,* **47,** No. 4, 85–115.

Fischer, E. (1928). Sur la faune littorale, du facies rocheuse en particulier, dans un millieu à salure tres variable. *Bull. inst. oceanog. Monaco,* No. 511, 1–8.

Fischer-Piette, E. (1930). Études dynamiques de bionomie marine. Variations dé la faune et de la flore d'une année à une autre. Résultats pour 1929–1930. *Bull. lab. maritime Saint-Servan,* **5,** 25–39.

———— (1931). Sur la pénétration des diverses espèces marines sessiles dans les estuaires et sa limitation par l'eau douce. *Ann. inst. océanog. Monaco,* **10,** No. 8, 213–243.

———— (1932). Répartition des principales espéces fixées sur les rochers battus des côtes et des îles de la Manche, de Lannion à Fécamp. *Ann. inst océanog. Monaco,* **12,** No. 4, 106–213.

———— (1933). Nouvelles observations sur l'ordre d'euryhalinité des espèces litorales. *Bull. inst. océanog.,* No. 619 1–16.

———— (1935). Histoire d'une moulière. Bull. biol. France et Belg., **69,** No. 2, 152–177.

———— (1940). Sur quelques progrès récents et sur les méthodes et tendances actuelles, en bionomie intercotidale. *Soc. de Biogéogr.,* **7,** 393–434.

———— (1948). Sur les élémente de prospérité des Patelles et sur leur spécificité. *J. Conchyliol,* **88,** 45–96.

Flattely, F. W., and Walton, C. L. (1922). *The Biology of the Sea-Shore,* pp. 1–336. Sidgewick and Jackson, London.

Ford, E. (1923). Animal communities of the level sea bottom in the waters adjacent to Plymouth. *J. Marine Biol. Assoc. United Kingdom,* **13,** No. 1, 164–224.

———— (1925). On the growth of some lamellibranchs in relation to the food supply of fishes. *J. Marine Biol. Assoc. United Kingdom,* **13,** No. 3, 531–559.

Fox, D. L. 1950. Comparative metabolism of organic detritus by inshore animals. *Ecology,* **31,** No. 1, 100–108.

Fraenkel, G. S., and Gunn, D. L. (1940). *The Orientation of Animals,* pp. 1–352. Oxford, Clarendon Press.

Fraser, J. H. (1931). On the size of *Urosalpinx cinerea* (Say) with some observations on weight-length relationship. *Proc. Malacol. Soc. London,* **19,** No. 5, 243–254.

———— (1936). The occurrence, ecology and life history of *Trigriopus fulvus* (Fisher). *J. Marine Biol. Assoc. United Kingdom,* **20,** No. 3, 523–536.

Fritsch, F. E. (1935). *The Structure and Reproduction of the Algae,* Vol. I, pp. 1–791. Cambridge Univ. Press, London.

———— (1945). *The Structure and Reproduction of the Algae,* Vol. II, pp. 1–939. Cambridge Univ. Press, London.

Fuglister, F. C. (1947). Average monthly sea surface temperatures of the

Western North Atlantic Ocean. *Papers Phys. Oceanog. Meteorol. Mass. Inst. Technol. and Woods Hole Oceanog. Inst.*, **10**, No. 2, 1–25.

Fuller, J. F. (1937). Feeding rate of *Calanus finmarchicus* in relation to environmental conditions. *Biol. Bull.*, **72**, No. 2, 233–246.

Fuller, J. F., and Clarke, G. L., (1936). Further experiments on the feeding of *Calanus finmarchicus. Biol. Bull.*, **70**, No. 2, 308–320.

Gail, F. W. (1918). Some experiments with *Fucus* to determine factors controlling its vertical distribution. *Publs. Puget Sound Biol. Sta. Univ. Wash.*, **2**, No. 43, 139–151.

———— (1922). Photosynthesis in some of the red and brown algae as related to depth and light. *Publs. Puget Sound Biol. Sta. Univ. Wash.*, **3**, No. 66, 177–193.

Galtsoff, P. S. (1930). The fecundity of the oyster. *Science*, **72**, No. 1856, 97–98.

Galtsoff, P. S., Chipman, W. A., Hasler, A. D., and Engle, J. B., (1938). Preliminary report on the cause of the decline of the oyster industry of the York River, Va., and the effects of pulp-mill pollution on oysters. *Invest. Rept. U. S. Bur. Fisheries*, **37**, 1–42.

Gardiner, J. S. (1903). *The Fauna and Geography of the Maldive and Lacadive Archipelagoes*, Vol. I, pp. 1–471. Cambridge Univ. Press, London.

Gauld, D. T. (1951). The grazing rate of planktonic copepods. *J. Marine Biol. Assoc. United Kingdom*, **29**, No. 3, 695–706.

Gislén, T. (1929). Epibioses of the Gullmar Fjord I. *Kgl. Svensk. Vetensakad. Skr. Nat.*, **4**, 1–380.

———— (1930). Epiboises of the Gullmar Fjord II. *Kgl. Svensk. Vetensakad. Skr. Nat.*, **4**, 380.

Goldberg, E. D., McBlair, W., and Taylor, K. M., (1951). The uptake of vanadium by tunicates. *Biol. Bull.*, **101**, No. 1, 84–94.

Gowanloch, J. N. (1927). Contributions to the study of marine gastropods. II. The intertidal life of *Buccinum undatum*, a study in non-adaptation. *Contribs. Can. Biol. and Fisheries*, **3**, No. 5, 167–177.

Gowanloch, J. N., and Hayes, F. R. (1927). Contributions to the study of marine gastropods I. The physical factors, behaviour and intertidal life of *Littorina. Contribs. Can. Biol. and Fisheries*, **3**, No. 4, 133–165.

Graham, M. (1935). Modern theory of exploiting a fishery, and application to North Sea trawling. *J. conseil, Conseil permanent intern. exploration mer*, **10**, No. 3, 264–274.

———— (1938). Rates of fishing and natural mortality from the data of marking experiments. *J. conseil, Counseil permanent intern. exploration mer*, **13**, No. 1, 76–90.

———— (1939). The sigmoid curve and the overfishing problem. *Rappt. et proc. verb. conseil permanent intern. exploration mer*, **110**, No. 2, 17–20.

Gran, H. H. (1931). On conditions for the production of plankton in the sea. *Rappt. et proc. verb. conseil permanent intern. exploration mer*, **75**, No. 2, 37–46.

———— (1933). Studies on the biology and chemistry of the Gulf of Maine. II. Distribution of phytoplankton in August, 1932. *Biol. Bull.*, **64**, No. 2, 159–182.

Gran, H., H., and Braarud, T. (1935). A quantitative study of the phytoplankton in the Bay of Fundy and the Gulf of Maine (including observations on the hydrography, chemistry and turbidity). *J. Biol. Board Can.*, 1, No. 5, 279–467.

Gross, F., and Raymont, J. E. G. (1942). The specific gravity of *Calanus finmarchicus*. *Proc. Roy Soc. Edinburgh* [B.], 61, Part 3, No. 21, 288–296.

Gross, F., and Zeuthen, E. (1948). The buoyancy of plankton diatoms: a problem of cell physiology. *Proc. Roy Soc. Edinburgh* [B.], 135, No. 880, 382–389.

Gurney, R. (1942). Larvae of decapod crustacea. *London Ray. Soc.*, 129, 1–306.

Haffner, R. E. (1952). Zoogeography of the bathypelagic fish *Chauliodus*. *Systematic Zool.*, 1, No. 3, 112–133.

Hahn, J. (1950). The rational exploitation of the sea fisheries with particular reference to the fish stock of the North Sea, by G. P. Baerends. Translation. *U. S. Dept. Int., Fish Wildlife Serv., Spec. Sci. Rept.*, No. 13, 1–102.

Hansen, K. V. (1951). On the diurnal migration of zooplankton in relation to the discontinuity layer. *J. conseil, Conseil permanent intern. exploration mer*, 17, No. 3, 231–241.

Harder, R. (1923). Über die Bedeutung von Lichtintensität und Wellenlänge für die Assimilation farbiger Algen. *Z. Botan.*, 15, No. 6, 305–355.

Harding, J. P., Marshall, S. M., and Orr, A. P. (1951). Time of egg-laying in the planktonic copepod *Calanus*. *Nature*, 167, No. 4258, 953.

———— (1952). On the biology of *Calanus finmarchicus*. VII. Factor affecting egg production. *J. Marine Biol. Assoc. United Kingdom*, 30, No. 3, 527–547.

Hardy, A. C. (1923). Notes on the Atlantic plankton taken off the east coast of England in 1921 and 1922. *Publ. circ. conseil permanent intern. exploration mer*, 78, 5–10.

———— (1926). The herring in relation to its animal environment. Part II. Report on trial with the plankton indicator. *Fish. Invest. London* [2], 8, No. 7, 1–13.

———— (1956). *The Open Ocean*, pp. 1–335. Collins, London.

Hardy, A. C., and Bainbridge, R. (1951). Effect of pressure on the behaviour of decaped larvae (Crustacea). *Nature*, 167, No. 4244, 354–355.

Hardy, A. C., and Gunther, E. R. (1935). The plankton of the South Georgia whaling grounds and adjacent waters. *"Discovery" Rept.*, 11, 1–456.

Hart, J. L., Marshall, H. B., and Beall, D. (1933). The extent of the pollution caused by pilchard reduction plants in British Columbia. *Bull. Biol. Board Canada*, 39, 1–11.

Hart, T. J. (1934). On the phytoplankton of the southwest Atlantic and the Bellinghousen Sea. *"Discovery" Rept.*, 8, 1–268.

———— (1937). *Rhizosolenia curvata* Zacharias, as indicator species in the Southern Ocean. *"Discovery" Rept.*, 16, 413–446.

———— (1942). Phytoplankton periodicity in Antarctic surface waters. *"Discovery" Rept.*, 21, 261–356.

Hartley, P. H. T. (1940). The Saltash tuck-net fishery and the ecology of some estuarine fishes. *J. Marine Biol. Assoc. United Kingdom*, 24, No. 1, 1–68.

———— (1947). Observations on flounders *Pleuronectes flesus* L. marked in the estuaries of the Tamar and Lynher. *J. Marine Biol. Assoc., United Kingdom*, 27, No. 1, 53–64.

Harvey, H. W. (1928). *Biological Chemistry and Physics of Sea Water,* pp. 1–194. Cambridge Univ. Press, London.

—— (1933). On the rate of growth of diatoms. *J. Marine Biol. Assoc. United Kingdom,* 19, No. 1, 253–276.

—— (1937). Notes on selective feeding by *Calanus. J. Marine Biol. Assoc. United Kingdom,* 22, No. 1, 97–100.

—— (1937a). The supply of iron to diatoms. *J. Marine Biol. Assoc. United Kingdom,* 22, No. 1, 205–219.

—— (1939). Substances controlling the growth of a diatom. *J. Marine Biol. Assoc. United Kingdom,* 23, No. 2, 499–520.

—— (1945). *Recent Advances in the Chemistry and Biology of Sea Water,* pp. 1–164. Cambridge Univ. Press, London.

—— (1947). Manganese and the growth of phytoplankton. *J. Marine Biol. Assoc. United Kingdom,* 26, No. 4, 562–579.

—— (1949). On manganese in sea and fresh waters. *J. Marine Biol. Assoc. United Kingdom,* 28, 1, 155–164.

—— (1950). On the production of living matter in the sea off Plymouth. *J. Marine Biol. Assoc. United Kingdom,* 29, No. 1, 97–137.

—— (1955). *The Chemistry and Fertility of Sea Water,* pp. 1–224. Cambridge University Press, London.

Harvey, H. W., Cooper, L. H. N., Lebour, M. V., and Russell, F. S. (1935). Plankton production and its control. *J. Marine Biol. Assoc. United Kingdom,* 20, No. 2, 407–442.

Hasle, G. R. (1950). Phototactic vertical migration in marine dinoflagellates. *Oikos,* 2, No. 2, 162–175.

Hatton, H. (1932). Quelques observations sur le repeuplement en *Fucus vesiculosus* des surfaces rocheuses dénudées. *Bull. lab. maritime Saint-Servan,* 9, 1–16.

—— (1936). Observations sur l'habitat et sur la croissance de *Patella vulgata.* L. *Bull. lab. maritime Dinard,* 15, 17–20.

—— (1938). Essais de bionomie explicative sur quelques espèces intercotidales d'algues et d'animaux. *Ann. inst. océanog. Monaco,* 17, 241–348.

Hatton, H., and Fischer-Piette, E. (1932). Observations et expériences sur le peuplement des côtes rocheuses par les cirripèdes. *Bull. inst. océanog., Monaco,* No. 592, 1–15.

Haurwitz, B. (1946). Insolation in relation to cloudiness and cloud density. *Harvard Meteorol. Studies,* Rept. No. 4, 154–165.

Hayes, F. R. (1927). The negative geotropism of the periwinkle: a study in littoral ecology. *Proc. Nova Scotian Inst. Sci.,* 16, No. 4, 155–173.

—— (1929). Contribution to the study of marine gastropods. III. Development, growth and behaviour of *Littorina. Contribs. Can. Biol. and Fisheries,* 4, No. 26, 413–430.

Henderson, J. T. (1929). Lethal temperatures of lamellibranchiata. *Contribs. Can. Biol. and Fisheries,* 4, No. 25, 397–410.

Hendey, N. L. (1937). The plankton diatoms of the southern seas. *"Discovery" Rept.,* 16, 151–364.

Hentschel, E. (1921). Über den Bewuchs auf den treibenden Tangen der Sargassosee. *Mitt. Zool. Mus. Hamburg, Beih. z. Jahrb. wiss. Anst. Hamburg,* 38.

Herpin, R. (1928). Étude sur les essaimages des annélides polychètes. *Bull. biol. France et Belg.,* **62**, No. 3, 308–377.

———— (1929). Études sur les essaimages des annélides polychètes. *Bull. biol. France et Belg.,* **63**, No. 1, 85–94.

———— (1935). Le peuplement d'une place vide dans la nature (La nouvelle plage de Cherbourg). *Ann Sci. Nat. Zool.* [10], **18**, 146–170.

Herrington, W. C. (1948). Limiting factors for fish populations. Some theories and an example. *Bull. Bingham Oceanog. Coll.,* **11**, No. 4, 229–283.

Hersey, J. B., and Moore, H. B. (1948). Progress report on scattering layer observations in the Atlantic Ocean. *Trans. Am. Geophys. Union,* **29**, No. 3, 341–354.

Hesse, R. (1924). *Tiergeographie auf oekologischer Grundlage,* pp. 1–613. Fischer, Jena.

Hesse, R., Allee, W. C., and Schmidt, K. P. (1951). *Ecological Animal Geography,* 2nd ed., pp. 1–715. Wiley, New York.

Hiatt, R., W. (1948). The biology of the lined shore crab, *Pachygrapsus crassipes* Randall. *Pacific Sci.,* **2**, No. 3, 135–213.

Hickling, C. F. (1938). The English plaice marking experiments 1929–1932. *Fish. Invest. London,* [2], **16**, No. 1, 1–80.

Hjort, J. (1914). Fluctuations in the great fisheries of northern Europe. *Rappt. et Proc. verb. conseil permanent intern. exploration mer,* **20**, 1–228.

Hoffman, C. (1929). Die Atmung der Meeresalgen und ihre Beziehung zum Salzgehalt. *Jahb. wiss. Botan.,* **71**, No. 2, 214–268.

Holme, N. A. (1950). The bottom fauna of Great West Bay. *J. Marine Biol. Assoc. United Kingdom,* **29**, No. 1, 163–183.

———— (1950a). Population-dispersion in *Tellina tenuis* Da Costa. *J. Marine Biol. Assoc. United Kingdom,* **29**, No. 2, 267–280.

Huntsman, A. G. (1948). *Odontosyllis* at Bermuda and lunar periodicity. *J. Fisheries Research Board Can.,* **7**, No. 6, 363–369.

Hurd, A. M. (1916). Factors influencing the growth and distribution of *Nereocystis luetkeana. Publs. Puget Sound Biol. Sta. Univ. Wash.,* **1**, No. 17, 185–197.

Hutchins, L. W. (1947). The bases for temperature zonation in geographical distribution. *Ecol. Monographs,* **17**, No. 3, 325–335.

Hutchins, L. W., and Scharff, M. (1947). Maximum and minimum monthly mean sea surface temperatures charted from the "World atlas of sea surface temperatures." *J. Marine Research Sears Foundation,* **6**, No. 3, 264–268.

Hutner, S. H., Provasoli, L., Schats, A., and Haskins, C. P. (1950). Some approaches to the study of the role of materials in the metabolism of microorganisms. *Proc. Am. Phil. Soc.,* **94**, No. 2, 152–170.

Iselin, C. O'D. (1936). A study of the circulation of the western North Atlantic. *Papers Phys. Oceanog. Meteorol. Mass. Inst. Technol. and Woods Hole Oceanog. Inst.* 4, No. 4, 1–101.

Isham, L. B., Moore, H. B., and Smith, F. G. W. (1951). Growth rate measurement of shipworms. *Bull. Marine Sci. Gulf and Caribbean,* **1**, No. 2, 136–147.

Ishida, S. (1935). On the oxygen consumption in the oyster, *Ostrea gigas* Thurberg under various conditions. *Sci. Repts. Tôhoku Imp. Univ.* [4], **10**, No. 3, 619–638.

Jansen, A. C. (1938). The growth of the plaice in the transition area. *Rappt. et proc. verb. conseil permanent intern. exploration mer*, **108**, 104–107.

Jenkin, P. M. (1937). Oxygen production by the diatom *Coscinodiscus excentricus* Ehr. in relation to submarine illumination in the English Channel. *J. Marine Biol. Assoc. United Kingdom*, **22**, No. 1, 301–343.

Jenkins, F. A., and Bowen, I. S. (1946). Transparancy of ocean water. *J. Opt. Soc. Am.* **36**, No. 11, 617–623.

Jensen, A. S. (1942). Two new West Greenland localities for deposits from the ice age etc., Kgl. *Danske Videnskab. Selskab. Biol. Medd.*, **17**, No. 1, 1–35.

Jesperson, P. (1923). On the quantity of macroplankton in the Mediterranean and the Atlantic. *Rept. Danish Oceanog. Exped. Medit.*, **3**, No. 3, 1–17.

———— (1930). Ornithological observations in the North Atlantic Ocean. *Oceanog. Rept. "Dana" Exped.*, **2**, No. 7, 1–36.

John, D. D. (1936). The southern species of the genus *Euphausia*. *"Discovery" Rept.*, **14**, 193–324.

Johnson, D. W. (1919). *Shore Processes and Shoreline Development*, pp. 1–584. Chapman and Hall, London.

Johnson, F. H., Eyring, H., and Polissar, M. J. (1954). *The Kinetic Basis of Molecular Biology*, pp. 1–894. Wiley, New York.

Johnson, M. W. (1939). The correlation of water movements and dispersal of pelagic larval stages of certain littoral animals, especially the sand crab, *Emerita*. *J. Marine Research Sears Foundation*, **2**, No. 3, 236–245.

Jones, F. R. G. (1951). The swimbladder and the vertical movements of teleostean fishes. I. Physical factors. *J. Exptl. Biol.* **28**, No. 4, 553–566.

Jones, N. S. (1950). Marine bottom communities. *Biol. Revs. Cambridge Phil. Soc.*, **25**, 283–313.

Jørgensen, C. B. (1952). On the relation between water transport and food requirements. *Biol. Bull.*, **103**, No. 3, 356–363.

Kelner, A. (1949). Photoreactivation of ultraviolet-irradiated *Escherichia coli*, with special reference to the dose-reduction principle and to the ultraviolet-induced mutations. *J. Bacteriol.*, **58**, No. 4, 511–522.

Kemp, S. (1938). Oceanography and the fluctuations in the abundance of marine animals. *Rept. Brit. Assoc. Zool.*, 85–101.

Ketchum, B. H. (1939). The absorption of phosphate and nitrate by illuminated cultures of *Nitzschia closterium*. *Am. J. Botany*, **26**, No. 6, 399–407.

Kikuchi, K. (1930). Diurnal migration of planktonic crustacea. *Quart. Rev. Biol.*, **5**, No. 2, 189–206.

Kimball, H. H. (1928). Amount of solar radiation that reaches the surface of the earth on the land and on the sea, and methods by which it is measured. *Monthly Weather Rev.*, **56**, 393–399.

Kitching, J. A. (1935). An introduction to the ecology of the intertidal rock surfaces on the coast of Argyll. *Trans. Roy. Soc. Edinburgh*, **58**, Part 2, No. 15, 351–374.

———— (1941). Studies in sublittoral ecology. III. *Laminaria* forest on the west coast of Scotland; a study of zonation in relation to wave action and illumination. *Biol. Bull.*, **80**, No. 3, 324–337.

———— (1950). Distribution of the littoral barnacle *Chthamalus stellatus* around the British Isles. *Nature*, **165**, No. 4203, 820.

Kitching, J. A., Macan, T. T., and Gilson, H. C. (1934). Studies in sublittoral ecology. I. A submarine gulley in Wembury Bay, South Devon. *J. Marine Biol. Assoc. United Kingdom,* 19, No. 2, 677–705.

Klugh, A. B. (1931). Studies on the photosynthesis of marine algae. No. 1: Photosynthetic rates of *Enteromorpha linza, Porphyra umbilicalis* and *Deleseria sinuosa* in red, green and blue light. *Contribs. Can. Biol. and Fisheries,* 6, No. 4, 41–63.

Knight, M., and Parke, M. W. (1931). Manx. Algae. *Proc. Liverpool Biol. Soc.,* 45, 1–155.

—————— (1950). A Biological study of *Fucus vesiculosus* L. and *F. serratus* L. *J. Marine Biol. Assoc. United Kingdom,* 29, No. 2, 439–514.

Knight-Jones, E. W. (1951). Gregariousness and some other aspects of the settling behaviour of *Spirorbis*. *J. Marine Biol. Assoc. United Kingdom,* 30, No. 2, 201–222.

Knight-Jones, E. W., and Stevenson, J. P. (1950). Gregariousness during settlement in the barnacle *Elminius modestus* Darwin. *J. Marine Biol. Assoc. United Kingdom,* 29, No. 2, 281–297.

Knight-Jones, E. W., and Walne, P. R. (1951). *Chromulina pusilla* Butcher, a dominant member of the ultraplankton. *Nature,* 167, No. 4246, 445.

Korringa, P. (1941). Experiments and observations on swarming, pelagic life and settling in the European flat oyster, *Ostrea edulis* L. *Arch. néerl. zool.,* 5, 1–249.

Kreps, E. (1929). Untersuchungen über den respiratorischen Gaswechsel bei *Balanus crenatus* bei verschiedenem Salzgehalt des Aussenmilieus. I. Mitt. über den Sauerstoffverbrauch in Wassermilieu bei verschiedenem Salzgehalt. *Pflügers Arch. ges. Physiol.,* 222, Nos. 1–2, 215–233.

Krogh, A. (1934). Conditions of life in the ocean. *Ecol. Monographs,* 4, No. 4, 421–429.

—————— (1934a). Conditions of life at great depths in the ocean. *Ecol. Monographs,* 4, No. 4, 430–439.

—————— (1939). *Osmotic Regulation in Aquatic Animals,* pp. 1–242. Cambridge Univ. Press, London.

Kuenen, P .H. (1950). *Marine Geology,* pp. 1–568. Wiley, New York.

Kylin, H. (1945). Weitere Angaben über die Ernährung von *Ulva lactuca*. *Kgl. Fysiograf. Sällskap. Lund Förh.,* 15, No. 3, 22–26.

Landes, K. K. (1951). *Petroleum Geology,* pp. 1–660. Chapman and Hall, London.

Laurie, A. H. (1933). Some aspects of respiration in blue and fin whales. *"Discovery"* Rept., 7, 363–406.

—————— (1937). The age of female blue whales and the effect of whaling on the stock. *"Discovery"* Rept., 15, 223–284.

Lea, E. (1930). Mortality in the tribe of Norwegian herring. *Rappt. et proc. verb. conseil permanent intern. exploration mer,* 65, No. 12, 100–117.

Leavitt, B. B. (1935). A quantitative study of the vertical distribution of the larger zooplankton in deep water. *Biol. Bull.,* 68, No. 1, 115–130.

—————— (1938). The quantitative vertical distribution of macrozooplankton in the Atlantic Ocean basin. *Biol. Bull.,* 74, No. 3, 376–394.

Lebour, M. V. (1933). The importance of larval molluscs in the plankton. *J. conseil, Conseil permanent intern. exploration mer,* 8, No. 3, 335–343.

———— (1934). Rissoid larvae as the food of young herrings. *J. Marine Biol. Assoc. United Kingdom,* 19, No. 2, 523–539.

Lee, R. M. (1920). A review of the methods of age and growth determination in fishes by means of scales. *Fish Invest. London* [2], 4, No. 2, 1–32.

Legendre, R. (1921). Influence de la salinité de l'eau sur l'assimilation chlorophyllienne des algues. *Compt. rend. soc. biol. Paris,* 85, 222–224.

Lenderking, R. E. (1952). Observations on *Littorina angulifera* Lam. from Biscayne Key, Florida. *Quart J. Florida Acad. Sci.,* 14, No. 4, 247–250.

Levring, T. (1945). Some culture experiments with marine plankton diatoms. *Medd. Oceanog. Inst. Göteborg,* 3, No. 12, 3–18.

Lindroth, A. (1938). Studien über die respiratorischen Mechanismen von *Nereis virens* Sars. *Zool. Bidr. Uppsala,* 17, 367–373.

Linke, O. (1939). Die Biota des Jadebusenwattes. *Hëlgoland. wiss. Meere-suntersuch,* 1, No. 3, 201–348.

Lloyd, A. J., and Yonge, C. M. (1947). The biology of *Crangon vulgaris* L. in the Bristol Channel and Severn estuary. *J. Marine Biol. Assoc. United Kingdom,* 26, No. 4, 626–661.

Lodge, S. M. (1948). Algal growth in the absence of *Patella* on an experimental strip of foreshore, Port St. Mary, Isle of Man. *Proc. Liverpool Biol. Soc.* 56, 78–83.

Loosanoff, V. L., and Nomejko, C. A. (1949). Growth of oysters, *O. virginica,* during different months. *Biol. Bull.* 97, No. 1, 82–94.

Loosanoff, V. L., Miller, W. S., and Smith, P. B. (1951). Growth and settling of larvae of *Venus mercenaria* in relation to temperature. *J. Marine Research Sears Foundation,* 10, No. 1, 59–81.

Lowndes, A. G. (1935). The swimming and feeding of certain Calanoid copepods. *Proc. Zool. Soc. London,* No. 3, 687–715.

———— (1942). The displacement method of weighing living aquatic organisms. *J. Marine Biol. Assoc. United Kingdom,* 25, No. 3, 555–574.

Lucas, C. E. (1936). On certain interrelations between phytoplankton and zooplankton under experimental conditions. *J. conseil, Conseil intern, exploration mer,* 11, No. 3, 343–362.

———— (1938). Some aspects of integration in plankton communities. *J. conseil, Conseil permanent intern. exploration mer,* 13, No. 3, 309–322.

———— (1947). The ecological effect of external metabolites. *Biol. Revs. Cambridge Phil. Soc.,* 22, No. 3, 270–295.

Lysaght, A. M. (1941). The biology and trematode parasites of the gastropod *Littorina neritoides* (L.) on the Plymouth breakwater. *J. Marine Biol. Assoc. United Kingdom,* 25, No. 1, 41–67.

Macbride, E. W. (1914). *Textbook of Embryology,* Vol. I, pp. 1–663. Macmillan, London.

MacGinitie, G. E. (1938). Movements and mating habits of the sand crab, *Emerita analoga. Am. Midland Naturalist,* 19, No. 2, 471–481.

MacGinitie, G. E., and MacGinitie, N. (1949). *Natural History of Marine Animals,* pp. 1–473. McGraw-Hill, New York.

Mackintosh, N. A. (1934). Distribution of the macroplankton in the Atlantic sector of the Antarctic. *"Discovery" Rept.,* 9, 65–160.

———— (1937). The seasonal circulation of the Antarctic macroplankton. *Discovery" Rept.,* 16, 365–412.

Mackintosh, N. A., and Wheeler, J. F. G. (1929). Southern blue and fin whales. *"Discovery" Rept.* 1, 257–540.

Madsen, H. (1936). Investigations of the shore fauna of East Greenland with a survey of the shores of other Arctic regions. *Medd. Grønland,* **100,** No. 8, 1–79.

Manigault, P. (1932). L'effet de variations de salinité, de température, de pH. sur *Littorina obtusata* L. subsp. *littoralis* L. *Bull. Inst. océanog.,* No. 605, 1–8.

Manton, S. M., and Stephenson, T. A. (1935). Ecological surveys of coral reefs. *Sci. Repts. Great Barrier Reef Exped.,* **3,** No. 10, 273–312.

Margetts, A. R., and Holt, S. J. (1948). The effect of the 1939–1945 war on the English North Sea trawl fisheries. *Rappt. et proc. verb. conseil permanent intern. exploration mer,* **122,** 27–46.

Marine Biological Association (1931). *Plymouth Marine Fauna,* 2nd ed., pp. 1–371. Marine Biological Assoc. Plymouth, England.

Marshall, N. B. (1951). Bathypelagic fishes as sound scatterers in the ocean. *J. Marine Research Sears Foundation,* **10,** No. 1, 1–17.

———— (1954). *Aspects of Deep Sea Biology,* pp. 1–380. Philosophical Library, New York.

Marshall, S. M. (1933). The production of microplankton in the Great Barrier Reef region. *Sci. Repts. Great Barrier Reef Exped.,* **2,** No. 5, 111–157.

———— (1949). On the biology of the small copepods in Loch Striven. *J. Marine Biol. Assoc. United Kingdom,* **28,** No. 1, 45–122.

Marshall, S. M., and Orr, A. P. (1927). The relation of the plankton to some chemical and physical factors in the Clyde Sea Area. *J. Marine Biol. Assoc. United Kingdom.* **14,** No. 4, 837–868.

———— (1930). A study of the spring diatom increase in Loch Striven. *J. Marine Biol. Assoc. United Kingdom,* **16,** No. 3, 853–878.

———— (1931). Sedimentation on Low Isles and its relation to coral growth. *Sci Repts. Great Barrier Reef Exped.,* **1,** No. 5, 93–133.

———— (1951). Time of egg laying in the planktonic copepod *Calanus. Nature,* **167,** No. 4258, 953.

———— (1952). On the biology of *Calanus finmarchicus.* VII. Factors affecting egg production. *J. Marine Biol. Assoc. United Kingdom,* **20,** No. 3, 527–548.

———— (1955). *The Biology of a Marine Copepod Calanus finmarchicus (Gunnerus),* pp. 1–188. Oliver and Boyd, London.

Marshall, S. M., Nicholls, A. G., and Orr, A. P. (1934). On the biology of *Calanus finmarchicus.* V. Seasonal distribution, size, weight and chemical composition in Loch Striven in 1933, and their relation to the phytoplankton. *J. Marine Biol. Assoc. United Kingdom,* **19,** No. 2, 793–828.

———— (1935). On the biology of *Calanus finmarchicus.* VI. Oxygen consumption in relation to environmental conditions. *J. Marine Biol. Assoc. United Kingdom,* **20,** No. 1, 1–28.

Marshall, S. M., and Stephenson, T. A. (1933). The breeding of reef animals. Part I. The corals. *Sci. Repts. Great Barrier Reef Exped.,* **3,** No. 8, 219–245.

Matthews, L. H. (1937). The humpback whale, *Megaptera nodosa. "Discovery" Rept.,* **17,** 7–92.

Mattox, N. T. (1949). Effects of drying on certain marine snails from Puerto Rico. *Ecology,* **30,** No. 2, 242–244.

Mayer, A. G. (1914.) The effects of temperature upon tropical marine animals. *Papers Tortugas Lab.,* **6,** No. 1, 1–24.

—————— (1918). Ecology of the Murray Island coral reef. *Papers Tortugas Lab.,* 9, 1–48.

Merriman, D. (1941). Studies on the striped bass (*Roccus saxatillis*) of the Atlantic coast. *U. S. Fish Wildlife, Fishery Bull.,* 50, No. 35, 1–17.

Merriman, D., and Warfel, H. E. (1948). Studies on the marine resources of southern New England. VII. Analysis of fish populations. *Bull. Bingham Oceanog. Coll.,* 11, No. 4, 131–164.

Miller, S. M. (1952). Phosphorus exchange in a sub-tropical marine basin. *Bull. Marine Sci. Gulf and Caribbean,* 1, No. 4, 257–265.

Milne, A. (1938). The ecology of the Tamar estuary. III. Salinity and temperature conditions in the lower estuary. *J. Marine Biol. Assoc. United Kingdom,* 22, No. 2, 529–542.

Miyazaki, L. (1938). On a substance which is contained in green algae and induces spawning action of the male oyster. (Preliminary note.) *Bull. Japan. Soc. Sci. Fisheries,* 7, 137–138.

Molander, A. R. (1938). Investigations into the growth-rates of the common dab and the flounder in the southern Baltic. *Rappt. et proc. verb. conseil permanent intern. exploration mer,* 108, Part 1, No. 14, 90–101.

Montfort, C. (1935). Zeitphasen der Temperatur-Einstllung and jahrzeitliche Umstellung bei Meeresalgen. *Ber. dent. botan. Ges.,* 53, 651–674.

Moore, H. B. (1931). The muds of the Clyde Sea Area. III. Chemical and physical conditions; rate and nature of sedimentation; and fauna. *J. Marine Biol. Assoc. United Kingdom,* 17, No. 2, 325–358.

—————— (1933). Faecal pellets from marine deposits. *"Discovery" Rept.,* 7, 17–26.

—————— (1934). The relation of shell growth to environment in *Patella vulgata. Proc. Malacol. Soc. London,* 21, No. 3, 217–222.

—————— (1934a). The biology of *Balanus balanoides.* I. Growth rate and its relation to size, season and tidal level. *J. Marine Biol. Assoc. United Kingdom,* 19, No. 2, 851–868.

—————— (1934b). A comparison of the biology of *Echinus esculentus* in different habitats. Part I. *J. Marine Biol. Assoc. United Kingdom,* 19, No. 2, 869–885.

—————— (1935). The biology of *Balanus balanoides.* Part IV. Relatïon to environmental factors. *J. Marine Biol. Assoc. United Kingdom,* 20, No. 2, 279–307.

—————— (1935a). A comparison of the biology of *Echinus esculentus* in different habitats. Part II. *J. Marine Biol. Assoc. United Kingdom,* 20, No. 1, 109–128.

—————— (1936). The biology of *Purpura lapillus.* I. Shell variation in relation to environment. *J. Marine Biol. Assoc. United Kingdom,* 21, No. 1, 61–89.

—————— (1936a). The biology of *Balanus balanoides.* V. Distribution in the Plymouth area. *J. Marine Biol. Assoc. United Kingdom,* 20, No. 3, 701–716.

—————— (1937). A comparison of the biology of *Echinus esculentus* in different habitats. Part III. *J. Marine Biol. Assoc. United Kingdom,* 21, No. 2, 711–720.

—————— (1938). Algal production and food requirements of a limpet. *Proc. Malacol. Soc. London,* 23, No. 3, 117–118.

—————— (1938a). The biology of *Purpura lapillus.* Part II. Growth. Part

III. Life history and relation to environmental factors. *J. Marine Biol. Assoc. United Kingdom*, **23**, No. 1, 57–74.

——— (1940). The biology of *Littorina littorea*. Part II. Zonation in relation to other gastropods on stony and muddy shores. *J. Marine Biol. Assoc., United Kingdom*, **24**, No. 1, 227–237.

——— (1949). Atlantic cruise 151 to the Mediterranean area. *Sci. Rept. No. 3. Woods Hole Oceanog. Inst.* Ref. No. 49-2, 1–7.

——— (1949a). The zooplankton of the upper waters of the Bermuda area of the North Atlantic. *Bull. Bingham Oceanog. Coll.* **12**, No. 2, 1–97.

——— (1950). The relation between the scattering layer and Euphausiacea. *Biol. Bull.*, **99**, No. 2, 181–212.

——— (1952). Physical factors affecting the distribution of Euphausids in the North Atlantic. *Bull. Marine Sci. Gulf and Caribbean*, **1**, No. 4, 278–305.

Moore, H. B., and Kitching, J. A. (1939). The biology of *Chthamalus stellatus* (Poli). *J. Marine Biol. Assoc. United Kingdom*, **23**, No. 2, 521–541.

Moore, H. B., and Sproston, N. G. (1940). Further observations on the colonization of a new rocky shore at Plymouth. *J. Animal Ecol.*, **9**, No. 2, 319–327.

Moore, W. G. (1942). Field studies on the oxygen requirements of certain fresh-water fishes. *Ecology*, **23**, No. 3, 319–329.

Mori, S. (1938). Characteristic tidal rhythmic migration of a mussel, *Donax semignosus* Dunker, and experimental analysis of its behaviour at the flood tide. *Zool. Mag. Tokyo*, **50**, No. 1, 1–12.

Mortensen, T. (1928–1950). *A Monograph of the Echiniodea*, Vols. 1–5. C. A. Reitzel, Copenhagen.

——— (1931–1938). Contributions to the study of the development and larval forms of Echinoderms, I–IV. *Kgl. Danske Videnskab. Selskab. Biol. Medd.* [9], **4**, No. 1, 1–39; [9], **7**, No. 1, 1–65; [9], **7**, No. 3, 1–59.

Morton, J. E. (1951). The structure and adaptations of New Zealand Vermetidae. *Trans. Roy. Soc. New Zealand*, **79**, No. 1, 1–51.

Murray, J. (1895). A summary of the scientific results obtained at the sounding, dredging and trawling stations of H. M. S. Challenger. *"Challenger" Rept.*, Summary, Part 2, 797–1608.

——— (1913). *The Oceans*, pp. 1–256. Williams and Norgate, London.

Murray, J., and Hjort, J. (1912). *The Depths of the Ocean*, pp. 1–821. Macmillan, London.

Naylor, G. L. (1930). Notes on the distribution of *Lichina confinis* and *L. Pygmaea* in the Plymouth district. *J. Marine Biol. Assoc. United Kingdom*, **16**, No. 3, 909–918.

Nelson, T. C. (1928). Pelagic dissoconchs of the common mussel, *Mytilus edulis*, with observations on the behaviour of the larvae of allied genera. *Biol. Bull.*, **55**, No. 3, 180–192.

Newcombe, C. L., Miller, C. E., and Chappell, D. W., (1936). Preliminary report on respiratory studies of *Littorina irrorata*. *Nature*, **137**, No. 3453, 33.

Newell, G. E. (1948). A contribution to our knowledge of the life history of *Arenicola marina* L. *J. Marine Biol. Assoc. United Kingdom*, **27**, No. 3, 554–580.

Nicholls, A. G. (1931). Studies on *Ligia oceanica*. I. A. Habitat and effect of change of environment on respiration. B. Observations on moulting and breeding. *J. Marine Biol. Assoc. United Kingdom*, **17**, No. 3, 655–673.

—— (1933). On the biology of *Calanus finmarchicus*. I. Reproduction and seasonal distribution in the Clyde Sea Area during 1932. *J. Marine Biol. Assoc. United Kingdom*, **19**, No. 1, 83–109.

Nicol, E. (1935). The ecology of a salt marsh. *J. Marine Biol. Assoc. United Kingdom*, **20**, No. 2, 203–261.

Nielsen, E. S. (1934). Untersuchungen über die Verbreitung, Biologie und Variation der Ceratien im Südlichen stillen Ozean. *"Dana" Rept.*, **4**, 1–67.

—— (1952). The use of radioactive carbon (C^{14}) for measuring organic production in the sea. *J. conseil, Conseil permanent intern. exploration, mer*, **18**, No. 2, 117–140.

Nikitine, B. (1929). Les migrations verticales saisonnières des organismes planktoniques dans la Mer Noire. *Bull. inst. océanog.*, Monaco, No. 540, 1–24.

Novick, A., and Szilard, L. (1949). Experiments on light-reactivation of ultraviolet inactivated bacteria. *Proc. Natl. Acad. Sci. U. S.*, **35**, No. 10, 591–600.

Odhner, N. H. (1915). Die Molluskenfauna des Eisfjordes. *Kgl. Svenska Vetenskapsakad. Handl.*, **54**, No. 1, 1–274.

Odum, H. T., and Odum, E. P. (1955). Trophic structure and productivity of a windward coral reef community on Einiwetoc Atoll. *Ecol. Monographs*, **25**, 291–320.

Orr, A. P. (1933). Physical and chemical conditions in the sea in the neighbourhood of the Great Barrier Reef. *Sci. Repts. Great Barrier Reef Exped.*, **2**, No. 3, 37–86.

Orr, A. P., and Moorhouse, F. W. (1933). (a) Variations in some physical and chemical conditions on and near Low Isles Reef. (b) The temperature of the water in the Anchorage, Low Isles. (c) Physical and chemical conditions in mangrove swamps. *Sci. Repts. Great Barrier Reef Exped.*, **2**, No. 4, 87–110.

Orton, J. H. (1920). Sea temperature, breeding and distribution in marine animals. *J. Marine Biol. Assoc. United Kingdom*, **12**, No. 2, 339–366.

—— (1928). On rhythmic periods in shell-growth in *O. edulis* with a note on fattening. *J. Marine Biol. Assoc. United Kingdom*, **15**, No. 2, 365–427.

—— (1929). Observations on *Patella vulgata*. Part III. Habitat and habits. *J. Marine Biol. Assoc. United Kingdom*, **16**, No. 1, 277–288.

—— (1933). Studies on the relation between organism and environment. *Proc. Liverpool Biol. Soc.*, **46**, 1–16.

Orton, J. H., and Lewis, H. M. (1931). On the effect of the severe winter of 1928–1929 on the oyster drills (with a record of five years' observations on sea temperature on the oyster beds) of the Blackwater estuary. *J. Marine Biol. Assoc. United Kingdom*, **17**, No. 2, 310–313.

Ostenfeld, C. H. (1908). On the ecology and distribution of the grass-wrack (*Zostera marina*) in Danish waters. *Rept. Danish Biol. Sta.*, **16**, 1–62.

—— (1918). Sea-grasses. *Rept. Danish Oceanog. Exped. Medit. Biol. Sec.*, **2**, 1–18.

Otterstrøm, C. V., and Nielsen, E. S. (1940). Two cases of extensive mortality in fishes caused by the flagellate *Prymesium parvum*, Carter. *Rept. Danish Biol. Sta.*, **44**, 1–24.

Pannikkar, N. K., and Aiyar, R. G. (1937). The brackish-water fauna of Madras. *Proc. Indian Acad. Sci.*, 6, No. 5, 284–337.

Pantin, C. F. A. (1931). The adaptation of *Gunda ulvae* to salinity. I. The environment. *J. Exptl. Biol.*, 8, No. 1, 63–72.

Parke, M. W. (1948). Studies on British Laminariaceae. I. Growth in *Laminaria saccharina* (L.) Lamour. *J. Marine Biol. Assoc. United Kingdom*, 27, No. 3, 651–709.

Parker, J. R. (1930). Some effects of temperature and moisture upon *Melanoplus mexicanus* Saussaure and *Camnula pellucida* Scudder (Orthoptera). *Bull. Univ. Montana Agr. Expt. Sta.*, No. 223, 1–132.

Patton, R. S., and Marmer, H. A. (1932). The waves of the sea. In Physics of the Earth. V. Oceanography. *Bull. Natl. Research Council U. S.*, 85, 207–228.

Pearse, A. S. (1929). Observations on certain littoral and terrestrial animals at Tortugas, Florida, with special reference to migrations from marine to terrestrial habitats. *Papers Tortugas Lab.*, 26, No. 6, 205–223.

———— (1939). *Animal Ecology*, 2nd ed. McGraw-Hill, New York.

Pease, D. C., and Kitching, J. A. (1939). The influence of hydrostatic pressure upon ciliary frequency. *J. Cellular Comp. Physiol.*, 14, No. 1, 135–142.

Petersen, C. G. J. (1914). Valuation of the Sea. II. The animal communities of the sea-bottom and their importance for marine zoogeography. *Rept. Danish Biol. Sta.*, 21, 1–68.

———— (1914a). Om Baendeltangens (*Zostera marina*) Aars-Production de danske Farvande. *Mindeskr. Steenstr. Føds, Kbh.*, 9.

———— (1915). On the animal communities of the sea bottom in the Skagerak, the Christiania Fjord and the Danish waters. *Rept. Danish Biol. Sta.*, 23, 3–28.

———— (1918). The sea bottom and its production of fish food. *Rept. Danish Biol. Sta.*, 25, 1–62.

Petersen, C. G. J., and Jensen, P. B. (1911). Valuation of the sea. I. Animal life of the sea bottom, its food and quantity. *Rept. Danish Biol. Sta.*, 20, 1–76.

Pickford, G. E. (1949). The distribution of the eggs of *Vampyroteuthis infernalis* Chun. *J. Marine Research Sears Foundation*, 8, No. 1, 73–83.

Pirrie, M. E., Bruce, J. R., and Moore, H. B. (1932). A quantitative study of the fauna of the sandy beach at Port Erin. *J. Marine Biol. Assoc. United Kingdom*, 18, No. 1, 279–296.

Poole, H. H. (1936). The photo-electric measurement of submarine illumination in offshore waters. *Rappt. et proc. verb. conseil permanent intern. exploration mer*, 101, Part 2, No. 2, 1–12.

Poulson, E. M. (1930). On the fluctuations in the abundance of cod fry in the Kattegat and the Belt Sea and causes of the same. *Rappt. et proc. verb. conseil permanent intern. exploration mer*, 65, No. 4, 26–30.

Pratt, R., and Fong, J. (1940). Studies on *Chlorella vulgaris*. II. Further evidence that *Chlorella* cells form a growth-inhibiting substance. *Am. J. Botany*, 27, No. 6, 431–436.

Pringsheim, E. G. (1950). The cultivation of algae. *Endeavour*, 9, No. 35, 138–143.

Pritchard, D. (1950). Notes on the dynamics of estuarine waters. *Proc. Colloquium on the Flushing of Estuaries, Woods Hole Oceanog. Inst.*, pp. 49–60.

Prosser, C. L., Bishop, D. W., Brown, F. A., Jahn, T. L., and Wolf, V. J. (1950). *Comparative Animal Physiology,* pp. 1–888. Saunders, Philadelphia.

Prytherch, H. F. (1934). The role of copper in the settling, metamorphosis and distribution of the American oyster, *Ostrea virginica. Ecol. Morongraphs,* **4,** No. 1, 47–107.

Pyefinch, K. A. (1950). Studies on marine fouling organisms. *J. Iron Steel Inst. London,* 219.

Rawlinson, R. (1934). A comparative study of *Metridium senile* (L.) var. *dianthus* (Ellis) and a dwarf variety of this species occurring in the river Mersey, with a discussion of the systematic position of the genus *Metridium. J. Marine Biol. Assoc. United Kingdom,* **19,** No. 2, 901–919.

Redfield, A. C. (1934). On the proportions of organic derivatives in sea water and their relation to the composition of plankton. In *James Johnstone Memorial,* pp. 176–192. Liverpool Univ. Press, Liverpool.

———— (1939). The history of a population of *Limacina retroversa* during its drift across the Gulf of Maine. *Biol. Bull.,* **76,** No. 1, 26–47.

Redfield, A. C., Smith, P. H., and Ketchum, B. H., (1937). The cycle of organic phosphorus in the Gulf of Maine. *Biol Bull.,* **73,** No. 3, 421–443.

Regnard, P. (1885). Phénomènes objectifs que l'on peut observer sur les animax soumis aux hautes pressions. *Compt. rend. soc. biol., Paris,* **37,** 510–515.

Reid, D. M. (1930). Salinity interchange between sea-water in sand and overflowing fresh-water at low tide. *J. Marine Biol. Assoc. United Kingdom,* **16,** No. 2, 609–614.

Remane, A. (1933). Verteilung und Organisation des benthonischen Mikrofauna der Kieler Bucht. *Wiss. Meeresuntersuch. Abt. Kiel,* **21,** No. 2, 161–221.

Richardson, I. D. (1952). Some reactions of pelagic fish to light as recorded by echo-sounding. *Fish. Invest. London.* [2], **18,** No. 1, 1–20.

Ricker, W. E. (1940). Relation of "catch per unit effort" to abundance and rate of exploitation. *J. Fisheries Research Board Can.,* **5,** No. 1, 43–70.

Ricketts, E. F., and Calvin, J. (1948). *Between Pacific Tides,* pp. 1–365. Stanford Univ. Press, Stanford, California.

Riley, G. A. (1937). The significance of the Mississippi River drainage for biological conditions in the northern Gulf of Mexico. *J. Marine Research Sears Foundation,* **1,** No. 1, 60–74.

———— (1938). Plankton studies. I. A preliminary investigation of the plankton of the Tortugas region. *J. Marine Research Sears Foundation,* **1,** No. 4, 335–352.

———— (1939). Correlation in aquatic ecology. *J. Marine Research Sears Foundation,* **2,** No. 1, 56–73.

———— (1941). Plankton Studies. III. Long Island Sound. *Bull. Bingham Oceanog. Coll.,* **7,** No. 3, 1–93.

———— (1946). Factors controlling phytoplankton populations on Georges Bank. *J. Marine Research Sears Foundation,* **6,** No. 1, 54–73.

———— (1947). A theoretical analysis of the zooplankton population of Georges Bank. *J. Marine Research Sears Foundation,* **6,** No. 2, 104–113.

———— (1953). Letter to the editor. *J. conseil permanent intern. exploration mer,* **19,** No. 1, 85–89.

Riley, G. A., and Georgy, S. (1948). Quantitative studies of summer plankton populations of the Western North Atlantic. *J. Marine Research Sears Foundation*, **7**, No. 2, 100–121.

Riley, G. A., and Von Arx, R. (1949). Theoretical analysis of seasonal changes in the phytoplankton of Husan Harbor, Korea. *J. Marine Research Sears Foundation*, **8**, No. 1, 60–72.

Riley, G. A., Stommel, H., and Bumpus, D. F. (1949). Quantitative ecology of the plankton of the Western North Atlantic. *Bull. Bingham Oceanog. Coll.*, **12**, No. 3, 1–169.

Ritchie, A. D. (1934). The habitat of *Procerodes ulvae*. *J. Marine Biol. Assoc. United Kingdom*, **19**, No. 2, 663–668.

Rodhe, W. (1948). Environmental requirements of fresh-water plankton algae. *Symbolae Botan. Upsalinenses*, **10**, 1–149.

Rounsfell, G. A., and Kask, J. L. (1943). How to mark fish. *Trans. Am. Fisheries Soc.*, **73**, 320–363.

Russell, E. S. (1931). Some theoretical considerations on the "overfishing" problem. *J. conseil, Conseil permanent intern. exploration mer*, **6**, No. 1, 3–20.

———— (1939). An elementary treatment of the overfishing problem. *Rappt. et proc. verb. conseil permanent intern. exploration mer*, **110**, No. 1, 5–14.

———— (1942). *The Overfishing Problem*, pp. 1–130. Cambridge Univ. Press, London.

Russell, F. S. (1927). The vertical distribution of plankton in the sea. *Biol. Revs.*, **2**, No. 3, 213–262.

———— (1932). On the biology of *Sagitta*. The breeding and growth of *Sagitta elegans* Verrill in the Plymouth area, 1930–31. *J. Marine Biol. Assoc. United Kingdom*, **18**, No. 1, 131–146.

———— (1932a). On the biology of *Sagitta*. II. The breeding and growth of *Sagitta setosa* J. Müller in the Plymouth area, 1930–31, with a comparison with that of *S. elegans* Verrill. *J. Marine Biol. Assoc. United Kingdom*, **18**, No. 1, 147–160.

———— (1933). On the biology of *Sagitta*. IV. Observations on the natural history of *Sagitta elegans* Verrill and *Sagitta setosa* J. Müller in the Plymouth area. *J. Marine Biol. Assoc. United Kingdom*, **18**, No. 2, 559–574.

———— (1935). A review of some aspects of zooplankton research. *Rappt. et proc. verb. conseil permanent intern. exploration mer*, **95**, No. 1, 3–30.

———— (1935a). On the value of certain plankton animals as indicators of water movements in the English Channel and North Sea. *J. Marine Biol. Assoc. United Kingdom*, **20**, No. 2, 309–332.

———— (1936). The importance of certain plankton animals as indicators of water movements in the western end of the English Channel. *Rappt. et. proc. verb. conseil permanent intern. exploration mer*, **100**, Part 3, No. 2, 7–10.

———— (1940). On the seasonal abundance of young fish. VII. The year 1939, January to August. *J. Marine Biol. Assoc. United Kingdom*, **24**, No. 1, 265–270.

———— (1951). A re-examination of *Calanus* collected off Plymouth. *J. Marine Biol. Assoc. United Kingdom*, **30**, No. 2, 313–314.

Russell, F. S., and Colman, J. S. (1934). The zooplankton. II. The composition of the zooplankton of the Barrier Reef lagoon. *Sci. Rept. Great Barrier Reef Exped.*, **2**, No. 6', 159–176, 186–201.

Russell, F. S., and Yonge, C. M. (1936). *The Seas,* 2nd ed., pp. 1–379. Warne, London.

Russell, H. D. (1941). The recent mollusks of the family Neritidae of the Western Atlantic. *Bull. Museum Comp. Zool. Harvard,* 88, No. 4, 345–404.

Russell, R. C. H., and MacMillan, D. H. (1952). *Waves and Tides,* pp. 1–348. Hutchinson, London.

Ruud, J. T., Jonsgärd, Å., and Ottestad, P. (1950). Age studies on blue whales. *Hvalrådets Skrifter Norske Videnskaps-Akad. Oslo* No. 33, 1–72.

Salt, R. W., and Mail, G. A. (1943). The freezing of insects. A criticism and an explanation. *J. Econ. Entomol.,* 36, 126–127.

Savage, R. E., and Hodgson, W. C. (1934). Lunar influence on the East Anglian herring fishery. *J. conseil, Conseil permanent intern. exploration mer,* 9, No. 2, 223–239.

Scholander, P. F. (1940). Experimental investigations on the respiratory function in diving mammals and birds. *Hvalrådets. Skrifter Norske,* No. 22, 1–131.

Scholander, P. F., Flagg, W., Hock, R. J., and Irving, L. (1953). Studies on the physiology of frozen plants and animals in the Arctic. *J. cellular Comp. Physiol.,* 42, Suppl. 1., 1–56.

Schreiber, E. (1927). Die Reinkulter von marinem Phytoplankton und deren Bedeutung für die Erforschung der Productions Fähigkeit des Meereswassers. *Hëlgoland wiss. Meeresuntersuch.,* 16, No. 10, 1–34.

Segerstråle, S. G. (1947). New observations on the distribution and morphology of the amphipod, *Gammarus zaddachi* Sexton, with notes on related species. *J. Marine Biol. Assoc. United Kingdom,* 27, No. 1, 219–244.

Seiwell, H. R. (1934). The distribution of oxygen in the western basin of the North Atlantic. *Papers Phys. Oceanog. Meteorol. Mass. Inst. Technol. and Woods Hole Oceanog. Inst.,* 3, No. 1 1–86.

Seiwell, H. R., and Seiwell, G. E. (1938). The sinking of decomposing plankton in sea water and its relation to oxygen consumption and phosphorus liberation. *Proc. Am. Phil. Soc.,* 78, No. 3, 465–481.

Setchell, W. A. (1926). Nullipore versus coral in reef-formation. *Proc. Am. Phil. Soc.,* 66, No. 2, 136–140.

Sewell, R. B. S. (1924). Observations on growth in certain molluscs and on changes correlated with growth in the radula of *Pyrazus palustris* (with a note on the radula by the late N. Annandale). *Records Indian Museum,* 26, No. 6, 529–551.

Sexton, E. W., and Spooner, G. M. (1940). An account of *Marinogammarus* (Schellenberg) gen. nov. (Amphipoda), with a description of a new species, *M. pirloti. J. Marine Biol. Assoc. United Kingdom,* 24, No. 2, 633–682.

Sheldon, S. M. (1915). Notes on the growth of the stipe of *Nereocystis luetkeana. Publs. Puget Sound Biol. Sta. Univ. Wash.,* 1, No. 1, 15–18.

Shelford, V. E. (1916). Physiological differences between marine animals from different depths. *Publs. Puget Sound Biol. Sta. Univ. Wash.* 1, No. 14, 157–174.

Shepard, P. S. (1948). *Submarine Geology,* pp. 1–348. Harper, New York.

Smidt, E. (1944). The effect of ice winters on marine littoral faunas. *Folia Geograph. Dan.,* 2, No. 3, 1–36.

Smith, F. G. W. (1946). Effect of water currents upon the attachment and growth of barnacles. *Biol. Bull.,* **90,** No. 1, 51–70.

———— (1948). Surface illumination and barnacle attachment. *Biol. Bull.,* **94,** No. 1, 33–39.

Smith, F. G. W., Williams, R. H., and Davis, C. C. (1950). An ecological survey of the sub-tropical inshore waters adjacent to Miami. *Ecology,* **31,** No. 1, 119–146.

Smith, G. M. (1951). *Manual of Phycology and Introduction to the Algae and their Biology,* pp. 1–375. Chronica Botanica, Waltham, Mass.

Smith, J. E. (1932). The shell gravel deposits and the infauna of the Eddystone grounds. *J. Marine Biol. Assoc. United Kingdom,* **18,** No. 1, 243–278.

Society for Experimental Biology (1950). Physiological mechanisms in animal behaviour. *Symposia Soc. Exptl. Biol.,* **4,** 1–482.

Sonneborn, T. M. (1947). Recent advances in the genetics of *Paramecium* and *Euplotes. Advances in Genet.,* **1,** 263–358.

Southward, A. J. (1950). Occurrence of *Chthamalus stellatus* in the Isle of Man. *Nature,* **165,** No. 4193, 408–409.

———— (1951). Distribution of *Chthamalus stellatus* in the Irish Sea. *Nature,* **167,** No. 4245, 410–411.

Spärks, R. (1936). On the relation between metabolism and temperature in some marine lamellibranchs and its zoogeographical significance. *Kgl. Danske Videnskab. Selskab; Biol. Medd.* [9] **13,** No. 5, 1–27.

———— (1951). Density of bottom animals on the ocean floor. *Nature,* **168,** No. 4264, 112–113.

Specht, R. C. (1950). Phosphate waste studies. *Eng. Progr. Univ. Florida Bull. Ser.,* No. 32, 1–27.

Spooner, G. M. (1947). The distribution of *Gammarus* species in estuaries. Part I. *J. Marine Biol. Assoc. United Kingdom,* **27,** No. 1, 1–52.

Spooner, G. M., and Moore, H. B. (1940). The ecology of the Tamar estuary. VI. An account of the macrofauna of the intertidal muds. *J. Marine Biol. Assoc. United Kingdom,* **24,** No. 1, 283–330.

Stauber, L. A. (1950). The problem of physiological species with special reference to oysters and oyster drills. *Ecology,* **31,** No. 1, 109–118.

Stephen, A. C. (1928). Notes on the biology of *Tellina tenuis* da Costa. *J. Marine Biol. Assoc. United Kingdom,* **15,** No. 2, 683–702.

———— (1929). Notes on the rate of growth of *Tellina tenuis* da Costa in the Firth of Clyde. *J. Marine Biol. Assoc. United Kingdom,* **16,** No. 1, 117–129.

———— (1929a). Studies on the Scottish marine fauna: the fauna of the sandy and muddy areas of the tidal zone. *Trans. Roy. Soc. Edinburgh,* **56,** Part 2, No. 14, 291–306.

———— (1930). Studies on the Scottish marine fauna: Additional observations on the fauna of the sandy and muddy areas of the tidal zone. *Trans. Roy. Soc. Edinburgh,* **56,** Part 2, No. 22, 523–535.

Stephenson, T. A. (1934). The breeding of reef animals. Part II. Invertebrates other than corals. *Sci. Repts. Great Barrier Reef Exped.,* **3,** No. 9, 247–272.

———— (1939). The constitution of the intertidal fauna and flora of South Africa. Part I. *J. Linnean Soc. London Zool.,* **40,** No. 273, 487–536.

———— (1944). The constitution of the intertidal fauna and flora of South Africa. Part II. *Ann. Natal Museum,* **10,** No. 3, 261–358.

—————— (1947). The constitution of the intertidal fauna and flora of South Africa. Part III. *Ann. Natal Museum*, **11**, No. 2, 207–324.

Stephenson, T. A., and Stephenson, A. (1933). Growth and sexual reproduction in corals. *Sci. Repts. Great Barrier Reef Exped.*, **3**, No. 7, 167–217.

—————— (1949). The universal features of zonation between tide marks on rocky coast. *J. Ecol.*, **37**, No. 2, 289–305.

Stephenson, T. A., Stephenson, A., and Day, J. H. (1940). The South African intertidal zone and its relation to ocean currents. VIII. Lamberts Bay and the west coast. *Ann. Natal Museum*, **9**, No. 3, 345–380.

Stephenson, T. A., Stephenson, A., and du Toit, C. A. (1937). The South African intertidal zone and its relation to ocean currents. I. A temperate Indian Ocean shore. *Trans. Roy. Soc. S. Africa*, **24**, No. 4, 341–382.

Stephenson, T. A., Tandy, G., and Spender, M. (1931). The structure and ecology of Low Isles and other reefs. *Sci. Repts. Great Barrier Reef Exped.*, **3**, No. 2, 17–112.

Steven, G. A. (1933). The food consumed by shags and cormorants around the shores of Cornwall (England). *J. Marine Biol. Assoc. United Kingdom*, **19**, No. 1, 277–292.

Stott, F. C. (1931). The spawning of *Echinus esculentus* and some changes in gonad composition. *J. Exptl. Biol.*, **8**, No. 2, 133–150.

Stubbings, H. G. (1938). Pteropoda. *Sci. Rept. Murray Exped.*, **5**, No. 2, 15–33.

Sverdrup, H. U. (1943). *Oceanography for Meteorologists*, pp. 1–245. Prentice-Hall, New York.

Sverdrup, H. U., Johnson, M. W., and Fleming, R. H. (1946). *The Oceans, Their Physics, Chemistry, and General Biology*, pp. 1–1087. Prentice-Hall, New York.

Swan, E. F. (1952). The growth of the clam *Mya arenaria* as affected by substratum. *Ecology*, **33**, No. 4, 530–534.

Taylor, H. F. (1951). *Survey of Marine Fisheries of North Carolina*, pp. 1–555. Univ. N. Carolina Press, Chapel Hill.

Taylor, W. R. (1950). *Plants of Bikini and Other Northern Marshall Islands*, pp. 1–227. Univ. Michigan Press, Ann Arbor.

Test, A. R. (1945). Ecology of California *Acmaea*. *Ecology*, **26**, 395–405.

Thamdrup, H. M. (1935). Beiträge zur Ökologie der Wattenfauna auf experimenteller Grudnlage. *Medd. Komm. Havundersøg. Kbh.*, **10**, No. 2, 1–125.

Thompson, D' A. W. (1917). *On Growth and Form*. Cambridge Univ. Press, London.

Thompson, H. (1930). Fluctuations in the North Sea haddock stock. *Rappt. et proc. verb. conseil permanent exploration mer*, **65**, No. 6, 35–44.

Thompson, T. G., and Wilson, T. L. (1935). The occurrence and determination of manganese in sea water. *J. Am. Chem. Soc.*, **57**, No. 2, 233–236.

Thompson, W. F. (1937). Theory of the effect of fishing on the stock of halibut. *Rept. Intern. Fisheries Comm.*, No. 12, 1–22.

Thompson, W. F., and Bell, F. H. (1934). Biological statistics of the Pacific halibut fishery. 2. Effect of changes in intensity upon total yield and yield per unit of gear. *Rept. Intern. Fisheries Comm.*, No. 8, 1–49.

Thompson, W. F., and Herrington, W. C. (1930). Life history of the Pacific halibut. 1. Marketing experiments. *Rept. Intern. Fisheries Comm.*, No. 2, 1–37.

Thompson, W. F., Dunlop, H. A., and Bell, F. H. (1931). Biological Statistics of the Pacific halibut fishery. 1. Changes in yield of a standardized unit of gear. *Rept. Intern. Fisheries Comm.*, No. 6, 1–108.

Thorson, G. (1936). The larval development, growth and metabolism of Arctic marine bottom invertebrates, etc., *Medd. Grønland*, 100, No. 6, 1–155.

——— (1940). Studies on the egg masses and larval development of Gastropoda from the Iranian Gulf. *Danish Sci. Invest. Iran.* Part II, 159–238.

——— (1941). Marine gastropoda prosobranchiata. *Zool. Iceland*, 4, No. 60, 1–150.

——— (1946). Techniques and future work in Arctic marine ecology. *Medd. Grønland*, 144, No. 4, 1–140.

——— (1946a). Reproduction and larval development of Danish marine bottom invertebrates. *Medd. Komm. Havundersøg Kbh. Plankton*, 4, No. 1, 1–523.

——— (1950). Reproductive and larval ecology of marine bottom invertebrates. *Biol. Revs.*, 25, No. 1, 1–45.

——— (1950a). Animal communities of the level sea bottom. *Ann. Biol.* 27, No. 7, 249–257.

Timmerman, G. (1932). Biographische Untersuchungen über die Lebensgemeinschaft das treibenden Golfkautes. *Z. morphol. Ökol.*, 25.

Tinbergen, L., and Verwey, J. (1945). Zur Biologie von *Loligo vulgaris* Lam. *Arch. néerl. zool.*, 7, Nos. 1–2, 213–286.

Trask, P. D. (1939). Organic content of recent marine sediments, pp. 428–453. In *Recent Marine Sediments*, pp. 1–736. Thomas Murphy, London.

Tressler, D. K. (1940). *Marine Products of Commerce*, pp. 1–762. Reinhold, New York.

Tully, J. P. (1949). Oceanography and prediction of pulp mill pollution in Alberni Inlet. *Bull. Fisheries Research Board Can.*, No. 83, 1–169.

United States Bureau of Fisheries (1913). A biological survey of the waters of Woods Hole and vicinity. *Bull. U. S. Bur. Fisheries*, 31, Nos. 1–2, 1–860.

Urie, H. C. (1948). Oxygen isotopes in nature and in the laboratory. *Science*, 108, No. 2810, 489–496.

Urie, H. C., Lowenstam, H. A., Epstein, S., and McKinney, C. R. (1951). Measurement of palaeo-temperatures and temperatures of the upper creataceous of England, Denmark and the southeastern United States. *Bull. Geol. Soc. Amer.*, 62, 399–416.

Van Oosten, J. (1929). Life history of the lake herring (*Leucicthys artedii* Le Sueur) of Lake Huron as revealed by its scales, with a critique of the scale method. *Bull. U. S. Bur. Fisheries*, 44, Doc. 1053, 265–428.

Verwey, J. (1930). Depth of coral reefs and the penetration of light. With notes on oxygen consumption of corals. *Proc. 4th Pacific Sci. Congr. Batavia*, 2a, 271–294.

——— (1931). Coral reef studies. II. The depth of coral reefs in relation to to their oxygen consumption and the penetration of light in the water. *Treubia*, 13, No. 2, 169–198.

Walford, L. A. (1938). Effect of currents on distribution and survival of the eggs and larvae of the haddock (*Melanogrammus aeglifinus*) on Georges Bank. *Bull. U. S. Bur. Fisheries*, 49, No. 29, 1–73.

Waterman, T. H. (1937). The relative effectiveness of various wave lengths for the photokinesis of *Unionicola. J. Cellular Comp. Physiol.*, 9, No. 3, 453–467.

Waterman, T. H., Nunnemacher, R. F., Chase, F. A., and Clarke, G. L. (1939). Diurnal vertical migration of deep-water plankton. *Biol. Bull.*, 76, No. 2, 256–279.

Watkins, E. E. (1939). The pelagic phase in the life history of the amphipod genus *Bathyporeia. J. Marine Biol. Assoc. United Kingdom*, 23, No. 2, 467–481.

——— (1941). Observations on the night tidal migrant crustacea of Kames Bay. *J. Marine Biol. Assoc. United Kingdom*, 25, No. 1, 81–96.

Welch, P. (1935). *Limnology*, pp. 1–471. McGraw-Hill, New York.

Wells, G. P. (1945). The mode of life of *Arenicola marina* L. *J. Marine Biol. Assoc. United Kingdom*, 26, No. 2, 170–207.

——— (1949). The behaviour of *Arenicola marina* L. in sand, and the role of spontaneous activity cycles. *J. Marine Biol. Assoc. United Kingdom*, 28, No. 2, 465–478.

Welsh, J. H. (1933). Light intensity and the extent of activity of locomotor muscles as opposed to cilia. *Biol. Bull.* 65, No. 2, 168–174.

Welsh, J. H., and Chase, F. A. (1937). Eyes of deep sea crustacea. I. Acanthephyridae. *Biol. Bull.*, 72, No. 1, 56–74.

——— (1938). Eyes or deep sea crustacea. II. Sergestidae. *Biol. Bull.*, 74, No. 2, 364–375.

Wheeler, J. F. G. (1937). Further observations on lunar periodicity. *J. Linnean Soc. London Zool.*, 40, No. 272, 325–345.

Whitaker, D. M. (1942). Unpublished. Quoted in *Turtox News*, 28, No. 7, 122–124.

White, F. D. (1929). Studies on marine wood borers. II. The effect of the experimental variations in salinity and hydrogen ion concentration upon the wood borers of the Pacific coast of Canada. *Contrib. Can. Biol. and Fisheries*, 4, No. 2, 9–18.

Whitney, L. V. (1941). A general law of diminution of light intensity in natural waters and the per cent of diffuse light at different depths. *J. Opt. Soc. Am.*, 31, No. 12, 714–722.

Wieser, W. (1951). Über die quantitative Bestimmung der Algen-bewohnende Microfauna felsiger Meeresküsten. *Oikos*, 3, No. 1, 124–131.

Wilson, D. P. (1937). The influence of the substratum on the metamorphosis of *Notomastus* larvae. *J. Marine Biol. Assoc. United Kingdom*, 22, No. 1, 227–243.

——— (1947). *They Live in the Sea*, pp. 1–128. Collins, London.

——— (1949). Notes from the Plymouth aquarium. *J. Marine Biol. Assoc. United Kingdom*, 28, No. 2, 345–351.

——— (1951). *Life of the Shore and Shallow Sea*, 2nd ed., pp. 1–213. Nicholson and Watson, London.

——— ' (1952). The influence of the nature of the substratum on the metamorphosis of the larvae of marine animals, especially the larvae of *Ophelia bicornis* Savigny. *Ann. inst. océanog. Monaco*, 27, No. 2, 49–156.

——— (1954). The attractive factor in the settlement of *Ophelia bicornis* Savigny. *J. Marine Biol. Assoc. United Kingdom*, 33, No. 2, 361–380.

Wilson, D. P., and Armstrong, F. A. J. (1954). Biological differences between sea waters: experiments in 1953. *J. Marine Biol. Assoc. United Kingdom*, 33, No. 2, 347—360.

Wilson, O. T. (1925). Some experimental observations of marine algal succession. *Ecology*, **6**, No. 3, 303–311.

Wimpenny, R. S. (1936). The size of diatoms. I. The diameter variation of *Rhizosolenia styliformis* Brightw. and *R. alata* Brightw. in particular and of pelagic diatoms in general. *J. Marine Biol. Assoc. United Kingdom*, **21**, No. 1, 29–60.

——— (1938). Diurnal variation in the feeding and breeding of zooplankton related to the numerical balance of the zoo-phytoplankton community. *J. conseil Conseil permanent intern. exploration mer*, **13**, No. 3, 323–337.

Winge, Ö. (1923). The Sargasso Sea, its boundaries and vegetation. *Rept. Dan. oceanog. Exped., 1908–10*, **3**, No. 2, 1–34.

Wirth, H. E., and Rigg, G. B. (1937). The acidity of the juice of *Desmarestia*. *Am. J. Botany*, **24**, No. 2, 68–70.

Wright, F. S. (1936). ' Report on the Maldon (Essex) periwinkle fishery. *Fish. Invest. London* [2], **14**, No. 6, 1–37.

Wynne-Edwards, V. C. (1929). The reproductive organs of the herring in relation to growth. *J. Marine Biol. Assoc. United Kingdom*, **16**, No. 1, 49–65.

Yonge, C. M. (1930). Studies on the physiology of corals. I. Feeding mechanisms and food. *Sci. Repts. Great Barrier Reef Exped.*, **1**, No. 2, 13–57.

——— (1930a). Studies on the physiology of corals. II. Digestive enzymes. *Sci. Repts. Great Barrier Reef Exped.*, **1**, No. 3, 59–81.

——— (1940). The biology of reef-building corals. *Sci. Repts. Great Barrier Reef Exped.*, **1**, No. 13, 353–391.

——— (1949). *The Sea Shore*, pp. 1–311. Collins, London.

Yonge, C. M., and Nicholls, A. G. (1930). Studies on the physiology of corals. II. Digestive enzymes, with notes on the speed of digestion. *Sci. Repts. Great Barrier Reef Exped.*, **1**, No. 3, 59–81.

——— (1931). Studies on the physiology of corals. IV. The structure, distribution and physiology of the zooxanthellae. *Sci. Repts. Great Barrier Reef Exped.* **1**, No. 6, 135–176.

Yonge, C. M., Yonge, M. J., and Nicholls, A. G. (1932). Studies on the physiology of corals. VI. The relation between respiration in corals and the production of oxygen by their zooxanthellae. *Sci. Repts. Great Barrier Reef. Exped.*, **1**, No. 8, 213–251.

Zenkewich, L. A., and Birstein, J. A. (1956). Studies of the deep water fauna and related problems. *Deep-Sea Research* **4**, No. 1, 54–64.

Zeuthen, E. (1947). Body size and metabolic rate in the animal kingdom with special regard to the marine micro-fauna. *C. R. Lab. Carlsberg, Ser. Chim.*, **26**, No. 3, 17–161.

Zobell, C. E., and Anderson, D. Q. (1936). Vertical distribution of bacteria in marine sediments. *Bull. Am. Assoc. Petroleum Geologists*, **20**, No. 3, 258–269.

Zobell, C. E., and Johnson, F. H. (1949). The influence of hydrostatic pressure on the growth and viability of terrestrial and marine bacteria. *J. Bacteriol.*, **57**, No. 2, 179–189.

Zobell, C. E., and Oppenheimer, C. H. (1950). Some effects of hydrostatic pressure on the multiplication and morphology of marine bacteria. *J. Bacteriol.*, **60**, No. 6, 771–781.

Index

Numbers in parentheses refer genera to their systematic position in the appendix, pp. 421–428.

457

Amphiura (301), *A. chiajei,* 305, 306;
  A. filiformis, 304, 306, 308, 312,
  314
Anabaena, nitrogen fixation, 92
Anaerobiasis, and glycogen, 83, 84
  survival of, 71, 83, 184, 191
  see also Oxygen
Anchistioides (349), molting, lunar
  rhythm, 81
  swarming, 82
  A. antiguensis, 81, 82
Animal behavior, texts, 5
  differences between broods, 157
Annual rings, 11, 280
Anomalocera (315), indicator species,
  276
  sinking factor, 40
  A. patersoni, 40, 276
Anomia (247), breeding season and
  depth, 312
  estuarine penetration, 401
  A. ephippium, 401; *A. squamula,*
  312
Anthomedusae, geographic distribution, 241
Antipatharia, maximum depth, 211
Antithamnion (99), salinity tolerance, 45
Aporrhais (210), in bottom communities, 304
  A. pes-pelecani, 304
Appendicularia, geographic distribution, 241
  seasonal cycle, 263
  see also Oikopleura
Arachnactis, larvae, indicator species,
  276
Arca (248), depth range, 48, 318
  intertidal importance, 362
  A. glacialis, 48, 318
Arenicola (197), and hydrogen sul-
  phide, 88
  and salinity, 395
  and substratum, 392, 394
  breeding, 394, 395
  burrow, 392–394
  burrowing, and soil hardness, 72,
  394
  and soil thickness, 73
  duration of spawning, 314
  intertidal distribution, 392 *et seq.*

Arenicola (197), mortality and temperature, 21
  oxygen requirements, 84
  respiration, 394
  temperature and salinity, 406, 407
  A. branchialis, 392; *A. ecaudata,*
  392; *A. marina,* 21, 72, 73, 84,
  88, 314, 392–395, 406, 407
Aricia (184), in bottom communities,
  303
  A. armiger, 303
Artemia (309), sinking factor, 40
  A. salina, 40
Ascidians, digestion, 107
  geographic distribution, 241
  maximum depth, 211
  see also genera 370–383
Ascidiella (372), biomass, 307
  estuarine penetration, 401
  A. aspera, 401
Ascophyllum (58), abrasion by, 66
  and salinity, 350
  and waves, 348, 350
  breaking stress, 56
  breeding, 348
  crowding and protection, 109
  estuarine penetration, 400
  float thickness and pressure, 46
  growth, 348
  intertidal distribution, 345, 346
  settlement, 348
  trace element concentration by, 93
  A. nodosum, 46, 56, 66, 109, 345,
  346, 348, 350, 400
Aspect, and insolation, 179
  and level, 344
Astarte (249), growth, 308
  in bottom communities, 306
  level and temperature, 373
  A. banksii, 306; *A. borealis,* 306; *A.
  elliptica,* 306; *A. undata,* 373
Asterias (298), biomass, 307
  breeding season and depth, 312
  speed-prey size relationship, 214
  A. rubens, 307, 312
Asterionella (33), size and temperature, 27
Asteroidea, depth distribution, 210
  maximum depth, 211
  see also genera 298–300

"Grass," and sandy beaches, 185
    see also genera 114–116
Grasshopper, development and temperature, 32
Grazing, and productivity equations, 256 *et seq.*
    and recolonization, 381
    area of food supply, 116
Gregariousness, see Crowding
Grouping, seasonal, 367
    see also Crowding
Growth, abyssal, 207
    and annual rings, 280
    and auxins, 95, 96
    and breeding, 13, 113
    and carotin, 96
    and conditioning agents, 96
    and crowding, 69, 103, 111, 363, 387, 388
    and currents, 63, 64, 357
    and depth, 320
    and dissolved organic matter, 363
    and feeding, 53, 102, 409
    and food, 102, 111, 289, 296, 298
    and level, 201–203, 387, 391
    and light, 14
    and longevity, 363
    and nutrients, 14, 91, 92, 121
    and photosynthesis, 121
    and pollution, 199
    and productivity, 306, 308
    and prosperity, 10, 38
    and sexual maturity, 113
    and size, 27, 30
    and temperature, 14, 25, 26, 28, 32, 121, 298, 314, 378
    and vitamins, 96
    and waves, 60, 61, 102, 202, 385
    effect of fishing on, 296
    in estuaries, 45, 201–203
    level, and feeding, 102
        and waves, 360
    light, nutrients and temperature, 91, 92, 121, 152
    measurements of, 11, 68
    of intertidal algae, 345 *et seq.*
    of intertidal animals, 331 *et seq.*
    of sublittoral organisms, 26, 308, 320, 321
    of whales, 253, 254

Guinardia, seasonal succession, 255
    G. flaccida, 255
Gunda (175), respiration and osmoregulation, 42, 86
    G. ulvae, 42
Gunnarea, intertidal distribution, 351
Gymnodinium (40), and conditioning agents, 97
    G. brevis, 97
Gymnosomata, geographic distribution, 241
    see also Clione

Haddock, brood success, and catches, 282, 283
    and currents, 286, 287
    development and temperature, 25
    effect of war on population, 293
    larval-adult competition, 289
    production and price, 282
Hake, lunar rhythm, 82
Halibut, fluctuations in fishery, 291–292
Halimeda (11), and coral reefs, 335
Halodule, intertidal distribution, 386
Halosaccion (96), depth–light relationship, 51
    H. glandiforme, 51
Hantzschia (38), diurnal rhythm, 387
    H. amphioxys, 387
Haploops (342); in bottom communities, 306
    H. tubicola, 306
Harpacticoidea, oxygen requirements, 84
    see also Tigriopus
Helcion (218), food, and form, 107
    supply, 116
    H. pellucidum, 107, 116
Hemigrapsus (362), activity and temperature, 380
    food, 381
    gills, and sediment, 377
        volume and level, 377
    intertidal distribution, 376
    leg length and agility, 378
    zonation and substratum, 376, 377
    H. nudus, 376–378, 380, 381; *H. oregonensis,* 376–378